Cranky Ladies of History

edited by
Tansy Rayner Roberts
&
Tehani Wessely

First published in Australia in 2015
by FableCroft Publishing

http://fablecroft.com.au

Cover art by Kathleen Jennings
Cover design by Amanda Rainey
Design and layout by Tehani Wessely
Typeset in Sabon MT Pro

National Library of Australia Cataloguing-in-Publication entry
Title: Cranky ladies of history / edited by Tansy Rayner Roberts and Tehani Wessely ; introduction by Tansy Rayner Roberts.
ISBN: 9780992553449 (hardback)
9780992553456 (paperback)
9780992553463 (ebook)
Subjects: Women—Biography—Anecdotes. Women—Conduct of life—Anecdotes. Women—Attitudes.
Other Creators/Contributors: Rayner Roberts, Tansy, editor, writer of added commentary.
Wessely, Tehani, editor.
Dewey Number: 305.4

Supported by Arts Tasmania

Selected work by the editors:

Written by Tansy Rayner Roberts

50 Roman Mistresses (FableCroft Publishing)
Pratchett's Women: unauthorised essays on the female characters of Discworld (FableCroft Publishing)
The Mocklore Chronicles (FableCroft Publishing)
- *Splashdance Silver*
- *Liquid Gold*
- *Ink Black Magic*

The Creature Court trilogy (HarperVoyager)
- *Power and Majesty*
- *The Shattered City*
- *Reign of Beasts*

Love and Romanpunk (Twelfth Planet Press)

Edited by Tehani Wessely

- *Insert Title Here*
- *Focus 2013: highlights of Australian short fiction*
- *Phantazein*
- *Focus 2012: highlights of Australian short fiction*
- *One Small Step, an anthology of discoveries*
- *Epilogue*
- *After the Rain*
- *Australis Imaginarium*
- *Worlds Next Door*

The editors would like to thank the following wonderful people:

- Liz Barr, for the initial inspiration for this anthology;
- Amanda Rainey for the amazing logo and cover design;
- Kathleen Jennings who, as always, has made astonishing art;
- Katharine Stubbs, because she is the best intern ever;
- Elizabeth Disney, whose proofreading talents are wonderful;
- all the brilliant backers of the Pozible campaign, because we wouldn't be here without you;
- the authors, for believing in the project and producing such marvellous stories;
- and our families, without whom we couldn't do what we do.

Contents

On Crankiness and Crowds and Ladies

Tansy Rayner Roberts

It began with a face, glaring out from an oil painting. Australian social justice and media blogger Liz Barr posted an image of Tsaritsa Sophia Alekseyevna of Russia on her Tumblr account and then, receiving a hugely positive response to Sophia's fierce expression, wrote a short essay about the woman in question, calling her a "would-be usurper, all-around cranky lady".[1]

There's something about that phrase: cranky lady. There was a time when it would have been seen entirely as a put-down, a dismissal of female strength and power. Yet the idea of celebrating women for their crankiness—rather than their beauty, their docility, their compliance—feels empowering and deliciously rebellious.

When we say 'cranky' and 'ladies' we also mean 'anger' and 'women'. Throughout history, women have struggled to express their anger at mistreatment and injustice—when they *have* expressed that anger, they have been punished for it by the men closest to them, by society, by the law, and even by other women.

The ability to express anger in a satisfying way has always been a privilege restricted to very few people in our society. Women's anger is more socially acceptable than it used to be, but we still have a long way to go about accepting and listening to the rage and unhappiness of those who are not rich, white, able-bodied and male.

1 https://lizbarr.wordpress.com/2013/10/16/tsaritsa-sophia-alekseyevna-of-russia-would-be-usurper-all-around-cranky-lady/

Tehani Wessely of Fablecroft picked up the idea of Tsaritsa Sophia as one of history's cranky ladies, and turned it into a book pitch. Tehani's personal superpower (and her mission in life) is to take authors she loves and inspire them to write amazing stories. She knew that 'Cranky Ladies of History' was a concept with something special behind it, something that would spark some of her favourite writers into producing work that she desperately wanted to read.

So she made it happen, and she pulled me along for the ride.

From the start, when Tehani and I talked about 'Cranky Ladies of History' as an anthology concept, people got excited. These days, when I give people advice about setting up successful crowdfunding campaigns, one of the first things I tell them is to choose the idea that sells itself—where people get excited from the first sentence, from *the title* of the project, before you've even explained all the nuts and bolts and rewards and payment options.

Cranky Ladies was one of those ideas. We found ourselves in a whirl of positive interest, not only from writers who wanted to pitch stories to us, but from mainstream media and many people who didn't have the time or the inclination to write for the book yet still wanted to support it, to promote it, and to help out with the campaign.

Crowdfunding is one of the new norms in publishing, and has helped many small presses remain viable in a time when the entire book industry is in flux. One of the best things about crowdfunding is the ability to test 'proof of concept' and find out if your publishing idea has legs before everyone invests all their time and money into it.

So many people we talked to wanted this book to exist, even if they weren't personally involved, and that turned out to be crowdfunding gold. We pulled in many of our most enthusiastic activists to help with the campaign, to blog about their favourite cranky ladies, and to spread the word. We had chosen March (Women's History Month) for the campaign almost on a whim, thinking it would be cute, but the further we got into the month the more we realised that people were hungry for these stories, not even just the fiction that we promised, but the anecdotes and essays about lost and misquoted and reclaimed women from history who were fierce, uncompromising and yes, angry.

One of the rewards I took personal responsibility for was the Cranky Ladies Calendar. I loved the idea of making a calendar that celebrated important dates in women's history, but also one using imagery like the Tsaritsa Sophia portrait that started it all—art depicting women who were angry. I was lucky in that several museums now have huge files of digital images of their art that are available for public use—but then I hit a wall because it turns out that art of named historical women isn't as common as it should be, and art of named historical women who aren't *smiling* is desperately rare. (Don't even get me started on how much of this art depicted women of colour, because the answer is 'almost none') But I got there in the end, and any project that allows me to celebrate Judith cutting off the head of Holofernes is always going to be dear to my heart.

The positive response we received to the Cranky Ladies crowdfunding campaign was invigorating and inspiring—especially when International Women's Day brought national media attention to the book that didn't even exist yet.

When you're making art that you think is challenging, rebellious and potentially controversial, there is nothing better than the feeling of having a crowd at your back, putting their money where their mouth is, cheering loudly, and keeping you company every step of the way.

Once the month of crowdfunding was over, the real work began. The authors whose pitches we had accepted had stories to write—and not every story was going to make it into the final volume. We weren't just looking for great stories, but also for a diverse mix of authors and historical figures, so that the book would cover a wide range of time periods, cultures and topics. We could, quite honestly, have filled the book just with female warriors of history, or pirates, or queens, but we wanted to show as many different ways as we could that women had rebelled against their society's conventions—or, in some cases, worked covertly within those conventions.

It was hard to accept that we couldn't have everything in this book. Every story we rejected felt like we were losing a piece of the big picture we had wanted to create. We also had to accept that some of the stories we had hoped for simply didn't come to us at all. We would have loved to include more pilots, sportswomen, scientists, and an even broader range of cultural diversity. We are particularly disappointed there are no Indigenous Australian authors in the anthology, and while we did receive a story that we deeply loved featuring an Aboriginal protagonist, we ended up having to let it go because of issues to do with cultural permissions that could not be addressed in time for us to go to print. This was possibly the most difficult choice we had to make with the book, and we remain very sad about it, though we stand by our decision to respect the cultural dictums in the matter.

Tehani and I are, however, so proud to be able to bring you this anthology, and to introduce you to spectacular women from history, as told by many of our favourite science fiction, fantasy and historical writers.

Thanks so much to all of our Pozible supporters[2], to Arts Tasmania for the Crowbar grant[3], and to every writer who pitched or wrote us a

2 http://www.pozible.com/project/178572

3 http://www.arts.tas.gov.au/funding/programs/crowbar

Cranky Ladies story, even if it didn't end up in the final book. We love you all. Special thanks to Kathleen Jennings for the astounding art wrapped around (and hidden within) this book, and to Amanda Rainey for another fantastic design job.

This book may look beautiful, but it has sharp teeth.

Cranky Ladies of History started out as a joke title in many ways. It was supposed to be ironic, to remind us all of the many ways that words have been (and often still are) used to patronise and belittle women. But the snarky title should not disguise the fact that this book is serious. Angry. Fierce.

Cranky Ladies of History is a book that doesn't smile at the camera (or the portrait artist) unless it wants to.

So let your cranky flag fly alongside those of Bloody Mary, Cheng Shih, Sacagawea, Countess Bathory, Hatshepsut, Nora of Kelmendi, Dr Lilian Cooper, Grace O'Malley, and many, many more.

These women deserve to be remembered.

Queenside
Liz Barr

My mother always said that nothing was so unbecoming to a child as a pout. So I told Lady Mary over our chess game, but she looked up at me with her pinched little face and asked if I thought her merely sulky and disobedient, and if so, wouldn't I prefer the company of her guardians, or perhaps even to return to court and the queen.

Truth be told, I regretted my words as soon as they left my mouth. And I did *not* prefer the company of her guardians, for Lady Shelton was aunt to Queen Anne, and I'd sooner look at Lady Mary's honest unhappiness than Lady Shelton's smiling ambition. As for the queen, I had known her when she was plain Anne Boleyn, lady in waiting to Queen Catherine, laughing and flirting and all the while plotting to destroy the royal family.

I could hardly say any of this out loud. But I didn't have to speak, because Lady Mary managed something very like a smile and said, "Elizabeth would miss you if you went anywhere. She loves you very much."

With that, she took my king and won the game.

Elizabeth was more interested in smearing damson jam around her mouth than winning at chess and expressing affection for her old Lady Governess. But she looked up when her name was mentioned and said, "My Margie."

In the King's family, love was very much like possession. I smiled, too, and said, "Eat your tart, your highness."

Out of the corner of my eye, I saw Lady Mary's face fall again.

Little wonder that she was unhappy, poor love. Once, she had been a princess, her father's heir, as happy and clever a girl as ever lived. She could read Latin and play the lute and talk philosophy and religion with learned men.

Then came the King's great matter, the Boleyn woman, taking it all away. In place of fine clothes and titles came bitter womanhood, unpredictable courses that kept Mary abed for days at a time, doubled over with cramps, and migraines that would leave her prostrate for a day, then linger as nagging headaches that made her bad tempered and unable to concentrate. Her mother was too far away to tell her that this was normal for some unlucky women, so she let the Spanish ambassador persuade her that the queen was having her poisoned. For two months I had to prepare all her food with my own hands, and I was no cook but the widow of a knight and a baroness in my own right.

Catherine died in January. Now I was all that Mary had.

I had been her Lady Governess when she was a child, and I loved her as if she was my own daughter, but she was a difficult girl.

◊Δ◊Δ◊Δ◊Δ◊Δ◊

It was a crisp, grey day in April, when the leaves were turning brown and the king—well, he had his own concerns, but we knew nothing of them until, just after noon, there was a bustle of movement outside, and we heard the servants calling, "The queen! The queen is come!"

Princess Elizabeth dropped her doll and climbed to her feet. "Mama! My mama is here!" She toddled over to her sister, sitting in the window with a book. "Let me up, Mary, my mama is here!"

Lady Mary made a great show of reluctance as she put her book aside, but she lifted her sister. I joined them at the window, expecting to see a great throng of people surrounding the queen. Royalty never travelled without their servants and courtiers, their courtiers' servants, their priests and fools and jugglers. Today, Queen Anne was alone but for two ladies in waiting, and her smile was strained as she accepted her aunt's embrace.

"Mama!" cried Elizabeth.

The queen looked up at the noise and waved to her daughter. She gave no sign of recognising Lady Mary or myself, but the strain around her mouth returned as she stepped inside.

"Why is she here?" Mary asked.

"To see her daughter."

"Alone?" Mary bit her lip. "She's planning something."

"What? To stab you with a dagger hidden in her farthingale? She's come to spend an hour with her daughter, child. Your mama did the same when you were small."

Lady Mary scowled at the comparison, but I was saved by a light footstep in the hall. The door opened, and there was the queen.

She wasn't beautiful, but neither was she the deformed monster her enemies portrayed. She had regular features, perhaps a little thin, but pleasant to look at. Her eyes were too wide and her mouth too thin, but cleverness made her eyes sparkle and her smile made her mouth seem kind.

She was not smiling today.

"Mama! I have a new doll and I learned a French song, and Mary has promised to teach me Spanish and Latin!"

While I bowed to the Queen, pushing Mary into a reluctant reverence, Elizabeth forgot all manners and formality. The queen seemed to shudder as Elizabeth ran towards her, though she concealed it quickly, forcing a merry note into her voice as she said, "My angel, how clever you are. The cleverest princess in Europe, I'll wager, and smarter than most of the princes as well. Sing me your French song."

She watched as the princess sang, her eyes hungry, committing this moment to memory. I had seen that look before, on Queen Catherine's face in the weeks before Princess Mary was sent away to her own court in Wales, in recognition of her status as the king's heir.

But Elizabeth was much too young for such a move, and surely the king hadn't given up hope of getting a son from Queen Anne.

"Why are you here, Mama?" the princess demanded as soon as she had finished her song. "No one told us you were coming."

"It's a surprise. Don't you like surprises?"

"Did you bring me a present?"

"Perhaps." This time, the Queen's smile reached her eyes. "That's a surprise, too."

"You *did* bring a present!"

From behind her back, the Queen produced a book.

"It's about the French court, where I grew up," she said. "Look at all the pictures! The lady in blue is Queen Claude."

"She's very pretty."

"Can you find a picture of a yellow apple? You have to look on every page." When Elizabeth had settled to her task, the queen turned to Mary and said, "We must speak."

I held my breath, hoping that Lady Mary would have the good sense to keep her sharp tongue to herself. That thin hope scarcely had time to form before it was dashed.

"Speak?" Lady Mary said. "About what? Sending my mother to a lonely death? Or leading my father and all of England into heresy?"

So sallow was Queen Anne that one might have mistaken *her* for the Spaniard, and the golden-haired, rosy-cheeked Catherine for the

Englishwoman. Anne Boleyn's colour rose only with her anger. Now, her cheeks flushed red and she spat, "Your mother died of old age and disease. As for heresy—" Miracle of miracles, she stopped and drew breath. When she spoke again, she was calm.

"Under different circumstances, I'd have enjoyed debating religion with you, Lady Mary."

"The Word of God is hardly a matter for debate," said Mary, but I saw her hesitate. Not quite distracted by the queen's ploy, but curious nonetheless. A mirthless little smile tugged at her lips. "Unless, I suppose, circumstances were *very* different."

"Do you remember the visit I paid you two years ago?"

I knew nothing of such a visit. I eased myself into a chair beside Princess Elizabeth, hoping the Queen and Lady Mary would not notice me. God forgive me, I've always enjoyed a gossip, and in Henry's England, a little knowledge can save a life.

Or condemn it.

"You told me," Lady Mary was saying in a low voice, "that if I renounced my mother and the Pope, I might return to court. You promised me," her voice turned bitter, "friendship."

"I meant it," said the Queen, "though you're as unpleasant a girl as ever lived. I had thought to send you to France."

"France." Mary, good daughter of Spain, made it sound like hell.

"You'd like Queen Claude. She's intelligent and educated, and appreciates clever women. She is a loyal friend to the Pope. You would have been happy in France."

"Why are you here?"

"I fear," the Queen's voice was even, "that the king loves me no longer. I fear that my daughter will be...cast out."

"As I was."

"Yes."

"Forgive me," said Lady Mary, "but why am I meant to care?"

"My daughter. Your sister."

"Perhaps she'll be sent to wait upon the next heir. No doubt I will follow. Who has my father's eye now?"

"Jane Seymour."

"I remember her. She was kind to me."

"She's as stupid as a turnip. She can barely write her own name."

"His Grace won't mind," said Mary. "As long as she gives him a son." She sat down, arranging her plain skirts around her. "What have you done to displease him?"

"I don't know." The queen's calm facade cracked at last. "I miscarried—our son died—but it was an accident, he knows it. But he was sitting with the Seymour woman in his lap—someone has filled his ears with poison, and so many lies, I can't even—"

"Did you betray him?"

"No!"

"He thinks you did."

"Lies," said the Queen. "All lies."

"Cromwell?"

"I believe so."

"He's as bad as Wolsey. Maybe worse."

"Then we have a common enemy," said the Queen.

It was true, I realised, but she did not mean that their common enemy was Thomas Cromwell. It was the king. I saw horror dawning in Mary's eyes—she loved her father, even now.

Such thoughts were treason. We'd be ruined, all three of us, and then who would protect Elizabeth?

Lady Mary stepped back.

"We have nothing in common," she said.

This was a victory for Mary. For years she had resisted the call to be pragmatic and sensible—*obedient to her father's wishes*—and ally herself to Anne Boleyn. Now the queen's position was precarious, and if she fell, Mary could say, "Look, I was right all along."

Jane Seymour—she was domestically-minded and dull, but she had always been kind to Mary. If the king married again, there would be no Spanish ghost hanging over his next wife.

For the first time in years, Mary's desires were in accord with her political well-being.

There was a fierce hope in her eyes. After these years of pain, she finally had a tiny shred of power.

She straightened her spine and said, "What do you want from me?"

"My daughter." The queen spoke softly, so that the princess, still absorbed in her book, wouldn't hear. "She will need someone to care for her."

"Me?"

"She is your sister. You seem to love her."

"My mother taught me to love all my father's bastards."

The queen's hand twitched. Many times she had said Lady Mary deserved to have her ears boxed, and occasionally I even agreed with her.

She did not move.

"Please," she said.

A bitter little laugh escaped Mary's mouth. "Would you put me in charge of her religious instruction? Or should I share my fond memories of her late mother?"

"Will I have to beg?"

"Lady Bryan will look after Elizabeth, as she always has."

I'd hoped I was forgotten. But the queen cast a dismissive glance in my direction and said, "She's not family."

As if *she* had been born to royalty. I swallowed my irritation and helped Princess Elizabeth turn back to the beginning of the book, still searching for that elusive yellow apple.

Mary shifted in her chair, straightening her spine and raising her chin. She took on a fragile, brittle dignity. I could almost see her future: a middle-aged woman with a bitter tongue that concealed the pains—not all of them physical—of her existence.

When she spoke, her voice was very soft. "You wore yellow to celebrate my mother's death. You persuaded my father to abandon their lawful, Godly marriage, then you hounded her until she died in a cold castle, miles away from those who loved her. Now you come to me and ask me to treat *your* daughter with kindness. Because you think—what? That I would treat my sister as badly as you have treated me?" Mary looked away, dismissing the queen. "You insult me."

She hesitated, then added petulantly, "She's a good, clever little girl, who will know her place and accept the one true religion, and whoever succeeds the King, we will serve him with humility and honour."

Not so many years ago, she would have added, *So there.* It was all I could do to keep from laughing and applauding. The queen thought she was dealing with an ignorant girl, but Mary was as stubborn and clever as her parents, and as touchy about her dignity. This was her first victory since the king remarried, and by God, she was savouring it.

Not for nothing had the queen spent these past years pleasing the king. Her cheeks were flushed and her jaw set, but she inclined her head and said, "My thanks." Then, so that Mary would not forget her place, she added, "Lady Mary."

Mary's lip curled, but she merely stood up, putting her hand to her temple.

"My head," she said. "I need to rest. Lady Bryan—"

"I'm coming, child."

As I got to my feet, Princess Elizabeth cried, "The apple! I found it!"

"Show me, my angel," said the queen, "and I'll read you the story."

Having got what she wanted, however unexpected or unpleasant the means, we no longer existed as far as the queen was concerned. I took Mary by her elbow.

"I did well, did I not?" she whispered as I led her upstairs to her room.

"Your mother would have been proud."

"It was my father that I had in mind." She eased herself down on the bed. "I think I'll sleep a little while."

"It's good for you."

"And tomorrow," she looked up at me, and through the pain, there was a new determination in her eyes, "I think I shall send my respects to Jane Seymour."

The Company of Women

Garth Nix

Summer. The sun noon-high in a sky clear as water, save for the merest scrape of cloud above the hills to the west. The meadow white with clover, the flowers so thick upon the ground no other colour could be seen, as if some strange snow had fallen out of season.

All through the meadow, bees. Single bees searching, groups of bees gathering, great swarms of bees swirling about the tall conical bee-houses arrayed in long lines, each one new-built every spring in its own place, as had been done for centuries past and all trusted would be done for centuries to come.

Godiva, Countess of Mercia, stood on the mound before the meadows proper, where the tips of the old standing stones could still be seen, the stone women of long ago buried by later Christian rulers but their presence still felt beneath the earth.

Lady Godiva was not alone. She stood in the very centre of the mound, at its highest point, albeit only a dozen paces above the meadow. Around her, ranged close, were the women of her household, at least those who had children, for all must be mothers who came that day to sing praise to the bees. Around them were the servants of the castle, and around them, in close-standing rings that extended to the edge of the mound and beyond, down into the white clover, were the mothers and grandmothers and great-grandmothers and even one ancient great-great-grandmother of the town of Coventry.

The song was as old as the buried stones, though the words had changed through several languages, and perhaps no longer made much sense, if anyone cared to examine them. But they did not look closely, for it was the feeling of the song that mattered, the sense of being at one with all the other women, and with the queens in their houses, the queens who were the minds and hearts and souls of this great metropolis of bees.

As the last note came from the assembled women and faded into silence, the bees answered. Deep in the hives there were thrummings and rumblings, and great droves of bees rose from the meadow and buzzed together, so many in number that the buzzing sounded like a mighty cascade, and a breeze blew across the mound, made from the beating of myriad tiny wings in unison.

Then the breeze faded, as the bees returned to their business. The women relaxed, letting go the slight stiffness of apprehension, that small fear that perhaps this year the queens would not answer the song, the meadows would fade early, and the honey would be sparse. To many families of Coventry, their bee-house and the honey it would provide might make the difference between comfort and privation, or for some, even a bare sufficiency and starvation. Few ate much of the honey themselves; it was too valuable. But sold at autumn fair, it would make silver to see them through the winter.

Godiva relaxed too, for it was a great responsibility to lead the singing, and this was only the third time she had done so. For a few minutes, lost in the song and the bee-sound, she had also managed to forget some things that were disturbing her mind, most principally the altered behaviour of her husband Leofric, the Earl of Mercia. In recent months he had become withdrawn, from his family and his court, and even more troubling, had taken certain decisions which were alienating the people of Coventry. Leofric had always been so reasonable, but now he would no longer listen to the counsel of Godiva or any of his former most trusted advisors.

This change in Leofric stemmed from the arrival in their court of one Ralph, a Norman knight and ferromancer, who Leofric had immediately appointed as his steward, replacing the good Athelbard who had served both him and his father before him well, and was not too advanced in years to continue for many years ahead.

Ralph had introduced a number of unwelcome changes, and at all times, Leofric had supported him. Most of the changes involved taxes and fees, Ralph suggesting new ways to gain money for the earl. As Leofric had never cared greatly for the accumulation of silver before, this was very strange. It was as if Ralph had some hold over the earl. Leofric wouldn't talk to Godiva about it. Whenever she tried, he would evade her and disappear hunting.

At least it would be a good season for honey, Godiva thought, as the women on the mound dispersed and she walked back with her handmaidens to where the dozen housecarls of her bodyguard waited. The men had stayed just within earshot, in case of need, back along the old Roman road behind the mound.

The harsh clatter of horseshoes on that road broke through the quiet murmur of the women, catching Godiva's attention. She frowned as she saw a black destrier ridden too fast coming towards them, sending the women returning to the town scuttling aside. It was, of course, Sir Ralph, as if her thinking of him had made him appear. Like the devil, she thought, and wondered. Ralph had also had his run-ins with the Bishop of Coventry and the gentler English church that still embraced much of the old Anglo-Saxon magic and tradition, the workings of holly and iron. The Normans followed the pope, of course, as the English did not, and claimed their ferromancy was the only true magic approved by God.

But she did not believe in the Devil incarnate. There was enough ordinary evil in the world and in people to not need any special manifestation. Ralph was clearly feathering his own nest while he worked to extract more coin for the earl, and surely this was explanation enough for his behaviour. But why had he ridden out to the bee-fields, on this day of all days?

Her housecarls lifted their axes as he approached, and spread out across the road. They had served her father or uncle before her, and were all veterans of numerous battles. In common with almost everyone else in the earl's household, they did not like Ralph. Godiva suspected if he gave them an excuse, such as trying to ride through to their mistress, they would happily cut him down and be contrite about it afterwards.

Ralph slowed his war-horse to a walk, and turned the stallion aside to calm him, allowing Aelfwyn, the leader of the housecarls to swagger up, his axe now on his shoulder. They spoke quietly, Aelfwyn shaking his head and pointing back to the town, Ralph in turn gesticulating and making some sort of vehement demand. Godiva walked more quickly. It would be better for her to find out what this was about, before Aelfwyn or Ralph lost their tempers.

"What brings you here, Ralph?" she called out as she drew closer. It was not a polite greeting, but she did not care to be polite to the man. He never seemed to notice, anyway.

"I am upon the earl's business," said Ralph loudly. "I have come to see his famous bee-meadow."

Godiva's fingers curled towards becoming fists and she had to force herself to relax them, to let her arms remain at her sides.

"The bee-meadow is not the earl's," she said calmly. "It is held by all the women of Coventry, direct from the king, as has always been."

"Is it?" asked Ralph, in his nasal voice that had little variation in pitch, and so disguised any emotion that might lie behind the words. "Yet there is no deed, no title, no *document* at all that says so, and in that absence, the bee-meadow, as anything else, must therefore be of the Earl's demesne."

Godiva felt an almost over-powering urge to meet this smug announcement with a command to her housecarls to cut the Norman down, and keep on hacking at him until the pieces were so small even the smallest dog, nay even the smallest rat could carry a piece away. But she resisted the surge of fury, for what he said was true, or at least true to a degree. There had been a grant of title, long ago, but it was believed destroyed when St Osburga's was burned in the first Viking raids.

"It is recorded as such in many records," she said. "And in the memory of the people. The earl himself I am sure would not contest it."

"The earl has given me the duty of ensuring his lands are properly managed," said Sir Ralph. "*All* his lands. Including this bee-meadow, milady."

Godiva felt rather than saw her housecarls spreading out in a line behind her, getting ready to charge this insolent Norman.

"Go back to the castle," she said to Sir Ralph, her voice cold and commanding. "I will discuss this with the earl."

Sir Ralph's eyes flickered, noting the barely-suppressed anger of the housecarls, axes held ready, knees bent to sprint forward before he could attempt to charge through and away, and there were probably too many, too close, for his ferromantic powers to turn their weapons aside. He looked as if he would say something, but instead he inclined his head with the slightest civility possible and turned his mount around.

"He needs killing," said Aelfwyn quietly to Godiva, sunlight flashing from his axe-blade across his face, lighting up his narrowed eyes. "You want me to see to it, milady? I've a wooden spear for such as he, in my arms-chest. Good oak, fire-tempered."

"No," said Godiva. "He is a Christian, of a sort, and he is the earl's man. No killing."

Aelfwyn nodded, but did not respond. Godiva was fairly sure he would obey, but only for a few days. If Ralph wasn't careful, he would meet an untimely end, and likely thus create even more problems. Godiva wanted to discover why Leofric was seemingly in Ralph's power before she did anything to remove the Norman from Coventry, permanently or otherwise. And now there was the additional problem of making sure the bee-meadow remained the common property of the mothers of the town.

"Let us walk," said Godiva. "Send someone back with the horses. I need to think."

Aelfwyn signalled to the men who held the horses, and to the housecarls. Soon the small host was walking up the road, with Godiva alone in the middle, until one of her women quickened her pace to join her company.

"I fear there is more trouble, milady," said Ceolwen, chief among Godiva's handmaidens. A fifteen years older cousin, Ceolwen was a widow now, her husband killed in the last year fighting the Viking raiders from Ireland, and her sons and daughters were grown and married. She was very close to the countess, godmother to Godiva's own son, and the two kept no secrets from each other.

"It seems so," replied Godiva quietly, so only the two of them could hear. She frowned. "I have to make Leofric talk to me. There is perhaps some simple explanation for...for everything."

"I doubt it is simple," replied Ceolwen. "Back there...that Ralph smelled of something worse then iron magic."

"Did he?" asked Godiva intently. She had little magic herself, and doubted most people who claimed to have greater powers, with a few exceptions. Ceolwen was one of them, for Godiva had seen her quell and send away a pack of wolves, and a great oak seemingly bend to speak to her, and though these things had happened in Godiva's childhood, she had not forgotten.

"It is not himself, exactly," said Ceolwen thoughtfully. "I think it is something he carries. Some object of forbidden sorcery."

"Ferromancy is not forbidden," said Godiva.

"It is not cold iron nor stone magic that he conceals," said Ceolwen. "Something more malevolent, something from the deep shadows."

"Something Bishop Osric can deal with?" asked Godiva, her frown lightening. This might be the opportunity she was looking for, if Ralph was found to be an evil sorcerer.

"I doubt it," said Ceolwen regretfully. "I caught only the faintest scent, myself. The wind from the bee-meadow is sacred, it made whatever it is stir itself. I have not noticed it before, and I think Osric would not be able to tell if anything is amiss. He is not of the sharpest, and his power slight."

"The dogs don't like him," added Godiva. "Ralph, I mean. I had thought it was because he kicks at them and is generally harsh, but it is likely he does that to hide whatever they scent."

"Yes," said Ceolwen. "The dogs would know."

They were silent for a minute or two, both thinking.

"You had best go to the great oak at Awsley," said Godiva. "I do not like to have that old hag looking into our court, but needs must. Ask her about Ralph and whatever he carries."

"She may not choose to talk," said Ceolwen carefully, who had a rather less orthodox opinion of the Wise Woman of Awsley and held her in much higher esteem than Godiva. "But of course I will go. What will you do?"

"First of all, talk to Leofric," said Godiva. "In bed, tonight. This time, I will make him listen!"

◊Δ◊Δ◊Δ◊Δ◊Δ◊

But Leofric wouldn't listen. He left their marital bed in his nightshirt, blustering and bellowing that he could not stand another word, a strange cry when he had avoiding listening to any word beyond Ralph's name. Godiva heard him shouting as he stomped across the hall, and out to the stables, calling for his grooms and housecarls to attend him, for he was away to his manor of Bercuswell where he would not be troubled by his woman.

Ceolwen passed the earl going out on her way in from her travels, and went to Godiva without taking off her cloak or boots.

"Leofric is afraid of something," said Godiva. "I cannot tell whether it is for himself, or me, or for the children. Ralph holds a great power over him."

"He does have something to fear," said Ceolwen. "The Wise Woman of Awsley was amenable today. She looked in the water to see what she might of Ralph."

"And?"

"She saw Ralph," said Ceolwen, very slowly. "But that was not all."

"What?" asked Godiva. "What do you mean?"

"She saw something of Leofric as well," said Ceolwen. "Bound within whatever Ralph carries on that dark chain about his neck."

"Something of Leofric?" asked Godiva, falteringly. "His soul?"

"The Wise Woman is not Christian, and she did not use that word," replied Ceolwen. "But I think it is what she meant. She saw others as well, what she called the 'bright shadows' of perhaps half a dozen living men, clustered about whatever Ralph wears, caught like bees on tar-paper. He has captured them, somehow. This is why Leofric does his bidding."

Godiva was entirely still for a moment, that shocked stillness of a warrior who has taken a wound and does not yet know it for what it is, whether a mortal blow or merely a cut to be shrugged off. Ceolwen began to reach out a hand to her, but pulled it back as Godiva drew a deep breath and spoke in measured tones.

"There is a mention of something like this in Saint Wulfstan's *Blessings and Maledictions*," she said. "Under "Maledictions", of course. A soul-thief who lived in the time of Urakazaar of Babylon. He had some foul device, a cursed amulet that could take souls and imprison them within."

"Yes," said Ceolwen. "The Wise Woman called Ralph something I did not understand, a word from the little folk of long ago. She said it meant 'creature who takes the light from others'."

"He must be forced to release Leofric. And the others...I wonder...five other souls caught. If they are also earls or nobles of Ingland, and Ralph a Norman...but would even Duke William employ such a wicked stratagem? He is like to take the kingdom in any case."

"Whether Ralph serves William or himself, the difficulty will be to force him to do anything," said Ceolwen. "Nor can he be simply killed. The Wise Woman was straight on that. She said to kill him would strand the bright shadows of the others in some nether place. They would live on, but as mere husks, without joy or savour of any kind."

"Likely he has other evil magic to protect him in any case," said Godiva. "Saint Wulfstan categorised a creature of his type, as I have said, but he did not offer any remedy...did the Wise Woman offer any suggestion for how we might free Leofric?"

Ceolwen hesitated a moment before answering, a hesitation instantly noticed by Godiva.

"What?" she asked, a smile flickering across her care-worn face. "I take it is something you fear I will undertake, and think it too dangerous for me, so you plan to not tell me and do it yourself?"

Ceolwen laughed, caught out. "I had resolved to tell you," she said. "I only thought for a moment I might turn you aside. In truth, I could not do what must be done in any case. It is for the leader of the women of Coventry, the singer to the bees. Or so the Wise Woman says."

"Ah," said Godiva quietly. "I think I understand. But surely that is only legend?"

"No. It is not simply legend. The tales speak truly of a great working of the old magic," said Ceolwen.

"But I have no power, no skills of magic," protested Godiva. "So how can that work?"

"You do not need power, nor arcane knowledge. The ritual itself is power," answered Ceolwen. "And it can only be done by she who leads the singing to the bees."

"And is the ritual as simple as the legend says?" asked Godiva. "To walk naked from the Mound of the Bee Field to the Bargain Stone in the market square?"

"You must also lay down a bunch of clover, an acorn, and a drop of blood new-pricked from a hawthorn branch. Then you may speak your lawgiving to anyone...or anything...and they must obey your rede."

"That does not sound so difficult," said Godiva. "Leofric will not like others to see my nakedness I suppose, but my housecarls can clear the road at least, blacken a few eyes—"

"It is not so straight a task," said Ceolwen. "No man may see you at all, or the spell is broken."

Godiva's mouth quirked in momentary frustration, but her mind moved swiftly.

"No, not so straight a task," she said. "But I think there is a way to do it, and we must do so with all speed, before Ralph hears of it. I need you to fetch Mother Halfgrim from the town."

"Mother Halfgrim!" exclaimed Ceolwen. "Now? In the night? That cantankerous old reptile?"

"Yes," said Godiva. "Tell her it is not the countess that needs her, but the Singer to the Bees. Before we are done, we will need many others too. There is a great deal to do."

"I will fetch Mother Halfgrim then," said Ceolwen, gathering up her kirtle to go. "I am eager to hear your thoughts, my lady!"

An hour later, Ceolwen returned with Mother Halfgrim, who strangely did not protest as she might be expected to do, in fact grumbling not at all. She was introduced into Godiva's bedchamber, the two speaking for little more than ten minutes, before Mother Halfgrim emerged and returned to the town, a curious, previously unsuspected smile twisting up her toothless mouth.

Later, other women came, speaking Mother Halfgrim's name to the sleepy housecarls, who scratched their heads and grumbled at this sudden flurry of midnight visitations, one likening it to a hive of bees all a-buzz over some invisible upset to the queen within.

Later still, a good hour before the dawn, Godiva called Aelfwyn to her, and explained what he and the other housecarls must do. He was aghast, and pulled at his moustaches, and blustered that she should not, must not, could not do as she intended. But Godiva spoke of Ralph and the thing he held, and the captive souls, and the captain quietened. At last he agreed to her commands, and went to rouse his men.

As the first small hint of the day began to show above the hills, Godiva went alone to the bee meadow. Along the way, she passed her housecarls, one by one, who were posted at fifty yard intervals, their backs to the road. They had already turned away the few folk who were about in the last dregs of the night, lawfully or not, save for those who were also following Godiva's orders.

On the hill, the Countess of Coventry disrobed until she stood naked, her only adornment remaining a tortoiseshell comb. She pulled this free and let her long hair fall, without any attempt to twine it about herself in some show of modesty. Then she called out once, twice, three times to the bees, asking for their permission before walking down the hill to pick a good bunch of clover. She had marked an oak some ways back toward the town, which doubtless would provide the acorn, and there was a hawthorn bush close from which she would gently take a thorny branch.

◊∆◊∆◊∆◊∆◊

While Godiva picked her clover, back in the town a man no one had seen before came from an alley, smiling and rubbing his hands. He met a band of idlers by the market square who were meant to be assembling a stand but had not yet even begun to think of doing so. In the dim, pre-dawn light none noticed that their visitor did not cast a shadow.

"A rare day today," laughed the fellow. "Not every day a common man sees a countess naked!"

"What's that you say?" asked Alfred, sometime leader of his band of so-called workers. "A countess naked?"

"Sure as sure," said the man, rubbing his hands again. "As pretty a noblewoman who ever walked the land. Your own Lady Godiva, she is to walk naked as a babe through the town to the Bargain Stone."

All eyes went to the old, black stone that rose waist-high from the cobbles like some time-worn tooth, as in fact legend had it was, the tooth of the dragon of Wessex, now remembered only on the banner of the Godwin lords. It was where deals were sealed, buyer and seller signing or marking their mark on deed or bill laid upon the smoothed flat top of the ancient tooth, if tooth it was.

"Naked?" asked a man, licking his lips. "And what's the earl to do to any man who looks upon her? Flay him alive, or put his eyes out?"

"Earl's gone a-hunting, and none can gainsay the lady," said the man. "She walks alone, without her housecarls. Wait but an hour and you'll see her treasures, as will any man who cares to look."

"How do you—" Alfred began to ask, but the stranger was gone into the darkness, nimbly stepping between the first early rays of the sun, going elsewhere to spread his news.

"I'll not watch," said Begran firmly. "This sounds to be women's business, best left alone. I remember my old mum—"

His words were lost in jeers and catcalls, led by Alfred, who had caught the stranger's glee.

"You can close your eyes, old Begran, old gelding," he cried, slapping him on the back. "But we are true men and we will gaze upon any beauty that offers herself, and...and aye, more too, should she cast her own eyes back!"

There was a muttering at this, and others beside Begran slunk away. But soon enough the word spread, and more men came to the square, asking if it were true that the countess herself was walking naked to the stone, and if she was, where would be best to see all that they cared to see. Small scuffles broke out over vantage points, men trying to climb on top of stalls, and others dragging them down, scuffles made worse by the absence of the town constables who were nowhere to be seen, nor the Under-Sheriff and his men, nor the housecarls of the earl.

The greatest crowd gathered at the eastern side of the market square, where the road ran in, for it would be here that the countess would first be seen. Men jostled and pitched their elbows wide, maintaining their chosen spots, shouting and hitting as the smaller and more slippery eased between them.

All this ceased as the cry went up.

"Here she comes!"

A figure hard to see with the rising sun behind her was walking up the road. The crowd of men surged forward, then inexplicably faltered and slowed, those behind roaring with frustration until they too fell silent.

Behind the first figure there were more. And not only on the main road, but coming in from the alleys on every side, walking slowly toward the square. Dozens of naked women, nay, hundreds of naked women, and the one in the lead was not the naked body of a winsome countess, but the leathery, age- and sun-worn shape of Mother Halfgrim, leader of the laundresses, those fierce, take-no-prisoner women who could crack a man's skull with a laundry pole as easy as lift a great tub of wet clothes to their shoulders, and they were all behind her, and they were not alone.

"That's my old mum," said a suddenly deeply worried voice among the crowd, the harbinger of many, many other cries.

"My wife!"

"My daughters!"

"My grandmam and her sister!"

"Old Aunt Alys!"

"The ale-wife from the Oxen!"

"Oh! Oh! The lepers from Holy Cross!"

The women walked on silently, the men turning about in confusion, many shielding their eyes and looking down of their own accord, others being forced to do so as husbands and fathers and brothers and sons pulled down other mens' hats or hoods, or slapped them in the neck.

Mother Halfgrim stopped a few paces away from the now silent crowd of cowed and ashamed menfolk.

"Go home!" she cried, fierce as ever. "Go home and do not look out, do not look out until a woman says you may! Any who look will rue it for whatever few days remain to them thereafter! "

No one moved, until Mother Halfgrim suddenly clapped her hands and shouted.

"Go!"

At that the men broke like a rabble charged by knights, and fled back through the square, the women in the alleys parting to let them through.

Mother Halfgrim began to walk again, and the women followed. All the women, of town and castle and from villages for leagues around, all naked and marching for the square. Thousands of women, young and old and in between, and amongst them, perhaps a hundred paces behind Mother Halfgrim, walked Lady Godiva, with a smile upon her face.

The smile grew broader as the great crowd of women swirled about the market square, and Godiva weaved between them, drawing ever closer to the bargain stone, the dragon tooth. The tallest and broadest women walked with her, against the chance that some man still dared to look, but they saw none, and Godiva felt no cheating gaze, as she was sure she would.

At last, she came to the stone. The women drew close as Godiva knelt and laid the heather and the acorn upon the flat, and then with the prick of a hawthorn, added a drop of her own bright red blood. She felt a strange thrill rush through her as the blood fell on the stone, a quickening of something she had never known, a sense that she was now a part of some great and terrible power that had wakened at her call.

Lady Godiva stood and raised her voice, speaking not just to the crowd, but to the world beyond and the ancient magic that she knew awaited her call.

"I summon the Norman called Ralph, steward to my husband. Ralph, come to the stone to answer for your misdeeds!"

There was silence then, unbroken by any sound. In that stillness, women flinched at the sudden sound of heavy footsteps, boots upon the cobbles. Ralph emerged from the shadows between two houses, and advanced towards the Bargain Stone. But this was not Ralph as he was usually seen, simply a cold and remote man. The shadows companioned him now, and the sunshine itself flinched away. Even the bold laundresses stepped back, and Mother Halfgrim herself took only one of the three steps she intended to interpose herself between him and the countess.

"I come," said Ralph. His voice was angry, tinged with fire, no longer the passionless tone of a bailiff on his master's business. "Not because of your petty magic, your foolish ritual. It is time all was made clear to you, Lady, and to all you women. The earl does as I command, and so must you all. None can gainsay me."

"I summoned you to a law-giving," said Godiva, though the words were hard to find, and her teeth were inclined to want to chatter. But she knew if she faltered, all would falter, and everything would be lost. "And this is my rede. You shall recant all your works of darkness, and give up whatever you wear against your chest, so it may be destroyed."

"Recant?" asked Ralph scornfully. "Give up my amulet? No, rather I shall use it once again. I have not bothered to capture the soul of a woman before, it seems hardly worthwhile. But you...you are a thorn in my flesh that must be dealt with lest it fester."

He reached into his tunic, and lifted up the links of an iron necklace. A pendant hung from the chain, a small tablet of some dull red mineral. Though it was no larger than a thumbnail and seemed unremarkable, as Ralph held it high Godiva's eyes were immediately drawn to it, and then she could not look away, nor move her head or limbs.

Whatever power was in the amulet, it held her fast. Dread filled her, and her breath grew fast and shallowed, all her instincts demanding she flee, muscles rippling but failing to instigate any movement.

"You see," said Ralph with a sneer. "I command a greater magic than anything you think to conjure."

Ceolwen alone of all the women moved forward, bending to pick up a loose cobblestone. But even as she rose to throw it, Ralph made a negligent gesture with his left hand, and the stone ran through her fingers like water, while others gave way beneath her feet. Ceolwen was suddenly knee-deep in what had been a solidly paved surface, held fast by the ferromantic magic Ralph also had at his command.

"So," said Ralph. He brought the pendant closer to his lips, and spoke to it, in a language vanished from the world for five thousand years or more. With each word, Godiva felt as if chill, insubstantial claws were reaching inside her, going past skin and bone to pull at something she didn't even know she possessed, drawing it out of her body.

Her soul was being taken, Godiva realised, and there was nothing she could do.

She cried out, and in that same moment, some deep instinct told her there *was* still something she could do, a faint last chance. She still commanded her voice.

In that instant of realisation, Godiva transformed her cry of pain and anguish into the beginning of the bee-song.

For several long seconds, she sang alone, but then the women closest to her began to also sing, even as they were held fast in all other ways, made as steady and unmoving as the buried stones of the hill by the meadow. More and more women joined the song, and as their voices rose in unison, Godiva knew that more than their voices were joined. She felt suddenly anchored, that the bright shadow that Ralph sought to draw from her body was no longer alone and easy prey, but linked to all the women around her, and those around them, and so on and on through all the many circles.

Thousands of bright shadows joined, so many the weight of them was too great for the amulet to move, and now her own soul was coming back to her, and Ralph's hand was coming down as if the pendant had grown heavy, weighted down by the connection with more souls than it could ever drink. As it slowly fell, the oppressive force that had held Godiva ebbed as well, but she did not move. The song had to be completed first, and it was not yet done.

"No, no," growled Ralph. He fumbled at his side with his free hand, trying to draw the thin, sharp dagger scabbarded at his waist. But still the amulet was dragging him down, so that he could not balance and he tumbled forward to land sprawling at Godiva's feet.

"You cannot harm me!" he spat out. "I am no mere ironmaster, I am the Favoured of Urakazaar! No weapon wielded by man, woman or child can harm me, I cannot be slain and I will—"

His words choked off as the first great cloud of bees swarmed into his open mouth and cascaded down his throat, closely followed by the second and third that slammed into his eyes and ears.

More and more bees flew to their deaths as the song continued, thousands and thousands of them descending upon the toppled body of Ralph. As the last note slowly faded into breathlessness there was no longer an identifiable man there at all, just a lump on the ground that looked like a fallen log covered in a thick carpet of dead and dying bees.

Ceolwen stepped out of the holes in the paving and prised up a cobblestone. Very gently, she brushed back a layer of bees from Ralph's hand to reveal the chain his lifeless fingers touched, and the tiny amulet that hung from the chain. Lifting the stone high, she brought it down with all her might.

The blow bounced off what seemed only oven-baked clay, which should have been easily crushed to dust. Ceolwen gritted her teeth and raised her hand again, but stopped as she felt Godiva's fingers wrap around her own.

"We must do it together, I think," said Godiva. Other women drew close, and many hands gripped the stone.

This time, when it came down, there was a great crack, as if some mighty door had been burst asunder. The tablet exploded in a waft of reddish dust. There was the brief, sickening smell of something ancient and decayed, but both dust and stench were borne away by the fresh wind, and the shadows that had defied the sunlight shrank and were likewise gone.

A single bee alighted on Godiva's hand as she straightened up. She raised it close to her face, and breathed upon it gently.

"Thank the mothers, sister," she said. "For all they have given us."

The bee flew up, and circled Godiva's head to take its bearing from the sun, before heading unerringly towards the bee meadow and the queens in their conical huts.

"They have given much," said Ceolwen. "There will be little honey this season, and perhaps the next."

"Yes," said Godiva. She felt very tired, and very dirty, and very naked. "But it is done."

"For now," said Ceolwen.

"For now?" asked Godiva quietly.

"Seasons turn, there is birth and death and rebirth," said Ceolwen. "For everything, even an ancient evil. Perhaps not in our time, but it will come."

"So," said Godiva. She looked around at the crowded market full of naked, determined women.

Her mouth settled in a grim line. This host needed no armour, no weapons, no boasts and shouting. But if she were the enemy, she would be greatly afraid.

Mary, Mary

Kirstyn McDermott

The woman in the bed makes a soft, parched sound that might be a groan, that might be a name long carried, never forgotten, or else a name more recently brought in careful, eager hands to the heart-shaped cage in her breast. *Fanny,* she might be saying, or *William.* Or perhaps she merely moans as thin rivers of fire course beneath her skin and her throat closes dry around each breath. A minute passes, or several, sickroom time stretched far beyond compassion, before her eyelids rasp open once more.

"Patience," she mutters. "A little patience."

In a chair near the door, a man sleeps slumped against the curl of his fist. Carlisle, the woman remembers, her husband's surgeon-friend with his large, kindly hands and eyes that fail altogether to mask his dismay, no matter the words of comfort he proffers. Carlisle, the *good* doctor, not the one who came before: those brusque and brutal fingers scraping at her womb, tearing the reluctant placenta loose piece by grisly piece; eighteen hours of labour and she would have suffered that pain tenfold in trade for its bloody aftermath.

Bear up, Mrs Godwin. We must have the whole of it out.

The woman has crafted her life in words; she can find none with which to approach such an agony.

A movement by the window on the other side of the room snares her attention and she rolls her head on the pillow. At first she surmises that a witching-hour breeze has billowed the drapes—though they have been drawn close now for days, the glass behind them a shield against the noxious vapours of London's air—but now a tall, dark shape frees itself from the shadows and moves towards the bed. Tallow-light flickers across a familiar countenance; narrow hands clasp and unclasp.

"I cannot help you this time," the Grey Lady says. "This is not a mouthful of laudanum. It is not the foul waters of the Thames with boatmen ready at hand. This is...beyond me."

The woman in the bed swallows. "I have never asked it of you."

"And yet."

"And yet."

The Grey Lady leans forward, nostrils flaring. Perhaps she smiles.

"I apologise." The woman in the bed averts her gaze. "The...odours are unpleasant." Sweat and blood, the stench of putrid flesh; she is rotting from the inside out and knows it, catches the smell of herself whenever she moves: arms lifted to steady a glass against her lips; the anguish of negotiating the chamber pot. Her body tells more truths than a priest—ah, how William's jaw would clench at such superstitious fancies. *I feel in heaven*, she recalls confessing, words floating on the tincture Carlisle had administered. A turn of her husband's mouth, his hand swaddling her own: *I suppose, my dear, that is a form for saying you are in less pain*. Her own dear Horatio.

"Mrs Godwin?" The good doctor himself, as though stirred by these recollections, rises from his chair. "How do you feel, may I enquire?"

"No worse," she says. "I fear, no better."

"There's naught to be gained from such conjecture, Mrs Godwin." He crosses to the bed and presses a hand first to her brow, then to her left cheek. The coolness of his skin is welcome; the accompanying concern that pinches at his face, less so. "I shall rouse your husband. He wished to be fetched when next you woke." Carlisle leaves the room in hurried strides, sparing not a glance for the tall figure standing opposite.

"He did not see you," the woman in the bed remarks. Her tone is one of confirmation rather than surprise. "Good men would see angels, would they not?"

"I am not an angel," the Grey Lady says. "We have traversed this ground many times."

"A devil then. A demon."

"I know of no such creatures."

"Nor of heaven, nor hell."

"I cannot say such places do *not* exist, only that I know nothing of them."

"Yet, if shades such as yourself exist, might not angels? Might not heaven?" After so many years, the conversation is rote; it has worn grooves in her tongue.

The Grey Lady smiles. "I cannot say otherwise."

"I—" The woman in the bed grimaces against a sudden spike of pain. "I am dying."

"Yes."

"You are the first to speak it."

"There have never been untruths between us. There should be none now." Again, she leans close. Again, her nose twitches. "Mary Wollstonecraft, you smell of burnt sugar, and hyacinth, and…" Those colourless eyes widen. "And *hope*? Even at this juncture?"

"I am frightened," the woman in the bed whispers. Within her, a renewed heat builds and she can feel sweat beading fresh on her skin. The pain worsens. "I am very frightened."

The Grey Lady smooths a place in the rumpled bedclothes and sits. "I will not leave." A small yellow wasp emerges from the collar of her blouse to crawl over her clavicle and along her throat. She moves as though to swat it, then pauses, hand hovering by her face. The insect takes flight and describes a slow, buzzing circle before alighting on the Grey Lady's knee. Its segmented body twitches. "She, too, will stay."

The woman in the bed closes her eyes. Blood simmers in her veins. This is not her end.

"This is not my end."

"There is always an end," the Grey Lady reminds her. "What fascinates is the beginning."

◊∆◊∆◊∆◊∆◊∆◊

Rehearsing the words of aggrieved indignation she would consign to paper the very moment she returned home, Mary Wollstonecraft stalked across Westwood Common. How bitterly disappointing to have believed Miss Arden worthy of the highest friendship, only to find herself scorned once again in favour of other girls. Those whose better circumstances, no doubt, saw them placed unforgivably higher in Miss Arden's affections.

Mary could scarcely be blamed for her family's diminishing standing, or her father's foul temper and weakness for gambling. She suspected the whole of Beverley made barbed sport of Edward Wollstonecraft, yet it wasn't a single one of *them* who slept sentry on the landing outside her mother's door those nights he staggered home with pockets barren and fists full of drunken rage. On brash, abrasive Mary, he would not dare to lay a finger, and often she found herself regarding a new bruise on her mother's face with seething, unexpected contempt.

If only Elizabeth Wollstonecraft would refuse to yield to her husband. If only she would not *succumb*.

If that soulless bond was marriage, Mary wanted no part of it.

Nor friendship either, certainly not friendship with Jane Arden, who deigned to offer tea and lemoncake to Mary merely as an afterthought, it seemed, having first seen to the care and comfort of the evidently superior Miss Jacobs. Even Jane's mama had behaved with more politeness towards the girl, complimenting her pretty muslin petticoats and the stylish manner in which her blonde hair had been curled and cleverly pinned.

Mary fumed. She would demand the letters she had written Jane Arden be returned forthwith, lest her words pass between vulgar hands and be made the subject of gossip and scorn. The very notion of enduring such slights from a person she loved—and which affection she had supposed returned!—was too much to bear.

Her foot splashed the edge of a puddle and she recoiled, breath hissing sharp through her teeth at her own carelessness before a bright scrap of yellow attracted her eye: a bee struggled on the surface of the murky water, damp wings aquiver in their valiant effort to attain the sky. Sympathies aroused, Mary bent closer. Not a bee, she realised, but a wood wasp. Autumn winds had shed the surrounding oak trees of most of their foliage and it took Mary scarcely a moment to find a suitable leaf, brown and curled at the edges like a small boat. Gathering her skirts about her, she crouched by the puddle and extended the makeshift vessel.

"Do you suppose that a wise course of action?"

The voice was unexpected and Mary started, dropping the leaf in the puddle and almost toppling backwards. Regaining her balance, she looked up to see a tall, elegant lady in a grey silk redingote and matching gloves standing but a few yards from where she herself crouched, undignified as a washerwoman.

"That is a wasp, child," the lady said. "Rescue it and you'll likely be stung for your trouble."

"I am not a child," Mary retorted. "Nor do I see why the poor creature would have any reason to do me harm."

"It is a *wasp*. What greater reason would it seek?"

Ignoring her unwelcome interlocutor, Mary retrieved the leaf and positioned it beneath the creature in question, which was now clearly tiring. Carefully, she raised the leaf up, allowing the water to drain over an edge while the wasp remained safe, albeit sodden, within.

"There," Mary said, gaining her feet as she brandished her trophy for closer inspection. "She merely needs to dry her wings."

The lady stepped closer, right to the edge of the puddle. She bent forward as if to study the proffered leaf but her gaze never shifted from Mary's. Her irises were a pale, watery grey and strangely flat, without hint of sparkle or sheen, as though they drew light into themselves yet, covetous, hoarded all outward reflection. After too long a moment, her eyelids shuttered and she sniffed; a subtle, delicate motion that reminded Mary of nothing so much as the family's tabby cat taking scent of the kitchen while supper was being prepared.

At last, the lady opened her eyes. "Ah," she said. "You see?"

The wasp had crawled from the leaf and was making cautious progress along Mary's palm. Mary held her breath as spindly yellow legs tickled her skin. "If I remain still, she shall not sting me."

"But is that within your nature, Mary Wollstonecraft? To remain still?"

Startled, Mary glanced up. "I did not give you my name."

Without warning, a gloved hand snaked out and plucked the wasp from Mary's wrist. Wings pinned together, the insect twitched furiously between gentle fingers, its black-barbed abdomen seeking a target. "You smell of rising dough and jonquils and, ah, such wilful ambition," the lady in grey said. Then she thrust the wasp into her mouth as though it were nothing more than a boiled sweet and began to chew.

Mary looked on in horror. And with no small amount of curiosity. "But does it not sting?" she asked.

The lady's thin lips spread into something resembling a smile. Scraps of semi-chewed wasp blackened the gaps between her teeth. "I intend to keep a watch on you, Mary Wollstonecraft. I believe there will be much of interest to observe."

◊Δ◊Δ◊Δ◊Δ◊Δ◊

William Godwin, eyes red-rimmed and puffy, encloses her hand within his own. "Mary, my dear, it is necessary to talk of the children. Respecting their care while you are ill, as you may be for…for some time to come. Are there especial instructions you would leave me? For the children?"

The woman in the bed blinks. "The children?" He has a kind face, her husband. She has always thought so.

"The children," he echoes. "Little Fanny, and the baby. Remember, they have been sent to stay with Mrs Reveley until…until you are well once more."

She remembers, of course she remembers. Her daughter, Fanny, named in dearest memory of one by whose side she herself had kept helpless vigil so many years ago. Watching day and night while her sallow friend sickened and rallied and sickened once more. Watching, too, as the weak little creature her friend had birthed succumbed with barely a whimper, his gummy mouth limp against the wet nurse's breast.

"The baby is dead," the woman in the bed whispers.

"No, Mary," William says. "Our daughter is strong and in good health. Do not weep for her sake, I beg you; she is in no danger."

"The baby is dead," she insists.

On the other side of the room, the Grey Lady speaks up. "It was Fanny's baby who died, Mary, not yours."

"And Fanny, too. Fanny is dead."

"Yes, Fanny is dead," the Grey Lady agrees. "But your *daughters* are both alive."

Her husband pushes more words across the coverlet but the woman in the bed pays them no mind. "So many dead babies, and their poor mothers with them." Tears scald her eyes. "Oh, for naught, for naught."

On this matter, the Grey Lady remains silent.

◊∆◊∆◊∆◊∆◊∆◊

In Lisbon, the late November weather was more clement than what London might have offered, but Mary Wollstonecraft nevertheless harboured a deep chill in the marrow of her bones. She stood with her arms crossed, her back turned away from the bed where Fanny Blood—nay, Fanny *Skeys*, as her tombstone would newly have it—lay motionless and cold beneath the coverlet. If she had permitted herself a glance, Mary knew that she would see a yellow wasp perched on the dead woman's brow, its forelegs bent as though in prayer. But she would *not* look. Around her finger, she curled and uncurled a lock of brown hair, recently snipped.

"If Skeys had but married her sooner," Mary said bitterly. "If he had brought her across to Portugal a year or two ago rather than leave her behind to languish in London, her health might have been perfectly restored."

Beside her, the Grey Lady tilted her chin. It was a gesture approaching acknowledgment more than agreement, and one Mary had come to find exceedingly irritating. "Fanny was consumptive for a long time," the Grey Lady said. "An earlier marriage—an earlier pregnancy—might have equally exacerbated her condition."

Mary exhaled sharply. "You cannot know this."

"No, but I may decline to play such fateful games."

Pressing her lips tightly together, Mary shook her head. Her heart felt empty, scoured out by this most recent blow. Surely, if she closed her eyes and allowed her imagination free rein, she might follow once more the footfalls of her sixteen-year-old self. Might step into that neat little house and meet afresh the slender and elegant girl who had instantly and irrevocably captured the entirety of her passion, of her desirous soul, with the turn of a gentle cheek and diffident flash of a smile.

And might Mary not then hold this girl in safer keeping than the world hence had done? Might they not set up a home together, alone, Fanny with her painting and clever seamstress fingers, and Mary able to find like employment perhaps, or perhaps even secure a teaching position? Might she not be permitted to then love Fanny as she truly wished, wholly and without censure or rejection, to feel that small, flushed hand clasped tight within her own, until their breaths jointly expired?

Instead of this. A fractured and disparate decade, so small a span, passed in such grievous haste.

"What will you do now?" the Grey Lady asked.

Mary wiped tears from her face. "Once matters here are settled, I expect I shall return to Newington Green—though I fear my sisters will have sorely neglected our little school in my absence. Everina does well enough if someone is nearby to drive her along, but Eliza…Eliza is a helpless thing."

"Your own contribution to her state is not insignificant."

Mary stiffened. "My *contribution* was to remove a near-deranged young mother from her *oblivious* husband lest she commit some dreadful harm to her own person. She did not wish to remain with him; you heard her speak it on several occasions."

"She might not have wished to leave her infant daughter behind."

"Do not scold me for that in which I was given no choice. If children were not deemed to be the property of husbands, how many more wives might seek to escape their arduous marriages?"

The Grey Lady tilted her chin. "I apologise. This is not the time to remonstrate on such subjects."

"I could not know the baby would die. It was always my hope to reunite them once my sister was well."

"That is true, but it provides no comfort to Eliza."

Mary pulled the lock of Fanny's hair even tighter around her finger until the tip darkened and swelled. To attend so frequently upon illness and death might be thought to numb a person utterly, but Mary had been left in a state of raw sensitivity. It was she who had nursed her abject, querulous mother throughout the months of her final lingering disease, changing dressings that did little more than hide the seeping necrotic flesh beneath, all the while managing her father's ill-tempered impatience. It was upon her shoulders that care for poor, distraught Eliza had fallen—care and responsibility and blame for executing the only plan she thought viable, the sole desperate avenue of escape at their disposal.

And now Fanny, dearest Fanny, and her tiny newborn son.

Mary was exhausted, in her body and in her heart. "I cannot continue. Not without her."

"And yet you will," the Grey Lady said. "As you always have."

◊∆◊∆◊∆◊∆◊

"Has it grown dark?" the woman in the bed asks. "I cannot see you."

"I am here, Mary," the Grey Lady says. Her tone is smooth as velvet curtains.

Deeper, more strained voices entreat from the wings, but the woman in the bed pushes them aside. She will no longer be corralled by the demands of men.

"I am here," the Grey Lady repeats.

◊Δ◊Δ◊Δ◊Δ◊Δ◊

When she'd set off for St Paul's to see her publisher that evening, Mary Wollstonecraft's mood had been one of anxious despondency. As much as the decision grieved her, she would need to abandon her rebuttal of Edmund Burke's recent attack on the French Revolution, on the principles and passionate character of a people determined to dismantle a pernicious monarchy. Who was she to tackle so protracted and presumptuous a project, one so removed from her usual territory of pedagogy, fiction and the criticism, however barbed and insightful, that she regularly contributed to the *Analytical Review*?

Joseph Johnson had been encouraging of the proposed pamphlet, certainly, and she was painfully aware that he'd already had her first pages printed in anticipation of their completion, but her mind now floundered within its own argument. Clamorous ideas buzzed and batted within the confines of her skull, refusing to be pinned to the page: feckless parents, irresponsible aristocrats and spoiled eldest sons—her own brother, Ned, came readily to mind—who inherited familial wealth yet neglected to care for poverty-struck sisters; the inherent privilege entrenched in class and gender that bred selfishness and injustice within men, and forced desperate women into marriages little better than legal forms of prostitution; the dire need for social and economic reform, rather than dependence upon charity, which did merely gratify wealthy sensitives seeking to congratulate themselves on their benevolence while continuing to indulge in the vices of inequity.

So vast a problem, so much of which to speak, and—most insistent among her thoughts—who was Mary Wollstonecraft, former governess, sometime author and literary critic, to write *A Vindication of the Rights of Men*?

Now, as she mounted the steps to her George Street home, Mary did so with clenched teeth and renewed vigour. Her hands shook as she peeled away her gloves and hung her beaver-fur hat on its stand. She was not at all surprised to find a familiar figure waiting in her study.

"You are returned early," the Grey Lady remarked as Mary seated herself at her desk. "I thought you might have stayed for dinner."

"I find myself quite without appetite for food."

"Did Mr Johnson take your decision well?"

"Mr Johnson said that I should not struggle against my feelings. That I should indeed lay aside the work if that would better my happiness. That he would destroy all that had already been written and printed, and do so cheerfully." Mary snorted. "*Cheerfully* was the precise word he used. For such a *mutilation*."

The Grey Lady smiled. "All is well then, and you may continue with your other work. A review of that play you attended with *Henry Fuseli*, perhaps?"

At the mention of the name, Mary felt her stomach flutter. She released a deep breath and steeled herself. No matter how great their genius, no matter how seductive their whispers, certain Swiss artists could be given no place in her heart this night, nor for many nights to come.

"I will put nothing aside," Mary said. "Effusions of the moment these pages might be, but the moment is of no small import." Unhappy with its banishment, Fuseli's visage flitted across her mind. Undaunted, she flicked it away. "Tell me, why should genuine *passion* be so well regarded when it flows from the paintbrush of a man, but not from the pen of a woman?"

"It is the way of things," the Grey Lady said. "As those with means and power govern those without, that which is male governs all that is female."

"It need not be so," Mary countered. "France shines hope upon us, no matter the worn and tired *nostalgia* that Burke and his ilk parade as vaunted tradition. We should yet see a progressive society built upon talent and ambition, rather than unearned privilege. Why should it be our continued duty to repair an ancient castle, built in barbarous ages, of Gothic materials?"

"Do you say, we should allow such edifices to crumble?"

"I say..." Mary paused. Her eyes narrowed dangerously. "We should bring them to rubble ourselves."

The Grey Lady clasped gloved hands together at her waist. "I would very much like to see such a world as you describe."

Mary picked up her pen and found the place among her papers where her thoughts had stumbled and trailed off earlier in the day. Frowning, she crossed out a line or two. Then she cleared her throat, dipped nib into ink and began anew, words flying from her as furious wasps provoked from their nest.

◊Δ◊Δ◊Δ◊Δ◊Δ◊

She was called a *hyena in petticoats*, a *philisophising serpent*. She was accused of lacking reason, of seeking to poison and inflame the minds of the lower classes, of being too shallow a thinker.

Those at the *Gentleman's Magazine* confessed themselves astonished that a *fair lady* might seek to assert the *rights of men*, remarking that they were always taught to suppose that *the rights of women were the proper theme of the female sex.*

By *rights*, they did not refer to those of education or self-determination. *While Romans governed the world*, they pointed out, *the women governed the Romans.* The age of chivalry having thankfully not yet passed, women should content themselves with ruling from the boudoir—though it remained questionable that such a viper as Mary Wollstonecraft might gain for herself so coveted a position.

The rights of women, indeed! Oh ho, what fertile ground for sarcasm and jest!

◊∆◊∆◊∆◊∆◊∆◊

Lips moving silently as she walked, Mary Wollstonecraft rehearsed the words she would soon say to Sophia Fuseli, sounding them for depth and clarity. Hers was an inarguably practical solution, a proposal that would surely suit all parties, and a *rational* one at that. Despite her many impassioned letters to the man, Mary suspected a recent cooling of Henry's sensibilities and she required the situation between them to be resolved. Her mind would otherwise remain fragmented, her thoughts unmarshalled.

The printing of a second edition of *A Vindication of the Rights of Woman* had allowed Mary not only to correct some glaring errors of grammar and spelling, but to bolster arguments she feared too weak in the version Johnson had rushed to press this January—yet again! the Devil coming for the conclusion of a sheet before it was written!—but still she was unhappy. Although gratified by the book's reception—more welcoming than her previous *Rights of Man* had enjoyed—a second volume remained to be written, her ideas expanded beyond the core theme of female education. If women were ever to be the equal of men, they would need to be treated thus, with responsibilities greater than coquetry, manners and marriage placed upon their dainty shoulders.

Why should they not aspire to autonomy? To their proper place within governance, commerce and the intellectual life of their society? A woman who had not power over her own self would remain forever a slave, and surely no true progressive argument could seek to deny universal rights to one half of the population...

Residual anger warming her cheeks, Mary paused to compose herself; she could not arrive in such a visible state of consternation.

Sophia Fuseli was already seated by the window when Mary was admitted into the modest but charmingly appointed parlour.

"Miss Wollstonecraft." The younger woman scarcely smiled as she gestured towards a chair opposite. Her pretty face, those model features her husband so adored, remained stiff and unyielding. "May I offer you tea?"

Mary accepted both seat and beverage, though she perched nervously upon the edge of one and took little more than a sip of the other. Less than a quarter of an hour later, it was Sophia Fuseli whose complexion reddened and flushed. Her cup trembled on its saucer as she reached to place them on the table.

"You insult both my husband and his wife, Miss Wollstonecraft." The woman's tone was chilled, crisp as frosted glass. "And you make yourself a fool."

"You misunderstand me," Mary said. "I do not wish to share Henry with you in the manner of wife—"

"Kindly take your leave, *Miss* Wollstonecraft."

But how could she, when Sophia was clearly confused as to her intentions—for why else would the woman take such prompt and livid offence? "Please, I do not mean to insult your marriage. My proposal arises solely from the sincere affection which I have for Henry, I can assure you. We have an *intellectual* affinity, he and I, and I plainly find that I cannot live without the satisfaction of seeing and conversing with him daily."

"You shall have to find a means of living so."

"But if we all inhabited the same household—"

"Will you not quiet your tongue?"

"Consider the practicalities, Mrs Fuseli, if nothing else. We are none of us people of great means; to combine resources and share expenses within one household—"

"*Miss Wollstonecraft!*" Sophia Fuseli rose up in one violent motion. She thrust a finger at Mary, who struggled to gain her feet as readily. "You shall leave my house this moment and never again *stain* its rooms—or my husband's studio—with your presence. You are no woman of principle, to speak so boldly of your rights and yet seek to trample roughshod over mine. You are no *woman* at all, but a monster."

Escorted to the street by the Fuselis' housekeeper, Mary stumbled but a dozen steps before stopping to brace herself against a wall. Around her, London bustled through its afternoon. Pedestrians passed oblivious to her humiliation as the clatter of hooves on cobblestones, the wooden groan of coaches, assaulted her ears. Her heart was an empty, gnawing thing within her. She had lost Henry.

She had lost Henry.

Her scalp prickled with sudden regard. Blinking away tears, Mary looked about her. On the opposite side of the street, still and perfectly unjostled by the milling foot traffic, stood a tall woman wearing a hat dressed with ostrich feathers. The woman's face was stern, reproving, and even at this distance, Mary could glimpse the disappointment in those steely eyes.

Well? Though she but mouthed them, the Grey Lady's words pealed loud as funeral bells in Mary's mind. *Did I not warn you, Mary Wollstonecraft? Did I not say?*

◊Δ◊Δ◊Δ◊Δ◊Δ◊

If her heart was a cage, she was unduly careless of its latch.

Fleeing the whispers and sneers of London, she sought refuge in Paris scant weeks before the execution of the king, and so became witness not to her beloved revolution but to the bloody terror that would claim it. Helpless to do aught but write, she took up her pen with fervour, heedless of the danger in her very English observations. In her politics, in her words, Mary Wollstonecraft was fearless.

But her heart *was* a cage, and its door remained open long after Fuseli had slipped featherless from its hold. Open, inviting another who alighted upon the flimsy bars and sang of love and desire and the untasted delight of sweat-salted skin. Another who skipped inside to settle for a while, or at least to give appearance of settling, his brash American plumage so bright and strange that Mary found *herself* wholly captivated—in her mind and soul and finally, wondrously, in her body.

◊Δ◊Δ◊Δ◊Δ◊Δ◊

"She is exquisite, is she not?" Mary Imlay, as she now styled herself, held her newborn daughter against her breast. "Ten perfect fingers in miniature, and look! Eyes the very shade of my darling Gilbert's. Surely now that our Fanny is here, he will stay in Le Havre with us. Whoever could resist such eyes as these?"

"She is indeed a most agreeable child," the Grey Lady said.

Frowning, the new mother glanced up. "You mock me?"

"I have never mocked you, Mary Wollstonecraft. But I do worry."

Such concern was not misplaced.

Barely three months of shared parenthood were hers to enjoy that summer before Gilbert Imlay, her once-soulful lover, now less-than-official husband chafing under harness, left for London on matters of business similar to those that had dragged him away during her pregnancy. As before, he promised to send for her when matters were settled. As before, months slid past with no firmer word on when that might occur.

Her treatise on the French Revolution completed prior to Fanny's birth, Mary was without a literary project with which to occupy herself. Instead, her word-churned mind bloated and burst itself over a near constant production of correspondence to Imlay—longing, scornful, desirous, admonishing letters that scarce received a satisfactory reply. Bodily, she devoted herself to Fanny, nursing the baby through smallpox, encouraging her efforts first to crawl and then to stand, rubbing her gums with chamomile as the first tooth began to cut.

"She will need to be weaned," Mary said, wincing as the child mauled a nipple between her newly armed gums.

"She is not the only one," the Grey Lady remarked.

Abandoned and friendless in the port city of Le Havre, Mary bundled up her daughter and returned to Paris. With Robespierre fallen, the streets were at last clean of the bloody work of the guillotine, but that winter proved the harshest of her thirty-six years. It was a winter of poor harvests and famine-priced food, a winter of unobtainable coal and wood cut laboriously by her own chapped hands, a winter of despair and burgeoning suspicion.

Imlay, came the whispers from foe and well-meaning friend alike, never intended to send for her or Fanny. Instead, he frittered his money away on the company of pretty London actresses.

On one pretty London actress in particular.

She tried to not heed them, but the words sank into her marrow.

Mary's latchless heart was ill. Her soul was weary. The impish, smiling face of her daughter undid her daily; she loved the child more than she would have once thought possible, and yet those soft and vivacious features bore so solid a stamp of Imlay upon them, it was sometimes nearer cruelty than kindness to behold them.

At night, alone with the darkness and a silence that no sound save Fanny's fluttering breath could penetrate, Mary's thoughts thickened and set. She pitied the poor mite for being born a girl into a world run by men for their own ends, and wondered what earthly good she was showing herself to be as a mother. Certainly no better a mother than wife, or sister, or any kind of *woman* at all, and now that the child was no longer in need of her milk—

"I am nothing," Mary whispered to the empty air.

She required, and received, no reply.

◊∆◊∆◊∆◊∆◊∆◊

Finally, there came a summons to London, though she set off with little more than resignation in her breast. This was for Fanny, who deserved more from a father than the pauper-gift of his name, and it was for Fanny too that Marguerite accompanied them. The efficient new maid seemed as excited to see England as Mary had once been to visit France.

Mary's gelid, smoke-grey thoughts trailed them all.

They were settled at Charlotte Street, the lodgings comfortably furnished with all but Imlay himself who vacillated between affection and apology, but remained acutely stubborn in his refusal to adopt the role of *Paterfamilias*. A refusal of which, it seemed, all of London was jovially aware.

The laudanum, she later insisted, was an error of judgement.

She had not intended—

Certainly not—

She had once been Mary Wollstonecraft.

Movement was the key, as it always had been. If she remained still, in her body or in her mind, thick-thumbed gloom would smother her alive.

And so, to the astonishment of many, she agreed to Imlay's proposal of a Scandinavian journey—some long-outstanding business she might follow up on his behalf, a traitorous ship captain to track down in Sweden, a purloined cargo of silver and gold to pursue in foreign courts—with the insinuation that their personal situation might be further resolved over the months of her—and Fanny's—absence. Having sighted once more the woman who had so inflamed his passions in Paris, having held again the child those passions had born, might it not be that Imlay merely required time and space in which to unfetter himself from present entanglements?

At this barest hint of oil, Mary's heart flung open with a shriek.

◊Δ◊Δ◊Δ◊Δ◊Δ◊

It was dim inside the carriage, and her clothing was wet and stinking of the Thames. She stared at her trembling hands, at fingernails still tinged corpse-blue, as though they alone had managed to resist the pull of the wakeful world.

"You are a foolish, obstinate woman, Mary Wollstonecraft." The Grey Lady sat opposite, arms crossed over her breast, mouth drawn pencil thin.

"Mary *Imlay*," she corrected, as she had done countless times this past year. Her throat rasped with the sting of a thousand wasps; she would never forget the unexpected agony of drowning, the furious burn of all that water rushing to fill her. If she had been foolish, it was only in her expectation that such an end might be painless.

The Grey Lady snorted. "You have never been Mrs *Imlay*, in truth, and pray never shall be."

"He is resolved that another might take that name."

"You knew this."

"Until yesterday, I only suspected."

"You *knew*, Mary, let us not pretend otherwise."

Mary shook her head. All those letters sent speeding back through

Denmark, Norway, Sweden, all those notes received in turn from his deceitful hand, all those hints and promises that she and Fanny might still have a place by his side—only to return to find him setting up house with his *actress*. With the whole of London witness to her humiliation, to Imlay's callous desertion, she had seen no other way to extricate herself or her daughter from the wretchedness into which they had been plunged.

"It was you who saved me," Mary said.

"I breathed upon a fisherman's nape," the Grey Lady replied. "Encouraged him to turn towards Putney Bridge at the moment of your leaping; that was the furthest of my ability. It was he, and those in the tavern, who effected your resuscitation."

"You would play my guardian angel, then?"

"I am no angel, Mary. Must we tread this patch anew?"

"A monster then, to see me dragged back to life and misery."

"To life, yes, and to your child."

Tears coursed down her cheeks but Mary made no move to wipe at them. "I had—I had made provisions for Fanny. She was to return to France, to be raised safe from the taint of her mother's errors, beyond the scorn of those who would damn her for her parents' degradation."

"This performance is wasted," the Grey Lady snapped. "You are no martyr to wail in sackcloth and ashes."

"You cannot know what I endure! What I have endured these past months—"

"But I do. Each passion, each *degradation*, that has e'er passed through you, I have felt most keenly. I know you, Mary Wollstonecraft. I know that you suffer, I know that your suffering is genuine—but, oh, how you delight in *feeding* it."

"Do not presume to tell me—"

"I shall do more than *presume* and, for once, you shall do naught but listen." The Grey Lady leaned forward; her eyes were flat metal discs in their shadowed sockets. "You make of people what *you* would have them be—such superior beings! so worthy of your heart!—and then you mourn their failings, when you are not blinding yourself to them. Imlay, Fuseli, even Fanny Blood—yes, Fanny; do not appear so shocked—they are more vital to you in their absence, for their presence can never approach the chimeras you have fashioned in their stead."

"You take Gilbert's side in this?" Beneath her despair, a renewed anger simmered.

"Never." The Grey Lady's voice was softer now, its barbs for the moment withdrawn. "I will always stand with you, but I will not tip soothing lies into your ear, nor will I aid this melancholy. You are stronger than you imagine, Mary, and I would have you see *yourself* through clear, unclouded eyes."

Shivering, Mary rubbed her cheeks. Rain pattered on the carriage roof and she found herself wishing the journey would never reach its end. For all her intellectual accomplishments, her much-prized rationality, she was terrified. Alone and abandoned she had been on several occasions, and penniless too, but never in so dire a situation as this. Never with a child—a *girl* child—for whom to care and somehow shield from the world's most outrageous fortunes.

"Oh!" she cried as her daughter's round and rosy face flashed into her mind. "My little Fanny, I would have left you to them. How could I have thought..."

"Your thoughts were elsewhere," the Grey Lady said. "They have been elsewhere for too long now, and it is past time you collected them." She sniffed the air, her nose wrinkling in displeasure. "Spoiled yeast and calla lilies and desperation, still."

"I can smell only mud and sewage."

The Grey Lady chuckled. "That too, of course."

"My heart beats, yet this feels a living death."

"While it seems so, I will not leave you."

Mary pressed her face to the window. "It is dark outside."

"It is October; the days grow short."

"It is so very dark." For the barest of breaths, Mary imagined she could feel the squeeze of gloved hands about her wrists. She closed her eyes. "I am frightened."

"Know that I am here," the Grey Lady said. "And cling to this, if nothing else: you are *not* a fate-spun heroine from one of those Gothic Romances you so despise."

This time she was certain that she felt it, the touch of flocked velvet soft as infant skin against her bare, chilled flesh. The impossible pressure of those thin and gentle fingers.

"You are Mary Wollstonecraft, and you will die for no *man*."

◊∆◊∆◊∆◊∆◊∆◊

Even in darkness, words glimmered and beckoned, drawing her outwards. First, the mixed blessing of her journals, notes for the travelogue that Joseph Johnson had commissioned upon learning of her Scandinavian endeavour. She wrought from them an epistolary elevated by personal circumstance: a woman journeying alone with an infant; a woman caught in the process of betrayal and abandonment; a woman traversing the masculine spheres of commerce, politics, creativity and philosophy—and crafting such clever, such *candid* dispatches.

Behold: Mary Wollstonecraft, Traveller-Philosopher!

Her mind flexed, and lightened.

Invigorated, finding solid footing once more among the literary circles of London, she conceived a fresh project by which she rapidly became consumed. *Maria*, the novel would be titled, or *The Wrongs of Woman*, and from the first she was resolved on a slow and calculated execution. The crafting of a truly *excellent* book was an arduous task, and this time Mary would not allow herself to be rushed. This time, she would reflect and revise and reconsider. This time, her words would ring with utter clarity.

Behold: Mary Wollstonecraft, Polemic Novelist!

Her heart, too, discovered a new fascination. Or perhaps *re*discovered it.

Upon the occasion of their first meeting years before at one of Johnson's weekly dinners, Mary had found William Godwin irksome in his undiscerning admiration of supposedly eminent men. He had, in turn, thought her too outspoken in conversation, especially when he would have preferred to imbibe the opinions of others around the table. Other eminent *men*, an unspoken qualification she had perceived only too well.

Newly reacquainted within overlapping social circles, they found themselves drawn to one another with the inexorable, near imperceptible weight of planetary bodies whose orbits, previously misaligned, now moved in startling synchronicity. Mary's passions, never cooled, rekindled. William's, to his own astonishment, burned all the bolder for their hitherto untested state.

But non-planetary bodies, bodies of flesh and flagrant blood, follow their own particular, if not wholly predictable, paths and thus conceive *projects* of their own.

See William Godwin, famous for his very public repudiations of marriage as a moral institution.

See Mary "Imlay", already sensitive to gossip and the subject of much speculation.

Then imagine—oh imagine!—the fraught negotiation of these two proud and independent souls around the sudden expectation of a third. The small, private ceremony at St Pancras. The quiet series of announcements to friends. The united front against those who shunned them, those who mocked and scorned and professed outrage, or merely snide amusement, at a marriage for which the catalyst would soon became roundly apparent.

Behold: Mary Wollstonecraft, Mother-To-Be, Redux.

◊Δ◊Δ◊Δ◊Δ◊Δ◊

The woman in the bed opens her eyes and tries to focus on the figures surrounding her. There is William, dear William, his tired face so pale, his eyes sunken. The doctor, the good doctor, whose name she cannot for the moment recall. And, of course, the other.

"I did not finish," the woman in the bed croaks. "I thought there was time, at last, to be still."

William clutches her hand. "There is time, my love."

"There is no time," the Grey Lady says quietly.

No attention is paid to her by any soul present save the woman in the bed, who struggles now to sit up, who is restrained by the gentlest of palms placed against her panting sternum, who is entreated to rest, to save her words for when she is well. William's eyes are glossy with tears.

The woman in the bed stares past him. "My baby, who will teach her, who will protect her?"

"Hush." William brushes damp hair from her face. "There will be time to talk of such matters."

"There is no time," the Grey Lady repeats. "I will not lie to you, Mary."

"You must look to her," the woman in the bed pleads. "Look to her as you have me."

Hush, my love, do not worry yourself so needlessly.

"That is not my purpose," the Grey Lady says.

"Then *make* it your purpose. My daughter will not know her mother."

Carlisle? Carlisle, she is raving; see how her face contorts?

Mr Godwin, I can do nothing further to help her.

The Grey Lady moves closer to the bed. A yellow wasp crawls down her sleeve and into the palm of her hand. "I am sorry, Mary. If it were in my power, I would ease all the suffering in the world, beginning with your own."

"It is dark," the woman in the bed whispers. "It is dark as the Thames."

Carlisle, fetch that lamp here. Mary, see? There is yet light.

I fear it will not be long, Mr Godwin.

"I felt as one standing on a precipice," the woman in the bed says. "All the world bustled and buzzed below me and for once I need not race away. There would be time, the baby would come, and there would yet be time for all I wished to do." Her chapped lips crack around a smile. "I should be at my desk."

Mary, be still now. Hush.

"Do not leave me, I beg you."

Never, my love. I am here always.

"I will not leave you." The Grey Lady extends a hand. "But here, open your mouth."

Insect legs scratch and tickle as they crawl over her tongue. The woman in the bed presses the wasp against her palate, feels its barbed abdomen burst even as it sinks its sting into her flesh. Where she expected pain, there is instead a spreading languid heat and the taste of molasses on fresh-baked bread.

"It is all I can do," the Grey Lady says.

It is enough.

◊∆◊∆◊∆◊∆◊∆◊

Do not suppose this to be her ending.

It is a play truncated in its second act, a journey derailed before its terminus, a cloth cut short by miser's blades; you cannot decipher the whole pattern from but a fragment in your hand.

She would not have remained still. She *could not* have remained still.

There would have been more words. There would always have been more words.

Her story cannot be shaped to a convenient arc, to a neat and satisfactory conclusion.

This is not her ending; it is merely where she left off.

◊∆◊∆◊∆◊∆◊∆◊

It is not her purpose and yet the Grey Lady comes regardless, propelled by curiosity perhaps, or perhaps by some deeper compulsion. The baby is sleeping in a simple wooden crib which once rocked the Reveleys' own children to slumber, now retrieved from storage and pressed into tragic and unexpected service. Nearby, little Fanny plays mother to a favourite doll, fussing with its hair and dress and planting noisy kisses upon its porcelain cheeks. The child does not notice the Grey Lady's arrival in the room, just as she has never noticed her myriad comings and goings. That is as it should be.

The Grey Lady approaches the crib, drops to one knee beside it. "Let me look at you, then." Her eyes scan the infant's chubby features, hoping to discern some familiarity in the shade of the nose, in the turn of the mouth, but her efforts are ill-rewarded. Babies are, after all, babies. In time, there might be something of the mother in this one, or the father, but that time will not be the Grey Lady's to witness.

She sighs. "Good life to you, child, and to your sister."

The baby opens her eyes. Dark brown as her mother's were, and curious, they fix themselves upon the Grey Lady's face. Those eyes *see* her.

"Oh my," she whispers. Leaning forward, her nose inches from the newly fascinating creature in the crib, she takes a delicate sniff. Oh my, indeed. "Mary Godwin..." The Grey Lady frowns; the name feels unfinished on her tongue. "Mary *Wollstonecraft* Godwin, or however you shall be someday known, you smell of thunderstorms and secret truths and...and *monsters*?"

The baby makes a soft, gurgling sound. Tiny fingers flex.

"Oh, my dear girl," the Grey Lady tells her. "I shall be keeping a very close watch on *you*."

A Song for Sacagawea

Jane Yolen

There were forty-five before her:
frontiersmen, good hunters,
stout, healthy, unmarried,
accustomed to the woods;
watermen, robust sailors;
experts on botany, carpentry,
forestry, smithery,
navigation by the stars.
One was master of the universal Indian signs,
one a black slave named York.
They carried powder and balls,
pork, purgatives, Peruvian bark,
beads for the natives,
writing desks and "creyons",
six papers of ink powder,
a swivel gun with bullets,
casks of gunpowder,
a Newfoundland dog.

They knew how to read
words on a page,
points on a map.
But they could not read the rest:
how broad the mountain-hemmed plains,
how deep the winter chill,

how wide the river fords,
how far good faith could travel.
They did not speak
with the tongue of the Shoshone,
they did not know
the Hidatsa words for peace, for war.

She spoke for them,
helped them passage through
the rough divides,
She dug roots for them,
wild artichokes,
when all they had to eat was parched corn.
She put up the tent,
packed it down again,
her infant son in a cradleboard on her back.

Was she a hero?
Did she get a medal?
Was she counted an explorer
who charted the way?
These are notions of the white man.
She was a Shoshone woman,
slave to the Hidatsa,
won by a French trader in a bet.
Carrying her son on her back,
she did all the white men did,
all that had to be done
to keep them alive on the long trail.
She was Sacagawea.

It was enough.

Look How Cold My Hands Are

Deborah Biancotti

Look how cold my hands are.

– Last reported words of Báthory Erzsébet
8 August 1560 – 21 August 1614.

Erzsébet was at her desk. "Have you tallied the day's costs? The fence around the village paddock, the church fees."

Church fees again.

Costs were relentless for the Báthory estate. And a relentless aggravation.

"Yes, Countess." The simpleton, Fickó, crinkled his face into a frown. He sat sprawled on the floor with the parchment between his knees.

Erzsébet rubbed at her temple. "And then incomings?"

There were always fewer of those.

She picked at the cold roast lamb on the tray at her elbow and calculated the monies for collection. "Payments owed on our castle at Beckov. Sales from the hemp crops. Use the coarser parchment for your workings, Fickó."

"Yes, Countess."

She pulled a quill from the quiver of ink and wiped it on the cloth at her elbow. Then she trimmed the candle wick and returned to her letter.

To Ferenc Batthyány, December 30, 1610

May God bless you in all your endeavours. We are arrived at Csejte manor this eve, not yet advancing to the castle.

In the depth of winter, the castle took longer to warm. Erzsébet would save on firewood if she could.

We saw many of the poor by the roads. But all follow loyally our King and saviour.

She grunted when she wrote that about the king. The Slovak witch, Erzsi Majorova, had taught her many curses. She cursed the king now.

By God's grace, my health improves. The headaches and visitations of which I wrote previously have lessened.

It was mostly true, though the pain in her left eye was almost constant these days.

I trust it is your considerate words and the careful ministrations of my healer, Anna Darvulia—

"Another letter, Countess?'

Erzsébet jumped. "Anna! I didn't hear you come in."

Anna gestured. "I see you write to Batthyány again. Does he write back? Or has his young wife stopped him?"

"Business about our adjoining property." Erzsébet put a hand across her letter. "And I may write to whomever I please. I am the Countess Báthory. My husband was the greatest war hero in the Kingdom of Hungary. My uncle was King of Poland. I am descended from princes in Transylvania! My daughters' husbands—"

"You are the most powerful woman in Christendom," Anna supplied.

"Don't interrupt!" Erzsébet snapped.

She would punish that impudence in anyone else. But she had never punished Anna. They were closer than sisters.

"Which jewels will you wear, Countess?" Anna asked, as if Erzsébet hadn't spoken. "You never go anywhere without your jewellery."

"Go? We only just reached the manor—"

But then she heard the heavy footfall of visitors across the stone floors downstairs.

"Who's here?"

Some superstition shook her. She slipped a wristlet of emeralds and diamonds over her hand, almost by instinct. As if it might protect her.

"That's what I came to tell you," Anna replied with a smile. "It's the Lord Palatine."

Erzsébet rose to her full height. "The king's fool! And you let him into my manor without my permission?"

Anna's smile was cold. It was always cold. "He *is* the Palatine."

Second only to the king in Hungary. If the Palatine were here again so soon, it meant the witch's curse had failed.

Erzsébet checked the impulse to take out her rage on Anna. To hit her hard across the face and leave a grubby stain of ink and blood.

Anna stood unblinking. She was no more afraid of Erzsébet than a stone is afraid of the sky.

Perhaps *that* explained why Erzsébet couldn't hit her. Anna was the only one who didn't fear the wrath of the Countess of Báthory.

"Light a fire in the drawing room," Erzsébet commanded.

She crossed to her dresser to check her reflection in the copper mirror. Her dark gown was unbuttoned, her pale undergarments stained with sweat and dust. The ride to Csejte had left her skin pinched and red from icy winds.

She smoothed her hands across her face. "They come at midnight? And on Christmas Eve? Parliament is not in session. Can it even be the king's business they attend?"

Anna moved behind her. "Perhaps they are charged to deploy the king's debt to your title, Countess?"

Unlikely. The king had owed the seat of Báthory since before Erzsébet's husband had died.

But it was unusual for the Palatine to be on the roads so late in the year. She hoped it was only about the fighting, some border breach by the unchristian Turks.

She hoped it wasn't about the allegations against her. Surely she had convinced Thurzó an investigation was unwarranted.

She reached for the powders below her mirror and smoothed a pale tincture across her cheeks. She looked old. It had been a hard year and the king's debt weighed heavily.

"With what the king owes the seat of Báthory, I could buy nineteen castles. *Nineteen!*"

"Or you could afford to keep the castles you have," Anna said. "No more begging Batthyány for assistance."

"That is not what I was doing!" Erzsébet snapped.

But it was true, she relied on her neighbours more than she wanted to. There were recurring bills for the Nádasdy-Báthory lands, including villages and churches. Her husband, Ferenc, was dead these six years and it was up to her to ensure her children's futures. Her daughters were provided for, but Pál was the only surviving Nádasdy son, and he was still too young for leadership.

The king must pay his debts.

The king *must* pay his debts.

"Who hosts the Palatine? Is my son arrived?"

"Not yet. Lord Palatine requested Szuzanna accompany him."

Erzsébet froze.

Szuzanna had come from the Lord Palatine's own household. Consequently, Erzsébet had never trusted her.

"You left him with that idiot *maid*? She's not even nine."

"She seemed safe enough," Anna said. "They asked only to view the manor."

"To view it?" Erzsébet frowned. "What have they seen so far?"

Anna smiled that cold, empty smile again. "I believe they have seen everything."

◊Δ◊Δ◊Δ◊Δ◊Δ◊

Anna was irresponsible, not alerting Erzsébet immediately to the intrusion of the Palatine.

And then to leave him in the presence of young Szuzanna. He would take that as disrespect. The lady of the house should greet him properly.

Erzsébet may be close to broke, but her lands and assets meant she was still one of the richest women in the world. Her peers were the Protestant ranks of Hungarian nobility. Even Palatine Thurzó himself was a cousin.

She reached the drawing room. Empty, the fire unlit.

"Anna! Where is he?" She moved from the seating area to the long dining hall. "Where is he? *Where is he!*"

Tabitha appeared in a doorway. Tiny, porcelain-skinned Tabitha. Her eyes were shadowed from some winter sickness. It made her only slightly less beautiful, but her beauty came mainly from youth. All the young were beautiful for a time.

"The Lord Palatine is in the basements, lady," Tabitha offered.

"You idiot girl!" Erzsébet shoved her.

There was a hard thud as Tabitha collided with the wall. By then Erzsébet was already out of the room.

She hurried down the slippery steps without a candle, holding tight to the stone wall. Below, she could see the glow of lights and hear the murmur of men's voices.

She hesitated on the threshold, getting her breath. She was not used to creeping through her own home.

Through a doorway she glimpsed Palatine Thurzó with eight armed men, lit by tallow candles. Probably sourced from her own supplies. She quashed a moment of rage at whoever had furnished them with light.

Pál's tutor was also there, Imre Megyeri, a look of sly triumph on his face. Duplicitous meddler! Reverend Ponikenusz was with them, of course. Grasping, accusing Ponikenusz. The man who had called her out during

Sunday service and accused her of all sorts of sins. And in front of her own people!

Hadn't Erzsébet provided for the church? Hadn't she paid burial fees for every one of her dead girls?

Szuzanna saw her first. Fear pimpled the girl's grimy skin. She raised a hand to point.

Erzsébet swept into the room. The men turned to her as one. Even from here, she could smell the road on their filthy clothes. Their beards glittered with ice. Under a dusting of frost they wore heavy travelling cloaks. Where their cloaks were shouldered, the embroidered vests and coats of office showed.

Official business, then.

Too late she realised her sons-in-law were also there. Anna's husband, Count Nikolaus Zrínyi, and Katalin's husband, Count György Drugeth de Homonnay. Zrínyi at least had the decency to look away but de Homonnay met her glare with his own.

The guards held three of her serving women. Dorotya Semtész, Ilona Jó Nagy, and Katarína Benická. They looked at Erzsébet with defeat and pleading.

"My lady—" Dorotya sobbed.

Erzsébet silenced her with a hand.

She bowed once to the Palatine. Curtly, to let him know how he shamed her with his unannounced arrival.

"Lord Palatine Thurzó. What brings you to this lowly room?"

"We followed the sounds of screaming, Lady Widow Nádasdy."

Thurzó looked grim. He gestured once at the floor as if she had not noticed. Two girls lay there, naked, their wounds exposed. One was already dead, her bloodied hair lying across her dry eyes. Three fingers were missing and there were stab marks on her arms. Her corpse had fallen across the pliers that had been used to gouge her face and chest.

The other girl had burns on her palms and feet. Her face was purple with bruises. Ilona must have taken the whip to her. Erzsébet recognised the deep welts across the girl's neck and ribs.

"See to the girl," Thurzó said to the armed men. "Take this one's statement and administer to her wounds. If it's possible."

"And if it's not, Lord Palatine?"

Thurzó glared. "If you can't ease her suffering medicinally, at least dispatch her with humanity. It's certainly more than the good Lady Nádasdy was willing to do."

There was an expression of disgust on his face.

Erzsébet stood tall, staring back fiercely. Only two girls, she reminded herself. Only two. She was the Countess Báthory. They would not make her account for the wounds of just two girls.

So long as the Palatine remained Lutheran enough to avoid the disruption of graves, there would be only two.

"Seize her," Thurzó said.

De Homonnay complied. He stepped forward and took hold of Erzsébet's wrist, but she wrenched away.

"How dare you!"

Her wristlet snapped, spewing emeralds and diamonds to the floor. Some fell into the congealing blood of the dead and dying girls. Under that oily sheen the emeralds turned black, but the diamonds were lost like so much grit.

"Chain the three serving women," Thurzó said to the guards. "Then follow me to the Castle. We'll search it in its entirety."

"By what authority—" Erzsébet began.

Palatine Thurzó lurched towards her. He sank his fingers into her hair, wrenching her out of de Homonnay's grasp so hard and fast her knees buckled. In her shock she clung to his wrist with both hands.

She let out a cry of rage and Thurzó shook her until her vision blurred.

◊Δ◊Δ◊Δ◊Δ◊Δ◊

"Unhand me! *Unhand me!*"

Thurzó ignored her.

Her scalp was raw where he pulled her forward by the hair.

He dragged her through the manor and out into the winter night where the cold bit into her neck and hands.

Erzsébet stumbled. Thinking to pull herself free, she let her feet go out from under her. But Thurzó hauled her half-upright.

"Is this how you want your villagers to remember you?" he seethed.

At least thirty people from Csejte had braved the cold on Christmas eve to watch her shame. Erzsébet tried to stand tall, but Thurzó pushed her instead into a low bow.

"Help me!" she cried out to the villagers.

No one moved.

Thurzó began to drag her up the hill towards the castle. She could hear the murmurs and curses of the crowd. Curses! And no one stepped forward to save their lady's honour.

They would all pay for that later. When she was freed.

There was the clink of armour just behind her, and the snorts of horses forced to follow in a slow procession.

"Go on ahead!" Thurzó shouted. "Open the castle. Search the keep for more victims."

Erzsébet's throat went dry. "No."

By the time they breached the hill and crossed the drawbridge, her skirts were drenched with mud and snow. Her legs were frozen up to her thighs. Her knees were shaking. Her scalp burned and throbbed as Thurzó let her go.

She put her bare hands to the ice-cold wall of the castle to hold herself upright. She was gasping.

Thurzó grabbed her by the elbow and dragged her through the castle to her own drawing room.

No fire had been lit, of course. The stone walls seemed to trap the snow and ice and concentrate it more deeply here.

The only light was from a candle lit from one of the men's lanterns. Thurzó fixed the candle to the sideboard, letting it drip onto the polished wood. The weak light turned the space into monstrous shadows.

This room was stuffed with furniture, tapestries and carpets plundered from the war—blunt shapes in the gloom. The whole castle used to be like this, but over the years she had been forced to sell many pieces to cover bills.

Once, a room like this would have made her feel safe. Victorious. Now she felt hemmed in and crushed.

She hid her hands in her sleeves to hide their shaking.

"Leave us," Thurzó said to the men who followed them. "I'm sure the Lady Nádasdy poses no such threat to me as she did to those young women."

Erzsébet took a seat in the shadows. She waited until she was alone with Thurzó. "I should welcome you formally, my Lord Palatine. This castle was my wedding gift from the Nádasdy family."

"You know where the liquor is kept, then? By all that's holy, Erzsébet!" he snarled. "We've had reports. Six hundred dead. *Six hundred?*"

"Preposterous," she said calmly. "Who would claim such a thing?"

Thurzó was at the cabinet beside the empty fireplace, his thick cloak joining him to the shadows. "Szuzanna, for one."

"Who's going to believe a nine-year-old girl?"

"A good many people, I should think. She has an angelic little face. And you know the saying. Fools, children and drunken men will always tell the truth. People of Hungary still believe that."

He poured a generous shot of dark wine into a crystal glass. Then he reached under his cloak and pulled out a bloodstained cloth. He tossed it to her lap. Erzsébet made no move to withdraw her hands from her sleeves.

"Recognise that?" he asked. "The undershirt you wore on my last visit. After my entourage left, I understand you slew three serving girls in a rage while wearing that shirt."

Erzsébet kept her face blank.

"Szuzanna also tells me she has seen a register you keep on your desk. A list of the dead, written in your own hand."

"Was Szuzanna intended as your spy?"

Thurzó ignored her. "I've sent a man for the register—"

"Into my private chambers?" Erzsébet snapped.

But Anna would hide the register. Anna would do that for her.

Besides, Anna was too far implicated not to.

"What would *you* put the death count at?" he asked. "Four hundred? Two hundred?"

"None."

"Fifty?" Thurzó continued, almost to himself. "Thirty? How many is enough?"

He sounded calm. Perhaps, if he was calm, she had a chance. Perhaps he was only acting on orders from their greedy king.

She shivered. Thurzó must have seen the movement, because he leaned forward with the glass. When she made to wave it away, he snatched her hand and pressed the glass to her palm so hard the crystal dug into her cold skin.

"Take it," he said. "The good Lord knows there'll be few enough drinks for you after tonight."

He rose and returned to the sideboard. Erzsébet sipped at the wine. It had turned bitter in the frozen room.

"You'll want sustenance after your ride, Lord Palatine. Perhaps—"

"If you think I'll consume any foodstuffs served by you, Erzsébet Nádasdy, you're deluded." Thurzó said without turning.

"I meant only to be hospitable. You are my guest."

She emphasised the last word. Thurzó slouched back to the lounge, shaking dried mud into the fine weave of her furniture. "I heard what you did to Reverend Ponikenusz. You and your mad woman from the village. Erzsi, was it? You poisoned cake and then called out the evil spirits of—what was it? —*cats* to attack him. Of all things!"

"Ridiculous!"

"Isn't it?" Thurzó agreed with equanimity. "And yet, your sister was a witch and your mother-in-law was a witch. And so, I suppose, are you."

"We are all witches when you want to destroy us. All women."

Thurzó raised his glass in a kind of salute. "The priest refuses all contact with you. He trembled as much as that frightened girl, Szuzanna, when I called for him."

"You made a promise to my husband—"

"Ah, the Black Knight of Hungary! I wondered how long it would take you to mention him."

"—on his *deathbed*," she continued, enraged by his casual disregard, "that you would protect me from the king!"

"*And I am!*" he roared. "The king wants you hanged, naked, from a gallows in the centre of court. The whole village knows about you,

Erzsébet. In fact, the whole country! The Lutheran pastors at Sárvár, the ones your husband silenced eight years ago with his extravagant and absurd donations, even they would speak against you now, I think."

"They would not!"

"And the Catholic brethren at the Viennese cathedral on Augustinerstrasse. They used to throw their pots at the wall to cover the noise of your girls *crying out for mercy*. They will make for convincing witnesses, too, when it comes to that."

"Convincing for a Catholic king," she replied bitterly.

"Yes, a Catholic king. One rumoured to be the next Holy Emperor of Rome."

"A Habsburg Emperor?" she spat. "Their ambition is as limitless as the Turks'! So the King sends you, good Lord Palatine, to ensure I cause no embarrassment in this ridiculous crusade of his. If this is about the crown's debt to me—"

"Oh, it's far too late for that."

"My husband held the Turks from our borders when King Matthias did nothing. The armies were starving and dying in their beds, and the king did nothing. No soldiers, no roads, no medicine. No schools! *We* did that. All of it. The nobility of Hungary has been protecting its people for decades."

Thurzó grunted. His face was in darkness.

She rose and he leaned forward to stop her leaving.

"Where do you think you're going?"

"To ask for someone to light the fire," she replied.

"Light it yourself. You have no servants, not anymore. After tonight, you won't even have a title."

Erzsébet hesitated. "What are you saying?"

"It's over for you, Erzsébet." His voice was almost gentle.

She resumed her chair slowly. "Impossible."

"Your people hate you. They are poor—"

"We are all poor. That's why they mock the nobles now, calling us Lord of Five Apple Trees and Mistress of Nine Pigs. We were impoverished fighting the king's wars for him. And yet, the king leaves our fine capital of Buda in the hands of the Ottomans."

"The capital is Pozsony now," Thurzó reminded her. He leaned back into the lounge where the shadows ate at him. "You complain of poverty, Erzsébet, but my wife tells me your jewels are the finest in the country. Plundered from the Turks, I understand."

"Gifts from my husband," Erzsébet replied. "I will give some to your good lady wife if you let me rally my cousins in Transylvania—"

"I shall do no such thing," Thurzó replied. "Did you really kill all the girls in your gynaecium?"

"No."

"You did, Erzsébet. After what I've seen tonight, I know the truth of it," Thurzó said sadly. "It's the complaints of their noble families that forced me back here."

She should have cursed all of them.

"They are only lesser nobles, György," Erzsébet said. "Not like you or I."

"Don't call me that, as if we are friends. Don't call me by my given name."

She tried to soften her voice. "It's all lies, Lord Palatine. I have enemies—"

"Easily three hundred people will testify to finding bodies in shallow graves around your grounds."

"Lies."

"I heard about the handmaid you killed in Predmier on the way home from my own daughter's wedding."

"An accident. The girl complained she was too warm in the carriage."

"So you stripped her, stood her naked in a barrel and poured icy water over her until she died. In the middle of winter. In the middle of the village square, for all to see. You call *that* an accident?"

Her hands were clenched around the glass he'd given her. She downed the rest of the contents in a gulp. "I have seen many maids corrected by my noble peers."

"And killed?"

Erzsébet replied quietly, "Even killed, if it was needful."

"Needful? *Needful?*"

"I gave those girls shelter and honest work! I am lady and mother to all my staff."

Thurzó stood restlessly. He rubbed his temple and stared at the empty glass that hung from his hand. "To think, I once told my daughter to be more pious and responsible. Like the virtuous Countess of Báthory, I said. I find your crimes hard to even comprehend."

"Because none of it is true. "

"Stop *lying!*"

He threw his glass at the wall by the candle. The glass shattered. Broken shards flew through the air like a diamond rain, lit by the candle.

"Three dead on the way to your brother's funeral at Ecsed!"

"I was unwell," she offered. "The stress. The grief."

"Is that all it takes? My God! You have been *unwell* as long as I've known you. Always with a headache or a fit, or one of your strange little trances where you tremble and writhe in your bed."

"There is nothing little about my suffering!" Erzsébet snapped.

He looked at her with a kind of grim satisfaction. As if he had been proven right in some way.

"Was it Ferenc corrupted you?" he asked. "I would believe that. He was a vicious man."

"He was a war hero," she corrected him.

Thurzó grunted. "Is that why you refuse to take the widow's path, to retire and mourn your husband quietly? You hope to bask in the reflection of his so-called heroism?"

"How dare you," she said quietly. "I'm kept in the king's court by the strain of his debt—"

"Don't try to pin this on King Matthias, Erzsébet. Would you rather adopt the religious beliefs of the Turks than take up with your own king?"

"The king owes me."

"That's the very thing. He doesn't want to owe you."

"Then he should pay his debts!"

"And that's the other thing. He doesn't want to pay you."

"Then what does he propose?" Erzsébet asked.

"To take everything you own." Thurzó resumed his seat. "To impress the mighty Empire of Rome."

He said it with sarcasm. Thurzó was not Catholic, either.

Erzsébet felt the blood drain from her face. "He'll never get his hands on my lands."

"He will. He's the king. "

"No! I've already bequeathed all my lands. Didn't your friends the counts, my sons-in-law, mention that? My daughters and son own the properties now."

Thurzó looked at her thoughtfully. Then he rose and moved to the cabinet, already unsteady on her liquor.

The candle needed trimming. It guttered, its light low, its oily smell edged with smoke. Its shadows made a mask of his face as he reached for another glass.

"No wonder they call you the Beast of Csejte," he said. "You are inhuman."

She pushed the rage down. She felt the pulse in her temple. She felt the tightness of her face, the itch of blood filling her skin.

"They call me many things, most of them unflattering," she said, lifting her chin. "I like to think you know me better, my good Lord Palatine."

He grunted, pouring more bitter wine. "I'm not sure I know you at all. Why kill *girls*, Erzsébet? You were seen as a champion of women. But I suppose they were easier for your old crones to subdue."

He returned to his seat. But where he'd been standing, she saw a kind of fire erupt, dancing along his outline as if the air still held the shape of him.

"I never killed any girls," she murmured.

"Are you going to lie to me like you lied to Reverend Ponikenusz? Are you going to blame the cholera?"

"It was not *me* that killed those girls."

"Ah! So who do you blame, if it wasn't you?" He raised his glass.

"The maids."

"The...?"

"Anna Darvulia and the others. Dorotya Semtész and Katarína Benická. Ilona Jó Nagy was the worst. I could not stop them. I was afraid for my life."

Thurzó's face went blank. He was quiet a long time.

Then he put back his head and roared with laughter. "Merciful Mother, that's rich! You blame the *Darvulia* woman?"

Thurzó laughed some more, spilling wine across the lounge he sprawled on. "Oh, Erzsébet! Whoever digs a hole for someone else will fall in it themselves."

"You mock me, Lord Palatine? When I confess my greatest fear?"

"Please. You? Afraid! Hungary's mightiest noblewoman?" His laughter died. "I grant you, the Darvulia woman had an evil reputation. A wild beast in woman's skin. You might have had a chance, blaming her."

"Had?"

Thurzó chuckled softly.

"*Had?*" Erzsébet insisted.

"Before she died," Thurzó replied. "But who do you blame for the deaths that have piled up since? The girls keep disappearing, their bodies—"

"Anna has not died."

Thurzó's smile dropped. "Gods, it's true. You're mad."

"She is not dead," Erzsébet insisted. "She attended me in my bed chamber this evening."

"Stop it, Erzsébet," Thurzó said.

"Why do you say she is dead? *Why do you say that?*"

"That's enough! The fish stinks from the head. You are the Countess of Báthory. You are responsible for the actions of your people. Even those who died. Especially those, as it happens."

"She is. *Not*. Dead!"

Thurzó blanched. "She's been dead two years."

One of the guards entered the room unannounced. Erzsébet turned by habit to reprimand him.

"We've found more," the man said simply, not even looking at her. "Count de Homonnay asked me to collect you."

"Any alive?"

The man nodded gravely. "The old woman the villagers spoke of. The one who was taken for hiding her daughter from the...lady. But over a dozen found dead so far."

The man dared to glance at Erzsébet.

Thurzó dismissed the man at the door and got to his feet. "Come with me, Lady Nádasdy."

Erzsébet rose before he could manhandle her again.

Her head was spinning. A needlepoint of pain had bloomed behind her eye. Her hands began to jerk against her sides. There was a sharp, unpleasant feeling as if her skin was peeling off. White sparks of light danced in her vision.

She pressed her fingers to her temple, trying to stop the tingling. Trying to hold herself in. She felt stripped from her body.

Anna could not be dead.

She heard Thurzó from far away. "Don't play games with me, Erzsébet. Ferenc might have believed in your trances, but I don't."

When she was a girl, a healing woman told her the trances were the result of demons arguing under her skin. The arguments brought terrible headaches and pain.

Only Anna had taught her not to be afraid of them. That the demons were merely spirits, passing through her. She said Erzsébet should be glad for the pain. It proved the spirits had not abandoned her and never would.

"Hungary will not stand for your treatment of me," she murmured. She could feel the sweat on her face, despite the cold. "After all my husband has done! All *I* have done."

"Your husband was a sadistic soldier ill-suited for courtly life. As are you."

"How dare you! I demand the right to defend my name," she replied.

Thurzó's glare hardened. "You fool. That's exactly what the king wants. He knows what you fail to admit. No one is coming to your aid, Erzsébet. No one could withstand the embarrassment. Your uncle has practically disowned you. Your peers look the other way. Even that little neighbour of yours that you're so fond of—Batthyány?—he won't stand up for you. Because to defend you would be to deny the King, the entire Habsburg family and soon, the might of Rome."

"You cannot deny my rights. It would shame the kingdom. It would imperil every noble of this country."

For a moment she felt like a countess again.

Thurzó held out a hand in summons.

"I will go nowhere with you, not until my son arrives and the seat of Báthory is safe in his hands."

"Pál isn't coming, not tonight. When we passed his retinue on the road, I suggested other lodgings this evening." He would not meet her gaze. "I will protect your children, Erzsébet. But alas, you are lost."

"Thurzó," she said, pleading. "György. Please. I'll give you land."

"You have no land, remember?" Thurzó said. "Besides, land is worthless now. No one can afford to maintain it. Perhaps you could offer it instead to the Turks?"

◊Δ◊Δ◊Δ◊Δ◊Δ◊

They reached the keep.

Erzsébet had not been there in months. The stink of death was strong even for her. They had lit all the oil lamps they could find and hung them from hooks on the walls. But even their sooty stink did nothing to dampen the smell.

The armed guards were there with her sons-in-law, hands covering their noses. The fool priest was bent to the floor, murmuring prayers.

She hesitated on the threshold, blinking to clear her vision of the dancing, oily lights after the dark drawing room. "A cloth, if you will. Something for the odour."

No one moved to assist her. They barely looked at her. Their gazes were fixed on the mess on the floor.

The bodies had so disintegrated they barely resembled the girls they had been. They were blackened and icy, but at least the marks of torture were harder to discern.

Fickó was meant to bury these bodies in the forest.

Thurzó strode grimly to the centre of the room. "Lady Widow Nádasdy, I came here intending to place you in a convent—"

"A *Catholic* convent, Lord Palatine?" she spat. "For our king's sake? I am Protestant, as you know."

"—but having seen your crimes for myself, I cannot, in good conscience, allow you to be free. If even the priests fear you…" He looked to where Reverend Ponikenusz kneeled. "We treated even the Turks better than this."

"I demand a trial," Erzsébet said quietly.

"I won't let you dishonour your family's name with a public trial," Thurzó replied. He sounded tired. "I exercise my right as Palatine, second only to the King in Hungary, to sentence you privately. You will be walled up in this hellish castle for the rest of your life."

"You would have me *starve?*"

"We will leave some little space for ministrations. We will feed you, clean your pots."

"You took an oath to my husband."

"Your life will be spared, Widow Nádasdy, for your family's sake. But you will be declared legally dead. Your journals and letters will be destroyed. Your fortune stripped from you and granted to the crown."

"You dishonour me!"

"Your honour is already lost. It is your family's honour I protect now." Thurzó was calm.

"See reason, György. You cannot imprison a noblewoman. It would be the shame of Hungary!"

"By court order, your name shall never be uttered in public again. You will disappear from the world, Erzsébet."

"This is unheard of!"

"So are your crimes." Thurzó told her. "Be grateful I don't do worse. The women, your accomplices, will be tortured for their statements and their bodies burned. Even that young simpleton, Fickó, if I have my way."

The fire in her vision danced.

"I shall write to my cousins," she said. "To my neighbours, to my peers in the nobility, to all the Protestants everywhere. If the Catholic king takes my land, all of us are at risk, György. Even you."

Thurzó nodded. She saw he knew the truth of it. "But your letters shall go undelivered. You will die inside the walls of this castle. And your soul will forever burn in Hell."

"No!" Erzsébet lurched backward.

The guard beside her stepped back as if afraid to touch her.

Thurzó grimaced. "Still enough childhood Calvinism to fear Hell, Erzsébet? After everything you've done, did you really believe you could escape eternal damnation?"

Erzsébet felt more sharply aware than she had in a long time. She could see and feel and taste everything. Every *filthy* thing. No bright flickers of light danced in her eyes. No pain troubled her. She could hear the blood rush through her body. She could feel the thick, tainted air on her skin.

Perhaps Anna had been wrong. It was demons after all.

And at the end, perhaps even the demons would abandon her.

◊Δ◊Δ◊Δ◊Δ◊Δ◊

The air was full of smoke and the stink of burning flesh the day she stepped into what would become her catacomb.

If she cared to look again from the narrow window by her bed, she would see the gallows where Ilona and the others still hung.

She listened to the scrape of rock as the stonemasons walled her in.

"I need parchment," Erzsébet told them. "The fine parchment. For letter writing."

"There is some on the floor, Lady," the guard said from outside the wall.

"This isn't enough." She leaned down and fingered it. "And this is too coarse for my noble family."

"It's all you're allowed, Lady."

"If you will not bring me parchment, I shall write my message on the very walls! Báthory is not dead!"

"As you will, Lady."

She was afraid Anna would not visit her behind the walls.

"Do you hear that?" Erzsébet asked.

One of the stonemasons hesitated. He glanced at his fellow but the other man kept working. The guard continued to stare at her dully.

"The demons," Erzsébet said. "Do you hear them? They sing to me. They sing."

And so, the Lady Widow Nádasdy, last Countess of Báthory—Erzsébet of Ecsed and later Csejte and numerous other holdings in Hungary—began to sing to her demons.

It took her four years to die.

Bright Moon
Foz Meadows

"I'll be Khan, someday," Esen announced, with all the sage authority of his eleven years. They were out by the corral, watching the new foals trot and totter on spindly legs, their tufted manes waving in the spring breeze.

"I'll lead your armies," Khutulun said, excited by the prospect, "And hunt with a golden eagle!"

Esen scowled at her. "Women don't fight, and they don't fly eagles. You'll herd sheep and tend the ger, and then you'll marry a man, and tend *his* ger, and your sons will fight for me."

Khutulun shoved him, hard, though he was nearly two years older. "Well, *you'll* never be Khan! Altan will be, or Buri, or one of our other brothers. You couldn't lead a pig to mud."

Angry, Esen shoved her back, and Khutulun clutched the front of his coat to keep from falling. Esen staggered, grabbing her arms, and suddenly they were wrestling in earnest, each one striving to make the other fall.

"Women don't wrestle, either," Esen panted, trying to force her down. "Bokh is a sport for men. Give up and get married!"

But Khutulun was clever. To win at bokh, you had to make the other person touch the ground with something besides their feet; Esen kept trying to throw her whole body aside, chasing a dramatic victory ahead of an easy one. He was bigger than her, but that meant he had to lean down to her level, overbalancing whenever she made a sudden move. So Khutulun swayed with his shoving, using his strength instead of her own, lulling him into a rhythm. Then, as they hit the patch of muddy ground by the corral gate, she threw all her weight one way when Esen was braced to go another.

His feet went out from under him; he fell with a cry, and Khutulun twisted, forcing him to let go of her.

"Women *can* wrestle," she declared, "And I won't marry anyone who can't best me at it!"

"You're unnatural," Esen gasped, wiping mud from his face—but there was a hint of respect there, too. When he stood, he clasped her arm and grinned. "But you still can't have an eagle."

Their tussle had attracted an audience, and by evening, everyone knew about it. Reactions to Khutulun's victory ranged from amused to disapproving, and as her hasty vow was passed from ear to tongue and back again, it warped in shape, until her elder sister, Qutuchin, pulled her aside and demanded to know whether she had really sworn to kill her future husband in single combat.

Khutulun made a face. "The men in this camp gossip the way chickens scratch," she huffed, and told her sister what had really happened, unable to keep the pride from her voice as she did so.

Qutuchin, though, was unimpressed. "One lucky win, and you're full of yourself."

"It wasn't luck!"

"That doesn't mean you could do it again," Qutuchin shot back. "Even if you could, it wouldn't matter. You'll marry where our father says, like I will."

"I won't," said Khutulun, stubborn as a colt. "Not if they can't outwrestle me."

Deep, male laughter interrupted the conversation. Both girls jumped, wide-eyed as their father, Kaidu Khan, strode into the ger. "Oh, will you not?" he asked, one eyebrow raised at Khutulun. "Tell me, little moon, is marriage such a sour prospect? The right woman married to the right man can be a powerful creature indeed. Sorghaghtani Khatun didn't outwrestle Tolui to prove her worth."

"No," said Khutulun, "But she didn't rule until after he died, either. And Toregene Khatun, too—she only became regent after Ogedei Khan's death, not before it." She tossed her head, staring defiantly at her father. "Strong wives become powerful when they lose their husbands. But I'm strong *now*—why should I have to find a man, then lose him, to have others see it?"

Beside her, Qutuchin stiffened in shock. The Khan's eyebrows drew together in an expression of disapproval. Khutulun trembled, realising she had gone too far, but she couldn't make herself look away. For a long moment, her father was silent, the tension between them stretched like an overfull bladder.

Then Kaidu Khan huffed, and said, "Perhaps you shouldn't, at that."

He turned away from her, and for the first time, Khutulun remembered that they weren't alone in the ger—that both Qutuchin's mother and her own, along with several of their brothers, were listening to every word.

"If Khutulun wishes to wrestle," Kaidu said to everyone and no one in particular, "then she will wrestle. If she wishes to learn warfare, she will learn warfare. Anyone who opposes her in this will answer to me."

And then he strode out of the ger as though nothing extraordinary had just happened; as though Khutulun's heart wasn't beating in her chest like a rabbit's. But it wasn't fear, not any more. It was pride, and strength, and the knowledge that though Esen was the first boy she had ever thrown in bokh, he wouldn't be the last.

◊Δ◊Δ◊Δ◊Δ◊Δ◊

"Just once," Esen grumbled, "you'd think that Kublai Khan had bigger bears to poke than our father, and longer sticks to poke them with, too."

Khutulun snorted. Five years had passed since she first fought her brother beside the corral, and now they were both tall enough to comfortably rest their elbows on the fence-top. "Don't be stupid," she said, snugging her hands in her sleeves. "Any man stubborn enough to besiege two cities for six years is more than capable of raiding our lands for spite."

"But that's my point," said Esen. "He's up to his balls in war at Xiangyang. Why bother with us?"

"Because he can. Because he means to be Emperor of China, and he wants our father to remember what he denied him at the kurultai."

Esen blinked. "Our father never went to the kurultai."

"Exactly," said Khutulun. "He didn't go, and didn't vote, and Kublai still calls himself Great Khan, but by our great-great-grandfather's laws, he isn't. So now he besieges Xiangyang, and sends his skirmishers here to say, *My strength is great, and my memory long. I haven't forgotten you.*" She clicked her teeth, angry. "And for that, our gers are burned."

In the corral, the horses milled, their summer coats limned with dust in the dawn light. "I see that Mongke-Temur's grey mare is here," said Esen, almost idly.

"So she is," said Khutulun. "I heard her arrive last night."

Esen rolled his eyes. "Of course you did. Because sleep is for the weak."

"Sleep is for people who don't share a bed with Qutuchin," Khutulun said. "I pity her future husband. Beautiful our sister may be, but she snores like a drunk."

Esen laughed at that, but his face was grave. "Will the Golden Horde ride with us against Kublai's men, do you think?"

"Not against Kublai," Khutulun said. "The battle is too small to tempt his glory, and it would make us look weak to ask it. But against the Ilkhanate? Certainly."

"That may be, but last I checked, the Ilkhantate isn't responsible for burning our crops. Defending our people might not be glorious work in Mongke-Temur's eyes, but it still must be done."

"And who better to do it than us?"

For a moment, Esen simply stared. "You can't be serious. War isn't bokh, little moon. And even if we do ride out, you're too young. Our father agreed to let you train, but that doesn't mean he'll let you fight."

"He will, when he sees me win."

"You can't just sneak into battle!"

"Watch me." She bared her teeth, a determined almost-grin. "I love and honour our sister, Esen, but I'm not her, and I'm not about to wait around for the great Kaidu Khan to remember that Qutuchin is not his only marriageable daughter. I will fight, and I will be seen to fight, and that is an end of it. And if you try to stop me—" here the grin turned feral, dark, "—it will be the end of *you*."

Esen lent Khutulun his old armour, and didn't breathe a word.

◊Δ◊Δ◊Δ◊Δ◊Δ◊

The next day, accompanied by Mongke-Temur—who came for curiosity's sake, but left his own men behind—Kaidu led his soldiers out in search of Kublai's skirmishers. When they rode, it was easy enough for Khutulun to conceal herself, sticking to the rear of the column and speaking only with Esen. At night, in camp, it was harder. Not because of her sex, which was easy enough to hide, but because these men knew her face. Khutulun kept to herself, and prayed for luck to any spirit that might be listening.

On the morning on the third day, a scout found their quarry. Khutulun saw him returning and nudged Esen, casting her eyes meaningfully towards the front of the column. He frowned, then nodded, curiosity overcoming his fear of being caught. Together, they edged their mounts closer to the front of the line, the better to eavesdrop on the scout's report.

Kublai's men, they learned, were camped in a gorge, with sheer rock behind them and bare ground before. It was a mixed blessing: riding in would mean a pitched battle and no element of surprise, but once encircled, the skirmishers couldn't retreat. The timing, too, was on their side: the enemy was resting, and if Kaidu marched now, the still-rising sun would be at his back as they entered the gorge, putting Kublai's men at a disadvantage. It was this last fact that seemed to decide their father. He began issuing battle orders to his noyans, while Mongke-Temur watched the proceedings from atop his grey mare, a small, amused smile on his face.

Every soldier carried a bow, but for this fight, Kaidu wanted his dedicated archers to hold back, covering the others. This meant splitting the column before moving out—archers to the rear, swordsmen and lancers to the front—which left Khutulun uncertain of where to ride. The archers would hold a safer position, but there would be a greater chance to distinguish herself in the melee.

Or would there? She paused, conflicted. What would impress her father more: taking on a greater, unnecessary risk for bravado's sake—unlike Esen, she was better with a bow than a sword, and everyone knew it—or accepting a less glorious role for the greater good?

Put like that, the answer was obvious.

Khutulun quickly lost track of Esen, but that didn't matter; they both knew what they were doing. As before, Khutulun kept to the back, just ahead of the string of spare mounts, and when the signal was given, she readied her bow. She had half expected to feel afraid, but instead, the world became sharp and crisp: the creak of her armour against the saddle, the huff of her gelding's breath as he moved from trot to canter to gallop, warm sun, blue sky, and the screaming of men around her.

They burst into the gorge, and the battle began.

Khutulun had drilled with the archers in practice, and knew what place to take when the noyan shouted his orders. Her hands were steady as she drew an arrow, steady as she nocked the bow, steady as she picked her target—a skinny man, unhelmeted—and steady as she fired. Her arrow took him through the neck, and her own throat clenched in brief sympathy, but then he fell, and her training took over. Not every shot hit home, and once the fight was joined, it was harder to tell if the ones that did were mortal or merely wounding, but she killed at least one man for certain, and likely more.

The battle surged and screamed like a living thing. For all the skirmishers had been caught unawares, they were Kublai's men, and knew their trade. An arrow whipped by Khutulun's head as their archers finally formed up, and she hissed in shock and anger, firing off a retributive shot at whoever had marked her out. The noyan yelled again, and Khutulun groped for another shaft in her emptying quiver, searching for a target, searching—

The soldier looked so like Esen that, for a freezing moment, she half believed her brother had somehow wound up on the wrong side of the fight. But her enemy was a man grown where Esen, for all his pretensions, was not quite so, yet. There were Esen's quick eyes and sharp cheeks, but the face that held them was stubbled and lined, the body beneath it armoured in red lamellar and mounted on a quick brown mare whose sleek confirmation and narrow head betrayed more than just takhi blood. Khutulun's pulse quickened, breath coming sharp and fast.

Hello, cousin.

She looked for the noyan, wanting to report her realisation, but the man was too far away and busy with it. The choice was Khutulun's: speak or not? Fire or not? Her thoughts churned, but as the man on the brown mare moved—giving orders, she realised dimly; not shouting, but moving among his troops, disguised by them—a single choice stood out like a crystal spar in a rockface.

Khutulun raised her bow, and fired at his horse.

The mare screamed, rearing up as the shaft punctured her shoulder. Khutulun was already moving, urging her mount out of line as she plunged through the fray towards them. Heart hammering wildly, she steered with her knees and fired twice more, rapid shots to clear her path; her gelding swung and pivoted around a fallen man. Khutulun jerked in the saddle, sending a third shot wide as her gelding swung and pivoted around a fallen man. Almost, she lost sight of her target, but the brown mare screamed again, one leg buckling, struggling to stay upright. She was there, her bow swapped for a blade as she came alongside.

Up close, her cousin wasn't much older than Esen, nor—mercifully—much bigger, either. His mouth gaped as he struggled to control his plunging horse, and before he could draw his own sword—he had dropped his bow in a grab for the reins—Khutulun draw back her arm and smashed the hilt of her weapon hard between his brows.

Her cousin's eyes rolled back in his head. Khutulun sheathed her sword, and as her enemy slid one way while his horse shied another, Khutulun used that momentum to haul him out of his saddle, arms screaming with the exertion. She was strong, iron-hard from training and as broad in the shoulders as Qutuchin was narrow, but still, she almost dropped him, sweat-wet fingers slipping against the lamellar scales of his armour. And then, somehow, impossibly, it worked: her gelding snorted in protest, shoving away from the now-collapsed mare. Khutulun swore and heaved and tugged. When they came clear, her unconscious cousin was spraddled across the high front peak of her saddle, half in her lap and half on the gelding's withers.

Before she could drop him, she turned about and steered them back at an awkward half-canter towards her own lines, the limp body flopping awkwardly like a badly landed fish. Double-burdened, she was vulnerable and slow, but though she heard new shouts of outrage mixed in with the battle-sounds, no one pursued her; or if they did, other fighters blocked their path. Where was the noyan? Her unconscious cousin groaned and stirred. Khutulun smacked him across the back of his head, willing him silent as she pulled in between two of their own archers, solid men who stared at her like she'd grown wings.

"What's this?" one cried, as the other gaped at her burden. "What have you done, boy?"

Exasperated, Khutulun lifted her helmet. "I've captured my cousin. Someone tell the noyan and my father we have a hostage."

The two men exchanged frightened glances.

"Now!" she roared, arms aching as her captive moved again, and this time the man to her left obeyed, a swiftly muttered, *Yes, khatun* falling from his lips as he wheeled his horse.

The title took Khutulun off-guard; she had never been called khatun before. It was a word for great women, and she was not yet that. *But perhaps,* she thought, *I will become.*

"Khutulun!"

It was Esen's voice. She turned in time to see him riding towards her, trailed by three men: the archer she had sent away, her father, and—she gulped—Mongke-Temur. Sudden nerves made her mouth as dry as her hands were wet. Capturing her cousin was a gamble on a gamble on a gamble, and the third time paid for all.

"Little moon," her father growled, reining his horse beside her, "what have you done?"

Don't falter, Khutulun thought, and forced herself to meet his gaze as she had once done before. "I have brought you the son of Kublai Khan," she said, and as her arms chose that moment to give out, she made their weakness into a strength, shoving her captive to the ground as though she'd planned it all along. He moaned quietly, landing on his knees, one palm braced on the rocky earth as he peered groggily up at them. He coughed, and Khutulun barked, "Name yourself!"

"Nomukhan," he said. There was pride in the word, and fear.

Kaidu Khan stared down at him. "You've grown," he said, "since I saw you last." And then, to the archer, "Take this prisoner to noyan Alghu."

Faster almost than Khutulun could comprehend, the archer dismounted, binding Nomukhan's hands and tying that rope to his saddle, so that when he resumed his seat, the younger man was forced to stagger after him, stumbling over the rough ground. Esen was silent on his horse, head bowed; Mongke-Temur's face was unreadable. Beyond them, the battle was almost over, but Khutulun kept her eyes on her father, waiting for his judgement.

"How did you know him?" Kaidu's voice was stern, but curious. "A man you've never met, and spied from a distance? I rode closer to him than you, but didn't see."

Arms still trembling from her cousin's weight, Khutulun said, "He had Esen's look, father. Good armour, a rare-blooded horse. Who else could he have been?"

The silence of Kaidu Khan was broken by Mongke-Temur's laughter. "Your daughter is a striking hawk," he said. "Would that all my men had such good eyes!"

"I am fortunate in her," said Kaidu, the barest trace of a smile on his face. "As in all my children." His gaze flicked to Esen, who blushed at the praise, before turning back to Khutulun. "The next time we fight, little moon," he said, and her heart near burst at those words, *next time*, "you ride with me."

◊∆◊∆◊∆◊∆◊∆◊

When they returned, Esen's old armour was exchanged for a new set made to Khutulun's build. She drilled in it alongside her father's men, and when she next rode out, the metal plates turned an arrow that would otherwise have gone straight through her shoulder. Qutuchin fussed over the impact bruise, but it was the first such mark of many, and after a while, she became as inured to the sight of Khutulun's injuries as she was to the rhythms of their monthly blood: as pain to be endured in service of a greater, more necessary cause.

"Greater for you, maybe," Khutulun muttered, when Qutuchin expressed this sentiment out loud. She was sixteen now, and would no more countenance the future prospect of pregnancy than she could walk on water. "Here, let's summon a witch: I'll trade you my womb to use as a spare, and you can have children enough for the both of us."

Qutuchin cackled. "You would say something like that. But if Bolad has his way, you may not have a choice."

"Who?" said Khutulun.

"Bolad! You know him. Young, handsome, wrestler? Wants to marry you?"

"Wants to *what?*"

"Marry you," said Qutuchin, thoroughly exasperated. "Honestly, you spend all day with men you claim are terrible gossips—do you never actually listen to what they say?"

"Rarely."

"Well, you should." Qutuchin folded her arms. She was seventeen and sharp-tongued, as beautiful as the bright moon for which Khutulun was named. "He's going to try and wrestle you for it, just like you always wanted."

Khutulun took a moment to process this statement. The vow she had made in childhood had long since passed into clan lore, affirmed by both Khutulun and her father whenever the subject came up. This was the first time anyone had tried to put it into practice. She burst out laughing. "Gods of luck, you almost had me worried! I could throw Bolad with my eyes closed. When's this all meant to happen?"

"Tomorrow morning." Qutuchin rose from her bed, suddenly suspicious. "Khutulun, what are you thinking?"

"I'm thinking, why wait? There's still light out." She left the ger grinning, Qutuchin hurrying to catch up.

She found Bolad by the corral, surrounded by a trio of friends who smirked and stood back at her approach. Bolad looked her up and down, a wide smile on his face. He was, she supposed, not wholly unhandsome, but his archery was terrible, and he told the worst jokes of anyone she had ever met.

Khutulun crossed her arms. "I hear you want to marry me."

"I do," said Bolad, surprise giving way to confidence in the time it took to blink. "I'll even consent to wrestle you first."

"If you're so certain of the outcome," said Khutulun, cocking her head at the corral, "why not make it interesting? If you win, I marry you, and you take my black mare. If I win, we don't marry, and you give me—" she made a show of considering, "—oh, ten horses of my choosing."

It was an extravagant bet for him to lose, not least because Bolad's family herd was famed for its bloodlines. But Bolad, whose list of faults could now definitively be said to include overconfidence, agreed in a heartbeat.

Khutulun smiled. "Shall we, then?"

Bolad waved her forward. "After you."

There was no ceremony to it, none of the formality of true bokh; no zasuuls to coach them on, no dance beforehand to warm them up. Still, Khutulun took a moment to stretch her muscles, which were pleasantly sore from a day of horseback archery, and roped Qutuchin in as a witness. Her sister drew her eyebrows together, shooting Khutulun a look that was equal parts amused and disgusted, and said, in a voice that carried to the gathering spectators, "Begin."

Bolad closed with her quickly, but for all his cockiness—for all that he knew of Khutulun's martial prowess, the battles she had fought and the prisoners she had taken—his grip on her was tentative, almost playful, like he expected her resistance to be token. Khutulun had been quite content to let him lose with at least some dignity, but this insult to both her skills and determination was too great to bear.

She lowered her head, gripped Bolad beneath his arms, and stepped hard right with her left leg leading. Dropping her weight as she twisted, she turned and threw him over her shoulder. The move brought her down, too, falling as Bolad grabbed helplessly for purchase, but he hit the ground first, and everyone knew it. Khutulun stood and dusted herself off, fighting the grin that threatened to spread across her face. Two of Bolad's friends were laughing, though the third looked furious; Qutuchin raised her eyes heavenward, as though praying for patience.

"Khutulun wins," she said, and Bolad gawked up at them like a fledgling newly fallen from its nest.

"I'll come for the horses tomorrow," Khutulun said, and before Bolad could reply, she took Qutuchin's arm and walked back into the ger, the sound of cheers and laughter following her like music.

"You humiliated him," Qutuchin said, voice low.
"He humiliated himself."
"You know there'll be consequences."
Khutulun chuckled. "I'm counting on it."

◊Δ◊Δ◊Δ◊Δ◊Δ◊

If Bolad had hoped that Kaidu Khan would prove sympathetic to his plight, he was sorely mistaken. Though he begged and grovelled over the matter of the ten horses, Kaidu was unbending, and by noon the next day, the best of his herd had passed into Khutulun's hands. The story spread like fire through dry straw, and Bolad spent the next three days in hiding from the mockery of his fellows and the anger of his family, none of whom took kindly to the loss of their best breeding stock.

Four days after that, a man rode in from a neighbouring clan in the company of three of his brothers, their maternal uncle and a string of fine mounts. Was it true, he asked, that Kaidu Khan's daughter would marry any man who could best her at wrestling, provided he put up ten horses as proof of his intentions? Esen, who greeted him, said it was. Khutulun threw him even faster than she had Bolad, and once he was back on his feet, he slapped her shoulder and laughed, and said it was worth the loss of the horses three times over for having such a story to tell.

"You're building quite the herd," Qutuchin said that night. "What happens if you meet a man you want?"

"Then I pray that he's a good wrestler," Khutulun said. "And if not, I pray his taste in horses will cushion the blow."

◊Δ◊Δ◊Δ◊Δ◊Δ◊

Years passed, and Khutulun's legend grew—as, indeed, did her herd. By her twentieth birthday, she had won thousands of horses from hundreds of men. She sold and traded many, and those she kept were the strongest, hardiest and most beautiful of all. In battle, she rode at her father's right hand, her keen eyes seeing patterns in the chaos. She was known for taking valuable captives, darting into the fray and back, her prize slung over her saddle. It was Khutulun whose advice Kaidu sought above that of Buri and Altan and Esen; Khutulun who shared his jokes; Khutulun who, at Qutuchin's marriage, gifted their sister with two hundred horses. She had enemies, attracted envy and rumour in equal portion at least to praise, but so long as she had Kaidu's support, her position was unassailable.

Until the return of Mongke-Temur, khan of the Golden Horde.

Though the grey mare she had once coveted had long since been replaced, Khutulun recognised her lines in the gelding Mongke-Temur now rode. He arrived unexpectedly at midday while Khutulun was fletching arrows, and she watched patiently from a distance as her father was found. By then, she was accustomed to inclusion in Kaidu's councils, and expected him to call her in, but when she caught his eye, he shook his head and took Mongke-Temur alone into the ger. Khutulun felt a chill up her spine. She went back to her arrows, but the feeling of unease persisted. What did Mongke-Temur want?

It was dusk when one of her younger nephews ran to summon her to the ger. Khutulun wiped her hands and followed him, her face a mask of carefully sculpted stone. The second she stepped inside, she could tell that the men had been drinking; the heavy fermented smell of airag hung in the air, and Mongke-Temur's normally sharp eyes were glazed.

"Come sit with me, little moon," Kaidu said. Khutulun's head jerked up in shock; it had been years since her father had last called her that, and never in such a setting. Mongke-Temur chuckled. Khutulun sat, her spine arrow-straight with outrage.

"What is it, Father?" she asked.

It was Mongke-Temur who answered. "A month past, my son-in-law was widowed when my daughter died in childbed. He is a northerner, a Rus prince and a Christian, but has spent years living among our people, and wishes his sons to be raised by a Mongol mother. Had I more daughters to spare, I would bid one of them take their sister's place. But as I do not, in honour of the great love you bear your father, and the friendship he in turn owes me, you will do this thing instead, cementing an alliance of advantage to us both."

"Were Qutuchin still unwed," her father said, softly, "I would ask it first of her. But she is not."

And that leaves me. The words hung unspoken between them. Fury burned in Khutulun, but she yoked it fiercely, summoning the same intensity of purpose that she used in battle. She did not ask why Mongke-Temur had chosen her father, out of all the Golden Horde's allies, to furnish him with a daughter; there was no point. He had seen her fight a half-dozen times since the capture of Nomukhan—had seen at least four of his own men wrestle for her hand, and lose—and knew exactly what he was asking from her.

The question was, did he mean the match as humiliation? Did he have some deeper purpose in proposing such an alliance? Or was he simply arrogant enough to think that the offer of a Rus prince would turn her head?

"What is his name?" asked Khutulun.

"Theodore Qara," said Mongke-Temur. *Theodore the Black.* "Prince of Smolensk and Yaroslav."

"And does *Theodore* know of me?" said Khutulun, rolling the strange syllables of his given name against her tongue. "Does he know the conditions of my hand?"

"He does," said Mongke-Temur, with a glance at Kaidu. "And he accepts them. He is a skilled wrestler, for a Rus."

"And if he loses?" Khutulun persisted.

Kaidu met his daughter's gaze. "He will not," he said, and Khutulun clenched her fists until her nails cut her palms.

◊Δ◊Δ◊Δ◊Δ◊Δ◊

Mongke-Temur left at dawn, stating his intention to return with Theodore inside of two weeks. Khutulun watched him ride away, her fingers itching to put an arrow between his shoulders.

"This alliance will help us all," said Kaidu. He didn't look at her.

Khutulun nodded tightly, then walked away. She spent the rest of the day with her horses, who expected nothing of her company beyond a scratch behind the ears, and wished, with vehement selfishness, that Qutuchin had never married.

When night fell, Esen found her sitting beside an old mare. The horse whuffed gently at his approach, and when he came to a halt, Khutulun said, without looking up, "You know, then?"

"Everyone does." He hesitated, then sat down a few feet away, toying idly with the grass. The stars overhead were bright and clean, like salt spilled on fine silk. "Buri laughed so hard, he walked into a post."

Khutulun snorted. "Buri has all the sense and grace of a one-winged chicken."

"I can't argue with that."

For a moment, they were silent. Then Khutulun said, softly, "I won this mare from the first man who ever wrestled for my hand. She was the pride of Bolad's old herd, and became the founder of mine. There's meaning in that, I think, and I keep her to honour it." She turned to Esen, tense with anger. "Is my legacy worth so much less than hers, that it can be bartered so cheaply?"

Esen sighed. "Our father chose Altan's wife, and Buri's. He chose Qutuchin's husband, and when I marry, he will arrange that, too. For all the respect he has given you, is it really so hard to imagine that in this one thing, your will is worth less than his?"

"If this were truly his will," said Khutulun, bitterly, "I would respect it. But Mongke-Temur came to *him*, Esen. What do we want with a Rus prince? What could anyone want? We conquered them, and they pay us tribute. No matter his riches or his standing, how is that an alliance worth my freedom?"

To that, Esen had no answer.

◊Δ◊Δ◊Δ◊Δ◊Δ◊

The dust cloud stirred by Theodore and Mongke-Temur's arrival was so great that at first, Khutulun thought they were under attack. How many men had come to witness her humiliation? How many would see her brought low? She watched the approach from a spot on the hill, but it wasn't until the party came closer that she realised the reason for their great numbers: Theodore had brought horses. Unmounted, unsaddled, young and old, geldings, mares, foals, and stallions—a whole herd on the move, their numbers in the high hundreds, most the distinctive takhi favoured by her people, but others with more varied bloodlines. Heavy northern horses with spotted coats; small, quick horses with neat hooves and wide eyes; slender, deep-chested horses the colour of rare metal, all of them running together, a display so beautiful that, despite everything, she felt her heart lift.

When she walked down to meet Theodore, the gathering crowd made way for her like grain before a scythe. The whispers and laughter would cut at her if she let them, so she tuned them out, focussing instead on the three people who mattered most: Mongke-Temur, her father, and Theodore Qara.

The Rus prince was not a young man, but she had known that already; by Kaidu's account, he was already in his fifth decade of life, and had now outlived not one, but two wives, the first of Rus birth, and the second Mongke-Temur's daughter. Between them, they had given him three sons—the pressure of ensuring succession, at least, was one that Khutulun wouldn't bear—whose Christian names felt odd and lumpy in her mouth, like uncooked dough. She had asked about Mongke-Temur's daughter, too, and been told only that she had converted to her husband's faith, taking the name *Anna* as a sign of her devotion. Who she had been before that, though, was information her father either could not or would not share, as if the loss of one woman's name was not worth the effort of inquiring after it.

Khutulun would not give up her name. Once married, it would be all she had left of herself.

"Khutulun Khatun," said Theodore. His tone was deep and respectful, though his accent slid oddly over the vowels. His face was tanned and lined above a trimmed, brown beard; he was tall, too, long-limbed and broad in the shoulders. Khutulun looked him over with a wrestler's eye, and was not unimpressed.

"Theodore Qara," she said. And then, when neither Kaidu nor Mongke-Temur moved to mediate the conversation, "You know my terms?"

"I do," he said, and gestured to where his herd was fenced and tethered. "And in honour of the occasion, I have decided to up the wager." He pitched his voice to carry. "If I lose, you will have a thousand horses. On my honour as the Prince of Yaroslav and Smolensk."

His words stirred a murmur of surprise from those gathered. Khutulun gazed at the horses, and though she had promised discipline, a small smile tugged her mouth upwards at the edges.

"That is generous indeed," she said. "I accept."

Theodore gestured to the open space behind them, an arena already ringing by spectators. "Shall we set to it, then?"

Khutulun led the way onto the field.

As she walked, she stripped off her coat, rolling her shoulders in the crisp air. In all her bouts of wrestling for marriage, she had never once danced beforehand, but she did so now, moving effortlessly through the forms, soothing herself with the fluid ritual of bokh. She was surprised—pleasantly so—when Theodore joined in. His bare arms were pale and ropey, the skin wrinkled in places, but the muscles beneath were hard as iron. When they came to a halt and bowed, his strange eyes were determined.

Mongke-Temur approached them, stepping easily into the judge's role. He nodded at them both, and when he raised his hands, the rest of the world fell away.

"Begin!"

Unlike so many men that Khutulun had wrestled, Theodore didn't close with her quickly. They both went into a crouch, their swaying movements mimicking their earlier dance, each seeking to take the measure of the other. They turned in a circle, boots hissing softly against grass and stones.

Suddenly, Theodore was on her. He grabbed her arms—too chivalrous to try for a hold on her legs—and sought to throw her in one clean move. But Khutulun was better than that; she shifted her weight and pushed back, struggling to regain her footing while compromising his.

Time slowed. Though Theodore had come to wrestling late in life, he had an old soldier's cunning rather than a young man's rashness, and it showed in how he took his time; he was willing to break away from her and withdraw, circling as he planned his next move. For the first time, it occurred to Khutulun that perhaps she would have no need to throw the bout, after all, that Theodore might outmatch her on his own merits. Under different circumstances, she could have borne that; he did not, after all, seem wholly intolerable. But Mongke-Temur had made sure that everyone knew what the outcome was to be; that their match was more formality than challenge. Whether she lost honestly or not, it would be known as a submission. For duty. For family. For alliance.

For the will of the Golden Horde.

As she changed positions, Khutulun glimpsed Kaidu from the corner of her eye. The angry set of his shoulders surprised her, as did the dark look he shot at Mongke-Temur. Her heart leapt in her chest, and as Theodore took advantage of the lapse to close with her again, her thoughts flashed back to her very first battle, the fight against Kublai's men. She had gone with the archers because she had thought there was greater worth in obedience, but in the end, it was Nomukhan's capture that brought her glory. *A gamble on a gamble on a gamble.* And she had won.

Khutulun felt the moment move through her like sunlight through water, as sharp and perfect as steel. Theodore Qara tightened his grip, and Khutulun moved with him, finding his rhythm as once she had found Esen's, moving him across the grass until she felt the pattern shift like a battle-tide.

And then she dropped, and hooked her elbow under his knee, rising up like a cornered bear. Theodore grabbed her back, startled, his hands digging into her like claws, but Khutulun was strong and inexorable. The prince's feet came off the ground, and with a triumphant cry, she threw him over her shoulder. Theodore hit the earth with a sound like boulders falling, and for a split second afterwards, there was a deafening silence, like she had knocked the whole world clean of air, not just the lungs of a shocked Rus prince.

And then the cheering started, loud and exultant, heedless of the fury in Mongke-Temur's eyes, the bafflement in Theodore's. Khutulun raised her arms, and when she turned, her father's smile was wide as the heavens.

"Little moon," he said, the pride in his voice unmistakeable. "How bright you shine."

Charmed Life

Joyce Chng

It must be a privilege indeed to be an Empress.

I heard this all the time, from ladies of the Court and fish wives selling their wares. When they looked at me, they saw the magnificent food or the gorgeous robes or even the leisurely walks in the imperial peach and jasmine gardens. Of course, I enjoyed the calligraphy sessions and poetry recitals immensely. I even loved the delicacies presented in such artistry and beauty that they were art, not food.

I sat beside the Emperor, smiling demurely and waving politely to our subjects when we toured the towns and villages in our jewelled palanquins.

A charmed life, they told me. I had a charmed life.

◊∆◊∆◊∆◊∆◊∆◊

When I worked at my father's workshop, crafting metal ore into tools, weapons and ornaments, I wore homespun clothes and was often barefoot. I would stand beside Father while he plunged burning-hot metal and beat it into a sword commissioned by one of the lords and nobles of the Court. Father didn't mind having me in the workshop; he grinned, and taught me certain skills like curling of pliant metal and making of simple but efficient machines. We made water wheels and pulleys to carry the baskets of rice and grain.

It was in the workshop that my would-be husband found me, perspiring and curling filaments of metal into a brooch. It was to be a gift to a lady of the palace.

Later, when his visits became more regular, I learned that he was not an ordinary man.

"Daughter," my father told me one day, when we sat eating a simple meal of rice and pickled cabbage hearts. "My daughter, you are fortunate to have the emperor shower such attention upon you."

I stared at my father, at his honest sun-tanned and soot-covered face. "Emperor?"

"Yes, my dear daughter."

Realisation sank in, deep and painful. I had hot tears in my eyes.

"But I will miss you and Mother."

Father looked at me and simply said: "Remember us."

In the summer, I, Leizu, was betrothed to the Yellow Emperor.

In the next spring, I was married in a lavish ceremony and welcomed into the palace.

◊∆◊∆◊∆◊∆◊∆◊

At first, I chafed at the restrictions and rules, so many of them! How to sit, how to bow, how to eat, how to use utensils without having the long sleeves of my garment touch the table, how to...so many how-tos. I missed the heat of the workshop, the smell of the ores and metal, and Father's songs while he worked. *Ti oh oh, ti oh oh. The sky is dark, the storm is coming.*

My husband was kind and considerate. We often conversed long into the night about poetry and art, fragrant tea on the lacquered table between us. We talked about the metal workings and new inventions. I tried to hide my impatience; my fists gripped the fabric of my robes so tightly I swore I made tears. I itched to visit the workshops while the men worked. The empire was growing rapidly. Zhong Guo was indeed becoming the centre of the earth. Middle Kingdom.

So I negotiated, politely, for concessions. I wanted to have my workshop made. I wanted to have an orchard planted, so that I could grow berries and other fruits.

Two Winter Solstices passed, and I grew restless. While the palace busied itself with Spring Festival preparations, I longed to be out in the orchard enjoying my tea. While the maids and servants amused themselves with the making of jiao zi, I pretended to join the fun, folding the dumplings with my bare hands, but my heart was elsewhere. I was spiritless.

I painted. I wrote. I must have bored my trusted lady-in-waiting, Wang Li, to tears with my insipid poetry. I sang too, to her dismay, yet she was accommodating even when I was impatient and short-tempered.

I wanted to go out into my orchard.

◊∆◊∆◊∆◊∆◊∆◊

"Leizu, Leizu, my dear wife, can you please sit down?" my august husband said mildly. I was pacing up and down the chambers. It was Yuan Xiao, the fifteenth day of the New Year. The full moon gleamed, a big white pearl in the night sky. Lanterns in various shapes and sizes hung on trees and string. They bobbed in the breeze. Outside the palace walls were the sounds of laughter and celebration.

"I can't sit down," I told him. "I am restless tonight."

Up and down, up and down, wringing my hands, staring off the balcony.

"Are you having your monthly course?" My husband chuckled. Women's problems amused him.

"My monthly course hasn't arrived yet..." I muttered irritably and stopped in my tracks, mouth open, my heart fluttering. I felt as if I discovered something momentous happening within me. A revelation.

And so it was: I had conceived. Eight moons later, I gave birth to a boy I named Changyi.

My little prince grew fat and content with the milk from my breasts. For a while, I was happy to bask in the glow of motherhood. I told him stories, whispered to him songs. He would have his grandfather's hands.

When Changyi turned one, I started feeling that itch-in-the-heart again.

I visited the orchard, pleased with the grove of shang shu growing with such health and vitality. While Changyi played with his nanny and Wang Li beside the pond of colourful carp, I sat beneath the trees, admiring the ripening berries and the leaves turning gold in the sun, my cup of hot jasmine tea in my hands and a plate of nibbles to whet my appetite. Wang Li, the sun flashing in her hair, came to dance and distract me.

◊∆◊∆◊∆◊∆◊∆◊

My garments were rough, pretty as they were. It suited me to try to find ways to make fabrics more comfortable. I pored over books in my husband's library.

I found herbs that gave dyes. I also found that fabrics could be made from the spun coats of goat, sheep and yak. The women who laboured with the spinning of the fur worked most of the day, turning the rough fibres into yarn and then into thread. The process was time-consuming, tiring. I hated to see the women so exhausted after a day's work.

With Wang Li in tow, I scoured the countryside, picking weeds and herbs. I dried them how my mother did in her kitchen, hanging in bushels, letting the wind dry them. I made tinctures, mixtures and solutions out of those dried weeds and herbs. Some worked as dyes. Some became medicinal.

◊∆◊∆◊∆◊∆◊∆◊

I sat beneath the grove of trees, staring idly into the jasmine tea, wondering what I should do to help the women.

Changyi squealed. He had tripped over and his nanny rushed over to comfort him. Wang Li came running. She had a soft spot for Prince Changyi, and often gave him tasty treats and cloth toys she had sewn during her free time.

I rose, anxious, but the women waved me away. I sighed. I would lose Changyi as he grew older: to the world of men and politics, where truths are lies, lies are lies and smiles are daggers in disguise. His trusting face would hide under a mask and his real self under layers and layers of selves. Sometimes, men willingly forgot their real selves. At night, before we slept, I called him another name, a milk name, which I would use only in his presence. A reminder of who and what he was.

As I lifted my cup of jasmine tea, now cooled by neglect, I was surprised to see a white ball inside it. But no, not a ball, rather a cocoon of some sort, wrapped tightly like dragon beard candy. Curious, I poked it. It was soft, still dripping with tea, and I found the end of a fine thread, similar to the ones I used for embroidering. Daringly, I began to unwind the thread, delighting at the feel of it, at the resilience, around my fingers. It would not break. It was strong. I unraveled it until an egg-like object was revealed. It broke open to show a curled and shrunken worm.

Heart pounding, I looked up into the tree, and saw white-coloured caterpillars eating the green leaves. Further up, I saw the white cocoons.

I had to sit. My knees felt weak. I pulled experimentally at the fine white thread. Wonderful, wonderful, wonderful. *I have found something.*

◊Δ◊Δ◊Δ◊Δ◊Δ◊

I observed the caterpillars for a month or so. They grew plump from the leaves, spinning white threads when they were about to change. After a few weeks, moths emerged and repeated the cycle again.

Encouraged, I began to pick the white cocoons, much to Wang Li's consternation. I had her bring a cedar wood tub filled with boiling water; the steam filled the air like white clouds to Heaven.

I plunged myself into this activity, this discovery. In my head, I heard Father's singing and felt the heat of the workshop.

I harvested the threads from the boiled and soaked cocoons, pulling and twisting them with my fingers until they formed a substantial reel. The dead caterpillars were actually quite tasty, though Wang Li thought they were disgusting. I laughed and laughed.

"They are smooth and strong," I told Wang Li. "Touch it, feel it, stretch it!"

My ideas spun like bright fire, like the threads from the white caterpillars. While my august husband slept, I sat by the moon-lit and candle-lit table, sketching with a charcoal stick. Dawn broke to a drawing of *something*.

My husband watched while I began constructing the machine. The court ladies thought I had gone insane. Perhaps I had. But it was a lovely sort of insanity that filled my veins with brightness; I stood at the threshold of something new, something daring. I stripped to my undergarments and went barefoot. My orders were simple: fetch the most resilient wood, string and metal. Men and women ran in and out of the palace.

When the machine was done, I stepped back, wiping my forehead.

"What is this?" My husband asked me, tentatively, as if I would break with mere words.

"To make the lives of women easier," I said, sipping tea from a porcelain cup. "Didn't you see the women labouring to make threads?"

To show that the machine wasn't frightening, I demonstrated it, following the design and pattern in my head. The harvested thin thread from the cocoons was stronger when twisted. I showed them how to turn the thread into cloth, working the levers and moving the pedals. The machine made a lot of sound, like the clanging of temple bells, but the result took their breath away.

◊Δ◊Δ◊Δ◊Δ◊Δ◊

I wrote my idea down, turning it into a book. My husband, the Emperor, praised me and said that I was a brilliant woman.

Didn't he see that in me when I worked in my father's workshop?

We began to cultivate more of the shang shu and the caterpillars. I started a nursery in the palace where I supervised the feeding, the harvesting and the production of the threads. I also learnt how to plant cuttings from the trees and coaxed roots from them. As I grew more knowledgeable, I went into the villages to teach the women how to turn the threads into wonderful fabric. Some villages became centres of this new invention, turning the threads into fabric that subsequently became beautiful robes that slid on skin like water.

Imagine my fury when I found out my husband had taken credit for this discovery. I stormed at him, angry, and too betrayed to feel otherwise.

"How dare you?" I shouted and kicked out with my foot, causing the rosewood table to topple over. "How dare you, how dare you?"

"Leizu, Leizu," my husband, the lying traitorous bastard, tried to placate me. "I wanted to share your knowledge."

"Share your knowledge, my foot. You took credit for it," I yelled. "You turned it into *your* invention."

I was incensed. Without a word, I left the palace with my silkworm books, a squirming unhappy Changyi in my arms, and Wang Li who agreed to accompany me.

My father was surprised to see me. My mother gasped and welcomed me into her arms. She smelled of cooked rice and steamed sweet potato.

"What happened?" my father asked, still soot-covered, the honest hardworking man I had known since I was a little girl.

"I will tell you over rice and picked cabbage hearts," I said, shrugging off my rich Empress robes, feeling the heat of the workshop on my face. Changyi giggled in my mother's arms. Wang Li gazed around shyly and looked at me with trusting, adoring eyes. I leaned forward and kissed her on the lips. Such gentle and soft lips.

A charmed life.

Indeed, it was a charmed life. I am putting it behind me.

I now live my own life.

A Beautiful Stream

Nisi Shawl

Her daughter's hatred would be seen as Gabrielle's fault. What of it? Such an outcome was not to be lamented or evaded, but accepted. Better for little Gazouette to believe her mama indifferent than for her to be used as leverage. Or worse, to be trapped in identical coils.

Gabrielle-Sidonie Goncourt looked down at her sleeping daughter with deliberate coldness, taking in the rucked sheets, the petal-coloured cheeks, then walked from the room into the lampless passageway. She had never wanted to bear a child, anyway, she reminded herself. One would think that at forty the chance of doing so had passed.

She shut the bedroom's door and leaned against its dark panels, their wood creaking slightly.

Strength. She willed herself forward. There were appearances to keep up.

As she walked along the corridor, Gabrielle's skirts rustled, sweeping the tops of her shoes, rubbing against her silk sleeves as her arms moved forward and back, forward and back. Turning a corner, she heard with sudden clarity the sounds of the diners below: her lover, faithful Missy, and the ballet backers she'd brought with her—the loud, rather coarse ice magnate M'sieur Hanse; the abstemious M'sieur Falco Tessiter and his equally sober son Robert. And of course Gabrielle's husband. Who did not ask of her more than she could give.

The ballet was to be dedicated to Gazouette: a show, literally, of Gabrielle's maternal affection. Probably the child would want more. Too bad.

Gabrielle knew how to walk downstairs; her mother, Sido, had shown her how not to lower her head, how to keep the line of her neck taut and appealing. Hand on the banister, eyes on the chandelier, she glided along in a smooth descent. Wasted; not one of her guests had peered through the doorway of the dining room to see her coming.

The maids had cleared the plates with their unsightly burdens, brushed crumbs and fallen titbits from the damask cloth. In a proper household the ladies would have now withdrawn, but Missy remained in the chair where she'd been seated during the meal, and Gabrielle found a glass waiting for her as expected at her own place, filled with a tawny vintage.

Goncourt and the Tessiters rose quickly; Hanse lagged somewhat behind them, one hand on the back of his chair. "Madame," her husband began, "we have been wondering if, perhaps, there might be some discussion of business?"

Gabrielle nodded. Goncourt eased the padded chair beneath her as she resumed her spot. "We are on good enough terms now, are we not?" She turned to Tessiter Père on her left. "It is in my mind that you would like best to give us support in the matter of costumery, maquillage, scenery—the materials bought once. As soon as the war ends, of course. While you—" she faced the other way, towards Hanse, "—would be the one to supply ongoing expenses such as rents, advertisements, and dancers' and musicians' salaries."

"Yes, but how are the proceeds to be disbursed?" asked this worthy. "Proportionally to our costs? Our risks?"

Missy intervened. "There is no risk. In a few months, when the war ends, we proceed. Our composer is Ravel; our choreographer Nijinsky. Our shining star is Gabrielle."

The older Tessiter demurred. "It is 1915. Nearly ten years now since they rioted in the streets over your kiss, Mesdames." He looked long and meaningfully at Missy's handsome but aging countenance. "The sensation has died down. Forgive me if I seek some other surety for our investment."

"I am good for it," Missy replied. Her voice was heavy with disappointment, as if she scolded a cat of whom she anticipated nothing better than a certain level of misbehavior. "Goncourt also may be relied upon."

◊Δ◊Δ◊Δ◊Δ◊Δ◊

The evening went convincingly, she thought. From her seat on the chaise longue before her boudoir's velvet-draped window, Gabrielle watched the Tessiters' carriage rattle away in the dull moonlight with tempered relief. Now the die must be cast.

Goncourt would be expecting her in their shared bedroom, a long walk and two turns along the passageway. Let him wait. She had a private farewell to make.

Reaching behind her seat to where the other woman stood, she arrested the hand of her lover, captured it firmly in her own so Missy could no longer toy with the tendrils escaping from Gabrielle's carefully inexact coiffure. Still plump and smooth, the mound under Missy's thumb yielded softly to Gabrielle's teasing bite. A heavy sigh—a sound too soft to be called a moan—escaped her lover's lips. Gabrielle drew her down to kiss not her mouth but her neck.

Soon the chaise held them both, a pliant twist of flesh and pleasure. No fire filled the room's grate, so they didn't remove their clothing, merely rearranged it. Nor did they linger long in the chill that followed passion.

Missy sighed again as she moved away, pulling up her stockings and fastening them in place.

A third sigh. Gabrielle rose to put enough distance between them that she could ask what was wrong without the danger of a collapse into her arms.

"I wish I could go with you," Missy replied. The shadows thrown by the candle on the mantel showed only half her face. That half held a stoically sad expression Gabrielle knew from earlier separations.

"But it is to Goncourt's estate we go," Gabrielle objected. "Inviting you would not be fair to him. Here, in the house you let to us, it is different."

"Yes." Missy stood also, shaking out the skirts of her gown, smiling ruefully. "Here, it *is* different."

Kissing her lover goodbye, Gabrielle prayed silently that she and Missy would meet once more in safety. That someday she'd be free of the shadowy militarists who sought to bind Gabrielle to their service by threatening those she loved.

But not soon. Her ostensible masters would learn where she had fled to, eventually, though they wouldn't be able to manipulate her so easily at Rozven. Her husband's family was well-established, his retainers loyal.

In their bedroom, Goncourt, fully dressed, paced in front of the glowing hearth. "All is in readiness?" she asked, to give him a chance to reprove her.

"This past hour. Where have you been?"

"With the child," Gabrielle lied.

Goncourt laughed. "A likely story! Haven't I always known—"

Though she had instigated it, she found herself bored by the prospect of the coming lecture. So she simply stopped listening. As her husband thundered on, she glanced around, noting instead the table newly emptied of his cosmetics: wax for his moustache, cream for the shining skin atop his head. Cologne and manicure set were also gone. A carafe and drinking glass occupied the bedside table, but overall the room's air was of a location soon to be abandoned.

That was the doing of this so-called "great" war, which was to have been over by Christmas. Dragging on and on, it had brought "requests" from her government she couldn't afford to refuse outright: to travel, to spy, to report on their enemies. To monitor even their ostensible friends.

Now her view of the room was obscured by memories: the awkward approach of her would-be recruiter during a lull in business at the dim café down the street; his laughable attempt to force her capitulation by publicising her African heritage—as if that weren't a point of which to be proud! As if it weren't already widely known—and when that failed, his semi-obscure promises to do violence to Missy, which Gabrielle tried to face with equanimity, hoping that her lover's wealth would shield her from harm. And then his hints about visiting pain upon Gazouette. Which Gabrielle was not able to treat with the same disdain.

"Do you suppose we fooled them?" Gabrielle asked, and knew from Goncourt's face she had interrupted what he was saying.

After being forced to vent his anger he usually became a penitent lamb. As was now the case: he gathered her gently in his arms. "Can you forgive me? In the morning it will be all over town—I have allowed a reporter to write about our little project for the *Journal*."

Gabrielle grimaced, but answered cheerfully, "Then we had best be on our way, hadn't we?" By the time their departure was known, she and her child would be safe.

Her husband held the bedroom door open for her with a small bow, and repeated the gesture at the entrances to the kitchen and the courtyard. Inside the cramped stables the loaded automobile throbbed loudly, the purring of an immense, watchful cat. Their driver got out and let Goncourt take his seat, then helped Gabrielle take hers. He arranged the fur collar of her favourite coat so it protected her ears without tickling her chin. He opened the cat's eyes, or rather, uncovered its headlamps.

"Where is Gazouette?" her husband asked.

"Gone ahead, with her nanny."

"They are to meet us in Chartres?"

"No. Tomorrow night, in Le Mans." That was when she would tell him that their child had embarked for Canada. By then Gazouette would be gone.

"Fine. As long as you are satisfied." He waved at the driver to open the courtyard gates and they set off.

◊Δ◊Δ◊Δ◊Δ◊Δ◊

But Gabrielle's ruse didn't work. A miscommunication of some sort. Less than a week after she and Goncourt arrived at Rozven, Taylor and Gazouette arrived also. Taylor sat challengingly upright on the uncomfortable chair in Gabrielle's office, her timid charge curled at her feet. "There were no suitable lodgings on Guernsey, not on the entire island," the Englishwoman explained. "I would have continued on, but then I heard the news of the fire on the *Mauretania*."

Gabrielle had not heard of the disaster herself till this morning. The ship on which she'd booked Gazouette's passage to Quebec was out of commission—suspiciously so, as it baulked her from removing the child from the grasp of government manipulators. For how long the ship would be disabled she didn't know. Nor did she comprehend why the woman hadn't journeyed on to her homeland and stayed there till repairs were effected. Or until some other method of escape offered itself.

Nonetheless, she nodded. "Of course. The nursery is being readied for you."

That change would lessen the space available to board nurses, for the house would soon be filled with wounded soldiers. The nurses would have to be made to fit somewhere—perhaps an outbuilding? Later she would re-examine their disposition; at the moment what mattered was that her plans for Gazouette's safety were ruined.

Gabrielle brought the interview to a quick close and went to the library. It had been her site of solace for three years now, during every visit since her marriage: the narrow windows admitting sunlight, stormlight, moonlight, mistlight; the polished stones of the floor, reddish black, stubbornly refusing to reflect more than smudges of those who stood upon them; and, of course, the books.

Not many remained on the emptying shelves. A quarter of the room's former inhabitants. Gabrielle caught the top of one tall volume with a crooked finger and pulled it down toward her. An old favourite, this one, rescued from the sale of her girlhood home's contents. It was clad in blue twill, crammed full of coloured plates depicting classical myths. She sat on a footstool and idly turned its pages till she came to Rubens's portrait of Thetis bathing Achilles. Here was an idea.

Though the hero had died.

But perhaps his death was owing to an error on the part of his mother? Or, perhaps the River Styx's hellish nature had precluded a happy ending?

Marking her place with one finger, Gabrielle carried the book of myths with her to her bedroom in the turret. The afternoon's long shadows stretched themselves out upon the naked staircase, concealing and revealing its scars, the result of removing the runner which had covered it so many years. That worn strip of carpet had been rolled up and stored temporarily in the entrance hall. It was to be laid down the middle of the transformed ballroom, between ranks of the hospital beds still stacked in the front drive, awaiting their installation.

She had written yesterday to affirm that they'd be ready to receive their first consignment of the "great" war's wounded by March 1. A fortnight away.

Outside her door she paused. On the other side of the circular landing lay the nursery. From beneath the bottom of its door came murmurs, contented-sounding voices: low and womanly, high and prattlingly childish. Gabrielle wouldn't interrupt; she could picture the scene clearly enough. Taylor would be unpacking, Gazouette staggering like a drunken doll as she struggled to follow in her nanny's bustling steps. The jumpers and heavy knitted stockings, the bonnets and leggings and jackets so carefully selected in anticipation of Britain's cool climate would be stowed away in chests of drawers.

Couldn't Gazouette and her clothing stay here? Wouldn't she be safe enough at Rozven, safe as her father and mother?

Entering her half-moon-shaped bedchamber, Gabrielle rang for her fire to be lit. The sun would soon set, and she'd need the warmth and light. When the housemaid had come and gone she pulled a white-painted, flower-cushioned armchair to the hearth and reopened her book to the Rubens.

Bats. They besieged the painting, framed the subjects, surrounded them. In the distance, ghosts clamoured to Charon for release from their dull afterlives—understandably. The river's waters, green and poisonous-looking, showed nothing of the miracle they were supposed to instill in those brought by supplicants to its shores. Brought to be bathed in the chill and cold, to freeze the body but soothe the soul…

And Thetis, that foolish nymph, had subjected her child to this treatment—to preserve his life, of course—but had failed to do it thoroughly enough. Why had she not submerged her own hand in the Styx, if that would keep her son from harm?

Gabrielle studied the painting's reproduction till the dinner bell. Would she need a dog? Or a friend such as the spinner Clotho to hold up an illuminating flame?

No—no flames, no bats. She'd try what she could accomplish without them.

After dinner she fended off Goncourt's attentions. It took very little trouble. She looked in on Gazouette, spoke a brief word with Taylor about the program for the following day, and went to bed betimes.

◊Δ◊Δ◊Δ◊Δ◊Δ◊

Gabrielle woke, as always, without recourse to an alarm clock. Only the faintest clues announced the coming of the day: a sky like milk from a dark blue cow, a western breeze laden with the merest hint of brine.

There was a bit of fuss in the nursery. To save time and lessen the noise, Gabrielle accepted Taylor's accompaniment out of the house and across lawns crackling with frost, to the path she had discovered during her first explorations. She insisted on carrying the child herself, though.

Even leafless with winter, the beech trees cut off much of the dawn's growing light. Taylor stopped at the woods' edge to adjust her lantern to a wider aperture, but Gabrielle, impatient, darted ahead, trusting to the bark's silvery glimmering to show her the way. "Leave that thing there!" she called back over her shoulder. No flames.

Gradually, the land fell. The path, like a young girl, ran straight down precipitous slopes, then dallied flirtatiously with the stream at their bottom, climbing in opposition to its flow to the low granite bluffs occupying Rozven's eastern boundaries. At last, as glowing pink and yellow tints had just touched the clouds far above, they came to the sacred spring.

The source.

A curved wall had been built into the earth. From a crack between its grey stones poured a cascade of singing water. Caught momentarily in a round pool, it laughed and splashed itself out by way of a channel bridged with slabs of that same stone. Above the wall and to one side stood a gracefully bowed beech, its lower branches festooned with ribbons: gay and bright or tattered, faded, old. Each ribbon represented a prayer, so the old women seated before nearby cottages had intimated.

Gabrielle knelt on the ground, Gazouette in her lap. Taylor spread the rug she had stubbornly brought. Gabrielle was glad of it; the dead leaves were damp. She lay the drowsy child down on the rug and went to work on removing her clothes.

Despite the harsh temperature, Gazouette seemed to enjoy her nudity. No sooner had her mother divested her of the last of her garments than she hoisted herself to her feet, fully awake now, running and stumbling in spirals and zigzags as the two women chased her. To Gabrielle's pride it was she who gathered the giggling girl into her arms, not Taylor. But she had to relinquish her to the nanny anyway in order to remove her own boots, coat, and skirt, and to roll and tuck up her crinoline and her blouse's long sleeves.

For a ribbon she had brought the band off an old gardening hat of Sido's. That old straw hat was the only remnant Gabrielle had of her mother's practical wardrobe, which had been sparse at the height of its glory and was now all but vanished with time. The band's pale blue spoke of the dusty, sunny days she'd spent under Sido's watchful maternal eye, guarded with the best of care.

So many others had petitioned the spring before her. Rumors among the women of the village said every single one had gotten her wish. But as Gabrielle chose her twig and tied her prayer to it she wondered if some other sacrifice would be required.

Taylor parted with Gazouette reluctantly. Gabrielle carried the squirming, wriggling little child to the bridge and lay on her stomach on the big flat stone. Using both hands—she was not afraid, not she—she gently lowered her daughter into the babbling brook. Cold stole into Gabrielle's bones, but she held the girl firmly, swishing her back and forth, twice changing her grip to ensure every inch of skin received its blessing. Then she pulled the wailing, dripping wet and now hopefully invulnerable child back out of the water and wrapped her in the driest part of her under-chemise.

A weird, skirling cry split the air—getting louder and louder, sharper and sharper, hurting her ears. Gabrielle sheltered Gazouette beneath her breasts and shoulders, peered up and saw a swelling black *thing* falling toward her. Its wide wings unfurled—an eagle?—osprey?—she could see its grasping claws, its dark, hooked beak—

It swerved aside! With a crash, it hit the pool. Only a few feet away... And now she perceived Taylor squealing with fright, running forward with arms stretched out—what good would that do?

Gabrielle rolled to lessen her weight on the baby and saw the bird surface from the pool's depths and fly to the tree of prayers, a flash of silver held struggling in its feet. This it transferred to its mouth. It hopped higher, out of sight, but Gabrielle had no doubt the silver signified a fish, which the osprey—only ospreys dived so—would now eat in peaceful retirement.

Fending off Taylor's stupid attempts to take Gazouette from her, Gabrielle raised herself onto her hips. She'd received an omen, but what did it mean? She couldn't decide.

Her hands, as she resumed her dress, felt oddly nimble. Shouldn't they be numb? Yet she barely required Taylor's assistance with her ties and buttons. Gazouette's were more trouble, but just because the girl ran about like a zany, and even once caught, refused naughtily to submit to being clothed.

The way back seemed to take a shorter time than had the trek to the stream's source. They reached the house at the hour Gabrielle was accustomed to take breakfast. Early for visitors, and yet an unfamiliar car stood parked next to the piles of unassembled bedframes. It was empty. But Goncourt's man met her at the door and informed her of Missy's presence in the library.

Without any hesitation, Gabrielle gave Gazouette into the nanny's care and hurried to greet her unexpectedly-arrived lover, almost running along the gallery in her haste, plunging down the three steps to the Low Wing, thrusting open the library's door—and halting on the room's threshold.

Missy was not alone. She'd brought someone with her. A man.

A moment passed. Hardly any time. Gabrielle recognised her other guest: the younger Tessiter, M'sieur Robert. What could the fellow possibly want? The ballet's premiere was far in the future.

She walked forward at a seemly pace, hands open. "My dear! How good to see you!" Missy joined her in a swift embrace. The awkward pause went unremarked.

"Will you have tea? Chocolate?" She faced M'sieur Tessiter politely. "I am afraid I can't offer you a place to spend the night. You see, we are in an uproar—"

Missy's throaty chuckle interrupted her attempt at an excuse. "But that's the news I've come to share! Robert will stay with me. I've bought a new home not five leagues from here!"

Gabrielle wouldn't need to pressure Goncourt into hosting his rival, then. Yet Missy would be near enough to see, to touch. What measures, if any, could be taken for her safety?

Gabrielle cast about in her mind for the names of available neighbouring estates. "Not—Broceliande?"

"But yes! Broceliande, certainly! Is that—is there something wrong with it? The house? The lands? The—"

"No." Gabrielle forced herself to think rationally. "Only Goncourt's people have an old feud with the former owners. And there is an idiotic tradition involving a curse—"

"A curse!" Missy collapsed onto the footstool. "Don't say such a thing!"

"Mere silliness, I assure you. Nothing at all to worry about if it *were* true." Nothing more than eternal enmity between their households.

◊∆◊∆◊∆◊∆◊∆◊

Goncourt drove. Rozven was low on male servants. Of course a woman could manage an automobile as well as any man, barring a breakdown. Gabrielle herself, for example. Her newly sensitive hands were also strong. They longed to hold and turn the car's steering wheel.

By boat, Broceliande was no more than five leagues away. If small enough, Gabrielle and her husband could have sailed down the beautiful stream and over the dark pond into which it fed, then out again, past the farmers' fields and so on, and so at last to the sea. She pictured their vessel as a dried brown leaf, sides deeply curling, a sail of white samite attached to its stem. An idle fancy.

In reality there were no good direct roads such as they needed; it took them the better part of the afternoon to reach the prim-looking house of Gabrielle's lover. Its walls were a delicate, biscuity yellow, the colour of an aging beauty's complexion.

Missy served English tea: lavish cakes, plentiful sandwiches, hothouse pineapples and grapes. The grapes aroused in Gabrielle a startling greed.

The problematic M'sieur Robert Tessiter was still in attendance, a week after he'd arrived. Goncourt could be managed well enough: a hint that the house's previous inhabitants had left so hastily for South America that their cellars remained largely intact was sufficient to clear him from the stage. But M'sieur Robert was not so easily got rid of.

Gabrielle had him open a window so she could more easily admire the room's view of the sea. It was admittedly magnificent. She blamed this quality for dazzling her into a clumsy-handedness she never experienced these days and causing her to drop her diamond bracelet onto the beach below. Then she stared at the man half a minute, until he volunteered to go and hunt for it.

He left. Gabrielle wasted not one second. She sped to the divan. Missy half-rose and drew her down. Gabrielle tasted sweet juices dried to a slight stickiness on her lover's lips, a last trace of their shared meal.

Shouting floated in the open window. Impossible to distinguish any words in it, though the tone was querulous.

The women investigated only themselves. Each breathed the other's breath. The shouting outside continued, muffled by distance and the noise of the waves. Missy spoke over it, her voice close and low: "You will stay here tonight? And come to me?"

Gabrielle gave no answer.

"You hesitate—why?"

Gazouette would be safe. She must have faith in that. She must show her faith and stay.

Had she not seen proof? The day after her immersion the child had tumbled down the entire length of the grand staircase unhurt—just a bit frightened.

Then the head groom's mastiff had gone mad and dug up his stake, rushing chain and all at Gazouette, whom Taylor had lain to bathe in the unseasonably warm sun. With her own horror-filled eyes Gabrielle had watched from the terrace as the ravening dog ran toward her daughter, and as the stake caught on something not there—on nothing—on air—on the bare soil of the empty flower beds. Halting the beast till it could be shot.

"I will." A change in Gabrielle's attitude toward her daughter would be marked, were anyone watching.

As well she agreed. Her husband's hard-soled shoes sounded in the corridor. Automatically the two women moved a few inches apart. Nothing could have been more decorous, more placatory, than their attitudes as Goncourt entered.

Her husband's expedition to the cellar had been fruitful, and he was happy to accept Missy's offer of hospitality. That evening, with their supper, the four enjoyed several bottles of wines he deemed "satisfactory". More formally inclined than Gabrielle, Missy signaled her when it was the hour to withdraw from the gentlemen's company. But scarcely had they exchanged preliminary embraces than Tessiter and Goncourt followed them, to swallow more tea and converse ignorantly about the war—although M'sieur Robert's observations seemed oddly better than those of the older and more worldly man. They scanned, somehow, matching a rhythm of international affairs Gabrielle hadn't realised she'd internalised.

Not until she and Goncourt retired did Gabrielle find the note. Missy had apparently secreted it in her pocket. "Turn right, then left, then straight on till six," it read, a touch cryptically. Below that line it unambiguously added, "Midnight."

"What have you got?" her husband asked.

"A puzzle. Not a very interesting one." She threw it on the dying fire and set about to soothe him to sleep.

Gabrielle herself stayed awake, and when she judged it time, slipped from the bed and made her way across the invisible floor on bare feet. She had memorised the furniture's location; she made it to the door without incident, and exited quickly so that the candle left burning in the passage wouldn't disturb Goncourt with its light.

A right turn took her to where a narrow corridor branched off to the left. The crack beneath the corridor's sixth door glowed yellow. Inside, a curl of smoke rose above a high-backed armchair drawn up to face the bright hearth. As Gabrielle closed the door an arm clad in the tailored sleeve of a man's jacket appeared to one side of the chair, cigarette in hand.

"Is it not a little dangerous to dress so, even here in your home, my love?" she asked.

"I rather hope you are mistaken." Not Missy, but M'sieur Robert stood to welcome her in.

Gabrielle kept calm. "It would appear so. My apologies." She turned to leave.

"Oh, you have come to the right place," said Tessiter. He moved with surprising speed to block the door. "Congratulations. You executed my directions flawlessly."

"Your directions." Her voice lacked all intonation. She knew suddenly what was toward. The men who believed themselves her masters were again attempting to control her.

"The first set of them, at any rate." He gestured to the armchair. "If you'll be so kind as to seat yourself, I'll convey the rest."

She could scream. The room wasn't that isolated; someone would hear and come. But how to explain her presence in this unlocked room with a man to whom she wasn't married? Goncourt's smouldering jealousy would blaze up at the discovery, and servants, deplorably, talked.

She sat. With half her mind, she listened. An important spy had been gravely wounded. He was to be sent to her hospital. Via Tessiter the government instructed Gabrielle to tend to his needs herself. She was to ensure that whatever he said of his mission in Flanders fell on her ears alone: fevered ravings, lucid reports, deathbed confessions. She should record his pronouncements and pass them on to Tessiter, using Missy as their go-between. Simple enough, did she not think?

She thought. As before, the government's requests seemed reasonable. The war itself, though, was not. Bluntly, it was a flaunting display of cretinism, a contest between heads of nations desperate to determine who possessed the longest metaphoric stick between their legs.

The half of her attention not claimed by Tessiter Gabrielle devoted to calculation. If Missy was to play the role of a messenger in this scheme, she was perhaps more deeply involved than first indicated. The threats against her must have been mere charades. Or perhaps her lover's status had changed between this approach to Gabrielle and the earlier one. In either circumstance, Gabrielle had no need to protect her.

Goncourt she disregarded, as always. He could look after himself. His connections were more current, more powerful than Missy's—though if her lover was now an agent, their respective ambits might be evenly matched.

Which left Gabrielle with perhaps one regrettable vulnerability. Gazouette.

Would Gabrielle's compliance guarantee her daughter's freedom? Probably not. Leverage once gained would never be abandoned.

As for the stairs, the mastiff: they could have been coincidence as easily as evidence of an answered prayer.

Did she believe her daughter safe? Or not?

Abruptly, there was silence. No sound but the hissing of the flames. Reviewing her memory of the past few seconds she realised Tessiter had asked a question: Would she do the job? She shifted uncomfortably on the too-soft velveteen cushion and answered him.

"Yes."

◊Δ◊Δ◊Δ◊Δ◊Δ◊

At least the spy was handsome. Blond, almost silver-haired, with eyes an unusually deep green and a face like a young David—though Gabrielle couldn't help seeing him as a gape-mouthed fish caught in her talons. The wound to his thigh stank and seeped an ugly mixture of blood and pus when he arrived. She washed it thoroughly with lavender water and packed it with a special healing clay like one Sido had used. This was perhaps why the gaping hole in his flesh closed so quickly. Or it could be due to some supernatural quality in her touch, as many claimed.

Alas, the spy's mind recovered slowly. When she knew she wasn't going to be free to sit by his side, Gabrielle gave him drops of a tincture she'd brewed from valerian and poppy to still his broken ramblings.

The nurses and servants believed she tended Lieutenant Tranché because she desired him. Little matter that. Any story would do but the truth, and she took care to give their rumors no grounds. Nothing that could be laid before Goncourt as definitive.

Despite the house's pressing lack of living space, Gabrielle had maintained her private room. Here she wrote her tales of an irretrievable past. It made sense to use the same pen, paper, desk drawer, lock, and key for her secret work for the government. Scrupulously she inscribed every wandering sentence the lieutenant uttered, not venturing to decide its relevance. She sealed the results in scented envelopes and delivered them personally into the hands of her former lover at their too-frequent meetings.

She took care that they two were never again alone together. Nonetheless, Missy's eyes often spilled over with questions and unacknowledged tears.

For weeks there was no coherence to Tranché's speech. At last his green eyes focused on her, and not some phantom of his illness. She introduced herself, said the password Tessiter had revealed to her, received his countersign. From that moment commenced Gabrielle's real labours in the fields of intelligence. She always remembered the exact date. It was one month from the day she had sent Gazouette away a second time. For good.

◊∆◊∆◊∆◊∆◊∆◊

Gabrielle died at the age of eighty-one. Her estranged and cold yet dutiful daughter returned to attend her sickbed, travelling alone all the way to France from Greece, her most recent in a series of loveless homes.

Rozven had been sold years earlier, upon Goncourt succumbing to a malady of the heart; Gabrielle inhabited a flat in Paris, alone except for her beloved bulldog Beau and a paid nurse. The medal bestowed in exchange for her wartime activities hung framed above her headboard, in a spot where she didn't have to see it.

Propped up with massive quantities of pillows, as she insisted, she watched out her windows while the chestnuts blossomed, watched their leaves unfurl, darken, become brown. But she didn't see them fall.

When, at last, after two seasons of grudging patience, the inevitable moment came, Gazouette (who had never shaken her childish nickname) was where she knew she should be, holding her mother's always strangely youthful hands. She bent forward to catch Gabrielle's last words—for posterity, she told herself, because they could never be meant for anyone else.

"It was best that you not know," the old woman murmured. "I made my mind up never to tell you, and I never did. Even long after the danger."

Gazouette couldn't help questioning that. "Never to tell me what?"

Gabrielle seemed not to hear her, or at least not to make the effort to respond. "You never felt the smallest threat."

She shut her eyes a final time. "And even without you, I have had a beautiful life."

Neter Nefer
Amanda Pillar

I was the daughter and sister of gods.
But godhood was not my destiny.
It was my mother's.

Blood dripped down the khopesh's blade to pool on the sandstone tiles underneath my mother's sandalled feet. The drip, drip, drip trapped my eye, the life essence so red and raw once separated from its host. If I captured it all, could I pour it back? Give life once it had been taken?

"Are they all dead?" Mother asked. Her voice was faint, as if it travelled a great distance to reach me, though I was mere feet away. It did not matter; she was not speaking to me. I swayed, my eyes locked on her curved blade and the dripping blood. I dimly registered the sound of screams echoing from other areas of the palace.

"Yes, God's Wife," someone replied. "No one here survives."

Footsteps pounded as guards and servants rushed back and forth. I heard the scraping sound of clothing being dragged over sandstone.

"Neferure!" Mother's voice was a whip.

I jolted to attention. "Mother?"

She stood regal before me, fingers gripping her khopesh with white-knuckled fury. In her other hand, she held a dagger. Her white gown had lost its pristine crispness, the splashes of garnet speaking of the battle just past. "Are you injured?"

I looked down at myself, studying my limbs. Crimson trickled down my arm and I frowned. I had been cut? Fingers tracing the blood up to its source, I found an incision at my throat. It must have happened when one of the attackers grabbed me. Cupping my hand over the wound, I tried to force the blood back inside. I did not want to end up empty like the men on the floor.

Mother took a step closer, her foot sliding through the blood puddle that had formed next to her. "Daughter?"

"I have been cut, but it doesn't seem serious."

Mother threw her words behind her; "Fetch a *swnw*, immediately!"

My protest was instant, "I don't need a physician!"

Mother turned to one of the guards, ignoring me. "And a priest of Sekhmet."

"As you wish, God's Wife." The guard turned and shouted down the hall, "My lady Hatshepsut requires a *swnw* and a priest of Sekhmet immediately!"

I wanted to groan, but the look of concern she flashed towards me kept my lips sealed. She moved the hand from my throat, inspecting the wound. Gently, she placed my palm back. "I would kill them again for the insult they have done you. May their hearts be stones when compared to the feather of Ma'at."

"It would be justice," I said. Then, with Mother so close, I whispered, "Why did they attack us?"

Her dark brows drew together sharply. "Where is your father?"

My heart began to beat with alarm. "He is unwell and in his rooms; I was on my way back from him..."

Even gods could grow poorly. The demons of disease did not discriminate against those they cursed, and Father had surely been cursed. His skin was covered in raw, ugly looking sores; his purity corrupted by evil. Secretly, I feared he would join Osiris, the god of death, sooner rather than later.

Mother spun on her heel and ran from the room. My hand cupped awkwardly to my neck, I followed as she ran down stone-lined halls. Her footsteps beat out an uneven pattern of desperation, leaving a one-sided blood trail the guards could follow. The palace at Thebes was vast; the God's Wife had her own suite of rooms, with the Pharaoh in a separate quarter. I was breathing heavily by the time we made my father's rooms. Two guards lay dead at the entrance, discarded on the floor like broken toys. Blood pooled around them like fallen shadows.

The door banged against the wall as Mother thrust it open. She strode into the room, khopesh and dagger raised. Furniture was overturned and beautiful statues and bowls were smashed on the floor. Throwing open the door to Father's sleep chamber, we came to a sudden stop. He lay in his bed, head set in the middle of his headrest, clothing neat and tidy. A rusty cloth had been spread over his middle. He looked peaceful.

Rushing forward, Mother dropped to her knees at her husband's side; her weapons clattering to the stone floor. A high, keening sound filled the room. I had never seen her like this. I could not watch her pain, and so my gaze swept the room, avoiding Father as well. My eyes came to rest on a statue of the sun god, Horus, discarded on the floor at Father's side. During life, Horus and Pharaoh were as one. But the statue had been broken, smashed in two. Kneeling down, I picked up the pieces, stunned at the sacrilege. Mother's wail died to sobs. Looking over her shaking shoulders, I realised the cloth covering Father was stained with blood. His life had flooded out across the bed. A knife hilt jutted obscenely from his chest; his heart, the seat of his soul, punctured by violence.

I could not comprehend it.

"Who could have done this? What reason would they have?" Mother's words were quiet.

The voice that replied from the doorway was familiar and blessedly welcome in this foreign moment. "What other reason is there, Hatshepsut? Ambition." Senenmut was a friend of my mother and father, and was my tutor.

Her kohl-smeared cheeks turned to face Senenmut as he came into the room. "But who would benefit?"

"Who is the heir?"

"He is but a child."

"But other people can use his position to gain power for themselves."

Mother stood and wiped her cheeks, leaving smears of black across her face. It made her look fearsome, her eyes glowing like a cat's in surrounding darkness. For a moment, it felt as if the goddess Bastet herself was in the room. "They wouldn't undertake something like this."

They did not name names, but I knew.

Senenmut's gaze was locked on Father's still form. "Let us see if they managed to survive. That will provide part of the answer."

◊∆◊∆◊∆◊∆◊∆◊

My mewling brother was alive. He was covered in blood from a dead guard, but he was hale and hearty, as his nurse commented with pride. As was his mother, Iset, who wept uncontrollably as she prepared drinks for us. No matter how many times she would smile at me, pray for me, I could not like her.

I also had trouble liking my brother, no matter that he too was born of a god and that one day, I might rule at his side as queen. It made me a bad person, this ill will that festered within me, and I knew that Ma'at might judge me harshly when my heart was weighed against her feather. But I could not change how I felt.

Why had they lived and Father died? Couldn't Osiris have waited a few more years before claiming him?

"I am glad you are both well," Hatshepsut said to my brother and his mother. My mother took a sip of wine from a cup Iset handed to her. We were seated in an antechamber next to Iset's quarters. Servants and slaves were busy removing the dead attackers and guards from her rooms. I did not wish to think about how they would clean the blood and other fluids from the stone floors.

Hatshepsut waved over one of the guards. "I want a large pyre to be built. See that it is done. I want it constructed in the courtyard of the temple of Osiris. Organise for one of the priests to meet with me immediately."

Once the guard left, Mother turned back to face us. First, her eyes lingered on me, then her gaze flickered to my brother, Thutmose. "Someone orchestrated this attack on my husband, and all those closest to him."

Iset's eyes were downcast, her beautiful heart-shaped face dripping tears. "Do you have any idea who?"

Mother's eyebrows drew together in sharp lines. "Not as yet. But I will not stop searching. Re, Ma'at and Amun will be on my side. I have ordered that the assassins and any who helped them be cremated."

Iset gasped, her hand coming to rest protectively over her heart. I tracked the movement. "That will destroy their *ib*, *ka, ba, khu*, and *ren*—their soul and essence! They will have no second life."

Horror sat deep within my own chest, but I did not doubt Mother's choice. It would cause the architect of this nightmare to think twice about attempting to harm any of us again. The second life was as vital to the *ka* and *ba* as was the first.

"There is no more fitting punishment," Hatshepsut said, eyes like flints.

Iset was shaking her head, as if to refute Mother's claim, but she said, "I cannot believe he is with Osiris now."

"My husband, Thutmose II, will live on. I have set the arrangements in motion. Do not be irrational, Iset. He joins godhood forever this day."

Iset's hand came to rest on her son's shoulder. "And we have Thutmose, the next *Neter Nefer*."

Hearing his name, my brother looked up from his position on the floor, his toy soldiers set up in rows before him. Deciding he did not need to interact beyond this, he went back to his game: war.

Hatshepsut placed a protective hand over her stomach. "And we have my unborn child."

Iset's gaze came to rest on the swell. "Yes, we do."

Abruptly, I stood. I did not wish to linger here with Iset and my brother. My heart beat uncomfortably within the confines of my chest. "Mother, I wish to see Father." I took the wine from Mother and pretended to take a sip. A strange, sweet smell reached my nostrils.

Hatshepsut looked at me, the dark smears of pain still on her cheeks. "Of course. We shall go to the temple."

"I shall come too," Iset said, rising gracefully to her feet.

Rudeness was not a virtue, but my heart told me that Mother should not drink any more of the strange smelling wine. I set it down on a table, away from Mother. "No, I wish to be with Father and Mother alone."

Iset's stare met mine, unblinking like a snake. "Thutmose is the heir. He has a duty to spend this time with his father." She stretched her hand out to rest maternally on Thutmose's shoulder. He did not look up at the contact.

"Then he shall do so after Neferure has paid her respects and prayers," Mother said. "As you shall wait until after I have done the same."

Iset nodded, eyes downcast, but her knuckles grew white on her son's shoulder. Thutmose let out a soft whimper.

It was only when Hatshepsut said, "Come then," that we left.

"You must not be rude to Iset," she said when we reached the corridor.

"This time is for you and me, Mother. She must wait as is custom."

"That is why I held firm. But she is family and deserves respect."

I held my tongue.

Reaching the temple of Anubis through a series of tunnels and passages, we entered a large sandstone room that felt cool to the skin. Father was positioned in the centre of the room on a large embalming table. His head lay on a rest, his eyes open to the ceiling; staring into the second life that awaited him. Two priests of Anubis walked around the chamber chanting prayers and casting spells to protect Father's body. Each carried pots and bowls that spoke of foreign scents and the richness of the earth. Their masks were fearsome in the brazier-lit room, shadows of jackals dancing in their wake.

A priest placed a small table near Father while another set a dish of palm wine on its surface. He dropped pieces of linen in the bowl to soak. After watching them grow wet, I picked up a damp cloth and began to wash Father's arm. Mother did the same with his leg. Sores were visible on his torso and neck. The wound on Father's chest was an ugly, garnet-stained gash.

The priests' chants became comforting in their sacred monotony. Under their hum, I murmured, "I think Iset put something in your wine."

Mother's hand jerked before continuing its smooth strokes. "Nonsense. Iset is a friend and family. We have known each other since we were small."

"She does not like me. She is jealous of you."

"That does not mean she tampered with my wine." Hatshepsut put a hand on my shoulder. Her fingers brushed against the cloth that had been used to bind my wound. "You will marry Thutmose one day. It is important to be kind to family."

My jaw set. "I will not marry that fool."

Mother recoiled at my vehemence. "Neferure! That is uncalled for."

"Father is beyond this world. We no longer have his light or wisdom, and all Thut does is play with his toys."

She had no reply. We continued to wash Father until Iset arrived. Her gaze locked on Mother's belly, but she said nothing. She had to all but shove Thutmose into the room. I heard her speak of 'duty' and 'responsibility'.

Once we entered the God's Wife's chambers, Mother let out a small sigh. "It will not be easy, the next few months."

Fingers coiling around the garnet and carnelian charms I wore around my neck, I stared at Mother's back. She still wore the blood-soaked linen from the attack, but some of the stains looked fresh. "Mother, I think you are bleeding."

Turning to me, she opened her mouth to reply, but froze, her eyes wide. Blood trickled in a growing stream down her leg. She stared at me as a small puddle began to form at her feet.

"Get a priest of Taweret and Sekhmet quickly."

I turned and ran.

A *swnwt* came with the priest and priestess, but they could do little. They placed amulets and chanted spells. They inserted special charms into Mother, but the blood flushed them out. She grew pale and clutched at her stomach as cramps rocked her.

"This much blood is not natural," the priestess of Taweret said to the priest of Sekhmet.

They began chanting more spells. The *swnwt* reached up to an amulet that hung from a leather strap around her neck. "I must stop the bleeding."

Mother shook her head, rocking with pain. "My son!"

The two women and one man stared at Hatshepsut. The *swnwt* spoke, "He is lost."

Mother's head dropped back.

The *swnwt* opened the large amulet that was on the end of the leather strap, and pulled out a pinch of dried red stems. "I will need some warm oil, honey, water of carob, and milk."

The priest of Sekhmet shook his head. "We should pack her vagina to keep the blood within."

I feared that if Mother lost any more blood, she would become empty.

"What does this mixture do?" I asked the *swnwt*.

The woman looked at me. "It should contract her uterus and stop the bleeding."

"What does this?" the priestess of Taweret demanded.

"It is a very rare plant. I obtain it from Crete. It's called a crocus."

"Make this concoction now." I did not care to hear more. It was the will of the gods if it would work, but Mother had to receive the potion for it to have any chance.

The priest began, "But I said—"

"My mother will need your aid through spells and prayer. It will be in the hands of the gods and Father." I thought for a moment. "We will need a priest of Amun. Having the presence of her own father should help."

The priests and *swnwt* began to talk in low voices. Being the granddaughter of the sun god himself should have lent me the authority I needed, but they still resisted. "Mother was sired by Amun himself; he came to the God's Wife disguised as Thutmose I. Why do you stand there? Order the priest!"

A servant ran to the door.

I turned to the *swnwt*. "We will administer the potion now. How do you know about this medicine?"

The *swnwt* spoke as she mixed the ingredients together. "I heard about it from a trader. There are many herbs that when used with the right incantations, will cure most ailments."

Whispering the words of a spell, the *swnwt* tilted Mother's head forwards and poured the liquid between her pale lips. Moments later, the bleeding finally slowed, and relief spread through me. I looked at the *swnwt* with wide eyes. Knowledge was power.

And I wanted to be knowledgeable.

Six years later

"You must not allow this opportunity to go to waste," Hatshepsut said to Thutmose III, my brother the co-regent. Scrolls of papyrus and clay tablets lay spread out on the table between them. Mother, Iset, Iset's Vizier, Senenmut and a dozen nomarchs all watched my brother. My brother ignored her and the rest of us. He was staring intently at an arrangement of soldiers before him: they were displayed on a flat piece of timber that could be carried from room to room.

While I found his behaviour childish, Senenmut told me that Thutmose was a master of military tactics. I remained sceptical. Egypt did not need war, but prosperity through trade, building projects, and facilities for the poor.

"We do not need to trade with the Nubians. We can enslave them," Iset said and nodded at Thutmose.

He blinked at the word 'enslave'. He looked at the two women opposite him, one a former God's Wife and the other, God's Mother. "Our army would not win such a battle at this stage." Thutmose's gaze rested on his mother.

"I agree with my nephew," Hatshepsut said. "We can undertake this effort in peace."

"Why do we need to do it at all?" Iset challenged.

Iset rarely defied Mother openly. After Father's journey to the underworld, Iset had bowed publicly to Mother's wisdom; Hatshepsut had been trained to rule by her father, Thutmose I. The first few years had been prosperous. But then rumours started to swirl through the currents of the Egyptian court; Iset worried that Mother wanted the throne for herself.

Foolish woman.

If Mother wanted the throne, it would already be hers. It was Mother's birthright. And so I—with the covert help of Senenmut—murmured reminders of Mother's ancestry, and of Grandfather Thutmose's desire for her to rule after his journey to the second life. Of the Oracle of Amun's prophecy that Mother would one day wear the double crown.

Mother remained silent for several heartbeats, watching Iset eat grapes and drink wine, both costly imports. "Trade is the river through which we obtain food, goods, and communication. Good trade is vital to a strong country."

"Without it," I said into the following quiet, looking pointedly at Iset's wine, "you would be drinking beer right now."

Iset dismissed my comment with a wave of her hand. "Beer is for peasants."

"Thutmose, you should sign this agreement," Hatshepsut attempted, pushing the scroll towards him.

"My son will sign no such thing. The gold wasted on this venture could keep this court fed for weeks."

Days, more like.

"And furthermore, I think we should have a month-long celebration to commemorate Thutmose's seventh regnal year. This gold would go towards funding such an important event."

Hatshepsut remained silent, as did I.

Thutmose finally looked up from his toys and met his mother's stare. Then he glanced at Hatshepsut. "I will sign the agreement, Aunt."

Iset's hand slammed down on the table between them. "You will do no such thing."

Thutmose's eyes locked on his mother's. They were the same: long-lashed, dark and pretty. "It is my authorisation, not yours, that is required."

"I am God's Mother and you are too young to make this decision."

Thut drew himself up, looking over the heads of his soldiers. He reined in a visible flinch when he met his mother's cold stare. "I am *Neter Nefer.*"

Iset flicked a hand, dismissing his comment.

Thut looked to Mother beseechingly, who nodded almost imperceptibly. Taking a deep breath, he said, voice wavering, "My will is law."

◊∆◊∆◊∆◊∆◊∆◊

"You need to marry Thutmose as quickly as can be arranged." Mother was seated on a delicate wooden stool carved from ebony. Gold filigree marked its sides and back.

I sat opposite her, on an identical chair in our quarters. My words were more forceful than hers, and far less quiet. "*No*."

"Neferure, you must. Iset is taking over; her role as God's Mother outweighs mine. If Thutmose had been my son, or had my son lived, this would not be an issue."

"But your son didn't live," I said the words quietly.

A sound of crashing stone nearby was shocking in the otherwise quiet. Indistinct voices reached us, and then we heard screams. Mother grabbed her dagger and I plucked a ceremonial khopesh that hung from the stone wall. It was not designed for action, but it would do.

Men burst into the room, their faces obscured by masks of the Set animal. Five of them and two of us. Not fair odds; the men would die. Grunts and groans sounded from the outer hall; a battle raged within the corridors of the palace. Mother leapt into action, feinting right then ducking low, slicing an attacker's belly open. The man folded in on himself as he tried to keep his innards from falling out.

I spun to my closest attacker, hacking with the khopesh, deflecting his blow. Surprise lit his eyes. He had not expected me to fight. But I had learned from the attack I survived on the cusp of womanhood; to be unprepared was to be dead. There were too many people who lived in the palace who would gain from Mother's and my deaths.

The blade of my khopesh was blunt, and my hacking left more bruises than wounds. I needed to make the man bleed dry, until he was nothing more than meat. The guards emerged from the entrance, bloody and furious. The attack did not last long beyond that. Afterwards, I realised my arm had been sliced; I quickly placed my free hand over the wound. Blood was the river of life, and I could not bear to lose a drop.

Mother ordered that Thutmose be checked, her concern for him foremost in her mind.

I was unsurprised to hear both he and Iset had survived.

◊∆◊∆◊∆◊∆◊∆◊

A moan reached my ears.

Lifting the netting that hung over Iset's bed, I slid onto a stool next to her prone form. She lay on her back, head propped up by a headrest crafted from rich ebony. Gold bangles and chains draped her arms and neck;

amulets of healing and longevity draping her form. Carefully, I placed the small brazier I had carried through the empty palace halls at my feet.

I studied the woman who had worshipped Set with such blind, hidden dedication, etching her face into my memory. A new groan emanated from Iset, and she clutched at her belly before rolling to her left, vomiting into an amphora beside her bed. It wasn't until she turned back that she noticed me. "Neferure?"

The pungent stench of illness permeated the room. "Hello, Iset."

"What are you doing here? I heard you were also cursed by illness?"

Not unless drugging myself with purgatives counted as being cursed.

"I feel remarkably improved," I said.

I had been checked by a *swnw* two hours ago, while I was vomiting and defecating uncontrollably. After he left to enjoy Thutmose's coronation day, I took a remedy I had taught myself.

Iset's eyelids fluttered before she locked her gaze on mine. Her weakness betrayed her, and her focus slid from me again. "Why are you here?"

"We have much to discuss," I replied.

"I am unwell."

Reaching down to the knife sheath strapped to my thigh, I said, "It must be today." Her eyes slid shut. They snapped open again when I asked, "Why did you kill Father?"

"I did no such thing."

"You may not have plunged the dagger, but you arranged it."

That stare bored into me. "Lies."

"I found the leader of the assassins." Senenmut had actually tracked the criminal down. But I had been there when he was captured. The leader hadn't survived the interrogation. Mother had never known about it; she was too fair, and refused to believe ill against her friend, Iset.

"You have a fanciful mind."

"You put an abortifacient in Mother's wine the night Father was murdered."

Her gaze narrowed. "You have no evidence."

"The wine that night had a scent I could not place then, but now know is silphium."

"You have not remembered correctly."

"I know herbs."

This, Iset did not debate.

"You also orchestrated the attack several months ago, after Thutmose had taken Mother's side over the trade agreement."

She was silent.

With my free hand, I pulled on a gold chain around my neck, so the charm was no longer obscured by my dress. Iset's eyes widened when she saw it. The ostrich feather glowed in the dim light.

"You risk all of Egypt with your actions," I said, stroking the feather with my fingers.

"I have not done anything wrong."

"Being a representative of Set in your position risks the balance of order and chaos. It can't be allowed."

"I do not represent Set! I am named for the goddess Isis."

I stared at her. "If I were to go into your secret room, I would find evidence of his cult. I know, because I've already looked."

She shrank back in the bed. Shutting her eyes, Iset whispered, "I worship him."

"It can't be allowed to continue."

"I will renounce him."

I pulled the necklace over my head and stood. "It is too late for that. The seeds of chaos have been sown."

I placed the feather on my vacated stool.

"I will let you marry Thutmose," she promised. "You will be Queen." Seeing the blade in my hand, Iset struggled to rise, but she was too weak. I had been dosing her with purgatives masquerading as remedies for days.

I shook my head and said almost sadly, "It is not enough to atone for what you've stolen from the kingdom."

I plunged the dagger down.

Iset let out a gasp. Blood welled from the wound. I dragged the blade down and she screamed. But there were no servants or slaves to hear her. She screamed until her throat was raw.

And then she spoke no more.

I began my gruesome task. Iset had cost the life of my Father, my unborn brother, numerous guards, friends, her own followers and hundreds of Egyptians who had perished while sourcing her treasures from other kingdoms. Then there were the peasants who were dying to meet the new agricultural taxes. And I had not forgotten that she had nearly killed Mother and me twice.

Cutting the heart from Iset's chest, I held it up. The heart was the seat of the *ib*, *ba* and *ka*, the personality and soul. Blood dripped down my hand and fingers; the power of life running across my skin. Leaning down, I dropped the organ onto the brazier. The smell of cooking meat filled the room, the scent of burnt chances and life wreathing through the air currents. By destroying Iset's heart, I had denied her the second life.

Once the organ was ashes, I scooped it back into the cavity. I then placed the ostrich feather—the feather of Ma'at—on the wound and left.

◊∆◊∆◊∆◊∆◊∆◊

"Neferure!"

Someone shook my shoulders and I jerked awake, almost butting my head into Mother's. Running a hand over my face, I asked, "Mother, what is it?"

"Iset is dead."

I forced myself to look shocked. "How? The illness?" I met Senenmut's stare over Mother's shoulder.

I was in the chambers I shared with Mother. The sun slanted through the windows, and a warm breeze spoke of *Peret*, the time when life would re-seed and the cycle of fertility would begin again. A time of new beginnings.

"She was murdered last night during the celebration." Mother's gaze was haunted. "Someone cut out her heart and burnt it."

I gasped. Senenmut looked at the ground.

Cheeks drawn, Mother said, "They left a feather on her chest."

Looking at my clasped hands, washed clean of visible blood, I said, "She was judged by Ma'at."

"She was denied the second life! There is no crime worth that."

I faced Mother squarely. "Every man who was involved in Father's death was denied the second life."

She stared at me. "Iset—"

"—Killed your husband," Senenmut said as he came up to my bed.

She spun to him. "You don't know that. That is ridiculous! She was his concubine. She *loved* him."

"She loved the power she gained from him. But she told her servants she hated lying with him—especially after he grew cursed by disease. She said her skin crawled with disgust when he entered her chambers. When we discovered her body, we also found evidence that she was a member of the cult of Set."

"That does not mean she killed him!"

"No, but the confession of the assassin confirmed it."

Mother rolled her eyes. "How convenient; for you to find the assassin no one else could. Why did you not tell me? When did this happen?"

"Years ago."

"And you let her live all that time? You never spoke to me of it? This is preposterous."

"You would not have believed us even if he had confessed in your hearing. You trusted Iset foolishly. Iset was necessary for the kingdom's strength—for Thutmose's sake. She is no longer required."

Mother narrowed her eyes at him. "Did you kill her?"

Senenmut shook his head, and with complete honesty said, "No. But she made many enemies with the way she governed the Upper and Lower Kingdoms."

Raising a shaking hand, Mother pinched the bridge of her nose. "Iset's supporters will try and take control of Thutmose." She looked at me. "You will need to marry him."

"I am not marrying Thut."

"The bloodline—"

"You should become Pharaoh," I interrupted.

Mother was silent, her expression growing stony. "That—"

"Grandfather wanted you to be Pharaoh; he said that you were his preference!"

"I took the throne with your Father. I followed tradition," Mother argued.

I almost shouted, "You were sired by Amun himself! No other Pharaoh in recent generations has been blessed in such a way."

"I cannot take the throne. It is Thutmose's right."

Senenmut spoke, his voice deep and sure. "Thutmose is not ready for the responsibilities of being *Neter Nefer*. He is more interested in scrolls and war games. You could take the throne tomorrow and Egypt would prosper as it hasn't since your father's time."

Silence.

Then, so quietly it was almost unsaid, Mother murmured, "I do not want the throne."

◊Δ◊Δ◊Δ◊Δ◊Δ◊

Weeks after Thutmose celebrated his seventh regnal year, Mother was crowned with the *Hedjet* and *Deshret* of Upper and Lower Egypt. Her body spoke of power and vitality, the sword at her hip the trials and tribulations that had led her to the throne. The stones and jewels that draped her echoed the wealth of combined Egypt, but her eyes were resigned. Thutmose's shone with relief.

She took the name Maatkare: truth is the *ka* of the Re.

It was a tribute to Iset; friend, family and ultimately, betrayer.

I do not know if Mother ever guessed what I had done the night of Thutmose's coronation celebration, but in the years that followed I would sometimes catch her watching me, gaze thoughtful.

What I did was for the good of the kingdom.

For Mother.

The Good God.

Due Care and Attention

Sylvia Kelso

"Damn and blast it, Jo, it's that bloody Higgins again!"

"Now, dear, do try to contain yourself. The man's only doing his job—!"

"Job my—!"

The Humber stopped with a perfect screech. The light in the middle of Brunswick Street waved even more madly, and I fended myself off the dash. My lifelong friend Lilian is a superlative medical practitioner, beloved the length and breadth of Brisbane, but no one could slight her with the description "ladylike".

"So, *Constable*, what is it this time?" I pictured the kindest of suppressed additions as, *you prognathous ape*. "Speeding at ten miles an hour? *Eleven* miles an hour, down your benighted Queen Street at one o'clock in the morning?"

"Doctor Cooper—keep telling you—due care and attention—" It was too dark to distinguish features beyond our headlamps, but Higgins' sixteen-stone silhouette was all too familiar, as were his wheezing gasps.

"Ahhh!" A Lilian-snort easily expanded to, *You blighted official imbecile!* "Do the words prolonged labour, breech birth, haemorrhage, utmost urgency, mean *anything* to you?"

"Madam, your vehicle clocked...block between Albert...Edward Street, twelve miles an hour...!"

"Sssst!" Encapsulating, *Then lobby to change the laws! Waive them for medical vehicles! You bloated babbling blockhead, give me a chance to save* some *lives!* But when Lilian begins hissing through her teeth it is more than time to intervene.

"Lilian, Lilian, dear. You know the constable has no power to change the law. Are we not, ah, flogging the messenger somewhat—?"

"Sstt!!"

"Now, Lilian, *please*. Constable Higgins, this is an emergency. Have your station mail the speeding summons care of Auckland House, corner of George and Mary Streets. And are you not somewhat off your beat?"

"Biked two miles—catch up—"

"Sssstttt!"

"How very zealous. We will be in correspondence with your superiors. And now, we really must go. Lilian?"

The car backfired, as it does at the most inopportune moments. The constable's shadow vanished, but shreds of, "Doctor, complaint, law-breaking," vanished under Lilian's explosion as we roared round the corner toward New Farm Park.

"Flog the messenger be damned, Jo, this ape victimises doctors every bloody week! They're all nitpickers but he's the absolute bloody limit. I swear, next time I will run right over the obese officious—Scythian!—and leave his body in the street!"

"Yes, dear, but really, he may wear blue, but he doesn't tattoo it on himself. Nor does he eat raw meat; and he's not foreign, like Scythians when they served as police in Athens. Wasn't that the house number? 28 Moreton Street?"

Once more the brakes precipitated me into the dash. The engine spluttered into quiet. Closing the car door softly, if with extreme effort, Lilian snatched her medical bag and shot a glance to the gesticulating silhouette across the street, growling, "God grant there's still *something* I can manage here."

◊∆◊∆◊∆◊∆◊∆◊

Luckily, or perhaps one should say, thankfully, we were in time for the patient, which preserved Lilian's temper along with the girl's life. The prompt arrival of the summons induced another eruption—"Three *pounds* three and sixpence! That's a week's ordinary wages! Hell and damnation, if I see him again I *will* run over him!"

Some tricky operations at the Lady Lamington Hospital fortunately assuaged my friend's wrath, and only routine alarums and excursions intervened before a sudden night-call to Mount Mee. The two hour train-trip to Caboolture preceded seventeen miles on horseback, then a critical operation on a Northern Coast farmer's wife, an event Lilian summarised at breakfast on her return.

"So the husband had to do the anaesthetic yet again, Jo, good thing those cow cockies are used to deliveries, even if it's only calves—God blast and damn!"

"Lilian! Mind the marmalade, oh, not the *Truth* again? What is it now?"

"The *Truth*?" Down went the newspaper with a toast-snapping slam. "It's the bloody Parliamentarians! They're going to victimise *all* of us!"

"Another fuss about noise and petrol fumes?"

"Sttt! They're proposing a Bill—Police Jurisdiction and Summary Offences! To ban everything from Sunday newspapers to two-up games, and just listen to this: Speeding infringements to be penalised by hefty fines! Loss of licence! And arrest *without warrant!* "

"Goodness! One of those would surely be enough?"

The newspaper hurtled across the breakfast room. At the door Millie's mob-cap flashed and vanished but Lilian was already on her feet.

"Enough? This is *intolerable!* Am I to go in fear and trembling that the bloody *Scythian* will arrest me on the street? Jo, I shall telephone David! We must *do something* about this!"

"Yes, dear, this is certainly draconian, I agree, and so will he, but perhaps not at breakfast, do you think—!"

But Lilian had already stormed out into the passage to seize the telephone mouthpiece. "Exchange! Get me Doctor Hardie's residence. No, not his rooms, his residence. Yes, if you please. *Now.*"

◊Δ◊Δ◊Δ◊Δ◊Δ◊

Dr Hardie and Lilian have been confederates almost ever since he came back from overseas in the early '90s, to upset medical Brisbane with his pioneering X-ray machine. Cemented by their work in setting up the Lady Lamington, the alliance has only strengthened over their years as honorary medical officers at the Children's Hospital. As I poured more tea and nodded Millie to pick up the battered *Truth*, scraps of conversation floated from the passageway.

"No, never! Yes. Must act now! Damn it, David, this will cripple everyone!" Lilian is almost as explosive with Dr Hardie as with me. "No, agreed. Some kind of united front— That set of Sunday excursionists? Well, if you think…? New president? Hmmn! Yes, a good standing, I suppose. Hmmm. If you propose him, perhaps… Me? David, really—! Oh, damn it, if you're determined…"

The mouthpiece clattered, the telephone tinged. Lilian stalked back in, grumbling under her breath.

"David agrees we must oppose this, he wants some sort of public front. He says, the Automobile Club." We had joined as a matter of course, when the state Club was founded, in 1905, though Lilian missed the actual meeting due to an acute appendicitis. But four years later the Club seemed practically moribund. "David says they need a new president. He wants to propose Feez."

She raised her brows. I said, "Do you have time to finish your tea, dear? Mr Feez is eloquent in court, as we know from that battered-child case. And perhaps, for what you plan, a barrister would be a better choice than an automobile seller."

"That's so." Lilian began gulping tea. "But I'll have to waste time at the blasted meeting, and confound it, Jo!" She banged the cup down. "David means to nominate Feez, but he wants me to second it!"

"A very good idea. It's always difficult to speak publicly, I know, but this is only to say, 'I second'. And people do respect you, you know."

"Hmmph!" The cup clattered down again. "Hopkins, or Bancroft or—Eleanor Bourne could do it—!"

"Doctor Hopkins can hardly propose his own successor. Doctor Bancroft is not a Club member. Nor is our dear Eleanor, even if she is now the Children's resident physician. Now, Lilian…"

"Oh, very well, blast it." She flicked her eyebrows at me. "I'll do as I'm told." The teasing glint vanished. "But I must be off. A very tricky tonsilitis at the Mater, Jo, I may be late for consulting hours. I know your Playgrounds group meets today. Will you have time to keep an eye out here?"

"Of course, my dear. Telephone if you seem likely to miss altogether."

"You are an angel, Jo." She rose from her chair; paused, turned, and dropped a kiss on my brow. "I know I'm testy and impatient and swear like a trooper, and you're always so forbearing. I really don't deserve you, dear."

I stood up myself and gave her a hug. "Never speak of unequal deserts," I said, "between us." I kissed her properly. "Now off you go, and *bon chance* at the Children's Hospital."

I did not bother to add, *forget the meeting till the time comes*. That ogre would vanish the instant Lilian donned her surgical mask.

◊∆◊∆◊∆◊∆◊∆◊

The prevalence of male persons engaged with automobiles, and the male tendency to speechify, lengthened the eventual meeting predictably. Luckily it was at the dear old School of Arts, whose wide verandah and plenitude of fans mostly dispelled the October heat. I had made the heat reason to coax Lilian into a silk organdie evening-waist, whose ivory shade flattered her auburn hair, while the delicate fabric and fuller sleeves softened her somewhat angular figure. Reaching up to adjust the large bow that replaced her usual tie, I could not help patting her cheek and murmuring, "You really look very well, my dear."

The now looming ordeal ensured she arrived tight-lipped and pallid, but I managed to deflect all but a couple of well-meaning queries on whether she still had headaches from the dog-cart accident—fractured skull or not, it had been almost ten years! Nor, now the male doctors have finally acknowledged Lilian as a respected practitioner, did the usual number of foolish persons offer such remarks as, "Woman driver, y'know, t'isn't natural." And, "Ought to leave medicine to the men, haw, haw, haw," or, even worse, "By Jove, Miss Cooper, all you really need's a wedding ring." To which Lilian, goaded, had once retorted, "I could wear it on my big toe!"

These perils eluded, we went to ground halfway up the crowded hall. Avoiding such anodynes as, "You will only have to stand up for five seconds," I kept my mind on ensuring neither of us fell asleep before the actual appointments began.

Dr Hardie, his thick blond moustache abristle, had likewise spied out our seats in one sweeping glance, then confined his attention to the crescent of worthies on the hall platform. The then-president, Dr Hopkins, took the chair. Various persons orated about the dangers of the imminent Bill, of giving automobile or motor-cycle dealers office in the club, and the state of roads, signage, petrol and tyre costs. However, I had only extricated four moths from my hair before the real business commenced.

Since the lesser offices were apportioned first, it seemed another aeon before Dr Hopkins reached, "And, gentlemen, the nominations for President?" Over the general buzz Dr Hardie fairly trumpeted, "Mr Arthur Feez!" Beside me Lilian rose to her feet, just escaping unseemly haste, to follow up with a crisp, "Seconded!"

She sat down on an expulsion of breath only I could have heard. I patted her hand, which, as I had expected, was trembling. She in turn patted me convulsively. The gentlemen turned the matter over for a few minutes. Then, amid general applause, Mr Feez was voted in.

◊∆◊∆◊∆◊∆◊∆◊

The rest of the meeting passed on plans to rent rooms for the secretary, Mr Moloney, and measures, some actually practical and politically tactful, to contest the Bill. When we finally reached open air Lilian undid her high collar and drew a long, audible breath.

"Thank God that's over!" She did mutter, since we were still in the crowd. "David can take it from here. Come, Jo, I've another full card at the Lamington tomorrow morning. I only hope the Peril starts."

Lilian has a foible to buy yellow cars, and it is a foible of Brisbane persons to christen each the Yellow Peril. Discovering which, Lilian's somewhat uproarious sense of humour led her to dub our vehicle the Peril, though only in the best of moods. To my mind its chief peril is the damage repeated crank-turning can do to my or Lilian's skirts, when we are not at home, with liberty to call on Harry the gardener's strong back.

That night unfortunately proved no exception. After five tries Lilian began kicking the front tyre and using "bloody" every second word. More fortunately, her sixth attempt pre-empted my own second trial. I advanced the throttle a little, shut the spark and adjusted the choke as Lilian clambered hastily in. Slamming the door, she pushed in the clutch and panted, more than somewhat maliciously, "Now I really would like to run that fat pachyderm down. Just pray, Jo, that we don't encounter the Scythian!"

◊Δ◊Δ◊Δ◊Δ◊Δ◊

Plans to resist the Bill had culminated in a request for Mr Moloney to write strong if politely worded letters to all State Parliamentarians who might support us: this took less time than one would have liked. Dr Hardie kept us up-to-date. Lilian was in too much demand for more than occasional fulmination on a dire future. That is, until the Woolloongabba emergency.

We had just sat down to a somewhat belated Saturday luncheon, and were planning the afternoon excursion, with another basket of toys for the wards at the Children's Hospital, one of Lilian's favourite charities; then the telephone rang.

Lilian sighed and rose. I set the dish-cover over her roast lamb and potatoes. The conversation was exceptionally brief. An instant later Lilian's head shot round the door.

"Jo, can you fetch the car? Get Harry to crank for you. Annie Davis just pulled the copper over on herself."

"Oh, Lilian! Of course!"

I seized my emergency hat from the hall and scurried for the back door. "Mrs Tanner, can Harry please crank the car at once? A bad burn in Woolloongabba." Lilian had delivered twelve-year-old Annie, seen her through diarrhoea and diphtheria, and Mrs Davis had been an early patient at our first rooms in Russell Street. Mrs Tanner shouted and Harry raced from his own lunch.

Another miracle, the Peril started at second crank. I shoved in the clutch, found the elusive reverse gear, and had us round at the George Street gate as Lilian, bag in hand, came racing down the steps.

"Jo, you love!" The bag landed in the tonneau and I just cleared the driver's side before Lilian landed too. With a roar the wheels flung gravel as Lilian swept us round for the Victoria Bridge.

"I keep telling these women, don't let your children in the laundry! And especially while the copper's alight! Ahh!"

With a ferocious swerve we skirted a slow wagon and whipped into the Queen Street turn. Dust and a pair of cyclists scattered. Lilian jammed her hat down like a jockey and put the car at the Victoria Bridge, I held on and begged divine Providence to keep us clear of police. I knew God himself could not make Lilian slow down on a call like this.

As we feared, the full copper-load had been on the boil when Annie, trying to help her mother by fishing a sheet up with the copper stick to test its progress, had overset the lot. Though an oversize borrowed apron intercepted the main splash, her half-bare legs had not escaped.

I had anticipated more than the usual burn horrors, especially with a child we knew and cared for. We entered to very little noise beyond the usual babble of distraught family. But when Lilian shook her head at Mrs Davis and said in her usual brusque manner, "Miss Bedford will help me, please take the others out in the back yard," I did wish fervently that we employed an assistant nurse.

◊Δ◊Δ◊Δ◊Δ◊Δ◊

"Oh, Doctor Lilian, it hurts—!"

"We'll fix that, Annie. Let me take a look."

Small for her age like so many 'Gabba children, Annie was a mere huddle of wet garments on the big patchwork quilt. As I squeezed past to the tiny window and drew back immaculately frilled white curtains, Lilian already had her bag open, scissors in hand. "Don't worry about your mother's apron. She'll get another one."

And as always, her voice had changed. However often I hear it, the way she addresses children always astonishes, sometimes moves me to tears. No longer brusque or impersonal, though as always steadfastly confident; rather as if she and the child were equals, confederates in a medical magic that no adversary can defeat.

Four quick snips parted the big sacking apron's strings. As I reached her side she handed off the scissors without looking and began, with deceptive speed yet amazing delicacy, to free the apron itself.

I took the wet cloth one-handed. She reclaimed the scissors. Annie moaned and turned her head sharply so my pulse leapt at the first dreaded signs of pain biting through the shock. Lilian murmured, "Not long now, Annie," and I held my breath in earnest as the scissors, lightly wielded as a scalpel on flesh, cut away Annie's over-washed, over-skimpy gingham dress.

Annie whimpered as air reached her skin. Lilian murmured, "Miss Bedford and I saw you born, Annie. We know how you look." The cotton bloomers parted. Lilian muttered, "Jo," and I dropped the apron and went round the bed so I might hold the girl still.

With that same deceptive speed and lightness Lilian drew away both garments at once.

Scarlet skin glared up at us, but there were no huge bursting blisters, no seared-through, seeping flesh. Annie squirmed and moaned, but she did not writhe, let alone scream aloud.

For one instant I saw Lilian actually taken aback. Then she breathed, "Well, well." And with that surgeon's speed, settled her next step.

"Jo, get the Vasoline. Annie, just a couple more minutes now. I shall cover this for you." The scissors went down and Lilian's own hand flew into the bag for the big bundle of gauze and lint.

With the same speed she smeared Vasoline thick on three big gauze sheets, gathered the first, and with a, "Here we come, Annie," lowered it, feather-light and swift, over the girl's stomach and waist. A second followed over the lower abdomen and upper thighs, the third over the legs. Light swathes of bandage followed atop; at last, with equal speed and care, we lifted Annie off the ruined clothes and wrapped her round.

"Now, Miss Davis," the familiar little formality elicited a sketchy smile, "I shall give you a 'potion', as I used to. Presently, you'll feel much better; then, I shall want you to go to sleep. Can you do that?"

Annie's eyes were round, though not, I imagine, much more so than mine. She nodded gravely. Lightly, tenderly, Lilian brushed back the girl's disheveled hair. "All over, pet." In one hand she scooped up her medical bag, in the other, the ruined garments. "We'll ask your mother for a water-glass."

◊Δ◊Δ◊Δ◊Δ◊Δ◊

"Quite astonishing, Mrs Davis—yes, Aileen, then, I did remember!" Lilian's composure was still some way from her usual medical face. "Severe inflammation, especially on the body, but very much better than I feared. I've applied Vasoline, with very light dressings. She should be kept quiet. Is there a truckle bed you could fit beside the crib?" She meant, back in the main bedroom. "Here's a light dose of laudanum: a teaspoon in a glass of water now, then as necessary during the afternoon and evening. I'll call tomorrow, for a dressing change."

There she paused, with a somewhat puzzled frown. "Aileen, when it happened. Exactly what did you do?"

Mrs Davis's broad, sun-weathered face screwed up in alarm. "Why, why, Doctor, was there wrong… Could I have—what *should* I have done?"

"No, no, not wrong! But I was prepared for a great deal more damage— So tell me, please. Between when it happened and when we arrived: what did you do?"

"Why, I run down the street to the pub to beg a moment of their telephone, I hated to leave her but I knew we must fetch you soon as we could. I left her with Mary and Beth, Mary's only nine but steady as can be, I knew they'd not let her—damage herself."

"Then what did *they* do?"

"Why—why—so far as I can tell, nothing! Only, when I come back, they'd been dousing her with the cold water bucket; she was dripping all over, and Mary says to me, 'It hurt her so much and we couldn't find the salad oil so we took the buckets and poured water on her, Mama, and see, it's better, shall we not go on?'"

She stared at Lilian, anxious, half-bewildered. "So when I had her inside, and—and the pain getting worse, Mary says, 'Let's do more water, Beth,' and I let them, having nothing better, till, till we heard the car. Oh, Doctor, did I do wrong?"

"No!" Lilian exclaimed. "No, not wrong! What you did was right—righter than I can explain." A faraway look filled her face. "But, Aileen, if you ever meet another such accident, don't wait. Use the bucket instantly."

◊∆◊∆◊∆◊∆◊∆◊

"Do you think, Lilian, we could waive the fee?"

"Of course, Jo. Mrs Davis is prouder than Lucifer, but I'll say there was so little to do, it would be a token at best."

"And we will bring some replacement clothes, too."

"Mmm. Certainly." But Lilian had grown increasingly vague. As the little picket gate clicked behind us she muttered, "That girl, that Mary. I believe, I do believe, she's made a medical break-through. I swear, Jo, she may be an accidental genius!"

"Genius, Lilian?"

"Genius, Jo. No blisters, no skin loss, not a quarter of the usual pain! Cold water! Maybe running cold water, perhaps first thing, on a burn. We must experiment, Jo. This could prove an entire new treatment. I may have to write a paper, drat it. But if it works more than once, other people must know—oh, blast and damn!"

We had reached the car, parked somewhat crookedly in the dusty street beside the neighbour's picket fence. Now, around its back, appeared a familiar blue-clad, notebook-wielding shape.

Lilian's face went from medical euphoria to a thunderous frown. "Yes, Constable?" *Scythian* could have whistled out on the ice. Higgins actually drew himself up.

"A complaint, Doctor. There was cyclists on Queen Street when you come round that corner. Driving without due care and attention. You nearly skittled 'em both." As Lilian's eye flashed and I guessed her teeth had clenched, Higgins raised his voice.

"And you was clocked over Victoria Bridge doing sixteen miles an hour, Doctor! Twice the speed limit! On a Saturday arvo—afternoon—with pedestrians and horsecabs from here to kingdom come! You coulda killed someone!"

"Sssss!" But before I could speak Lilian had stamped round the bonnet and almost up against Higgins' heaving chest. "Do you have children, Constable?"

"What's that gotta do with—"

"Everything! Do you have children or not?"

It came in such a tone I dared not intervene. Higgins himself very nearly recoiled. Then produced a reluctant grunt.

"Girls?"

"Orright, I got kids, girl and two boys! What's that got to do with…"

"How old's the girl?"

"Look, Doctor—"

"Humour me, Constable." A less humorous tone I could not imagine. "How old is she?"

Higgins shuffled feet and pencil and would clearly have loved to exceed his position and return as good as he was getting. At last he growled, "Eight this year."

Lilian's back stiffened with a snap and she pointed furiously over the tumbledown picket fence, past faded zinnia flowers to the recalcitrantly dusty, out-at-elbows little Woolloongabba house.

"In there's a twelve-year old girl, Constable, who just pulled a copperful of boiling water on herself! Have your children ever been burned?" Higgins actually took a step back. "Have you seen what it's like?"

Higgins' face spoke for itself. Lilian's voice suddenly went soft and she almost whispered, "How long would you want *your* daughter to suffer before a doctor arrived?"

Higgins did hold his tongue, but his neck reddened, up and out to the tips of his ears. I too wanted to cry, *Oh, a foul blow, Lilian!* But I still dared not speak.

Higgins had no such recourse. He fell back on officialdom, his only possible riposte.

"Doctor," through definitely gritted teeth. But his glare added, *Wait for the new law. Just wait!* "I am an officer of the police. It's not my place—or my duty! —to decide, decide medical matters. My duty is to enforce the law—including speed limits!"

"Ssssstt!"

Lilian whirled about and almost flew to reach the crank. Higgins was so close to the bonnet she might well have assaulted his knees had I not gestured frantically at him and mouthed, "Post the summons!" He gave me a stare as vicious as the one he had aimed at Lilian, but he moved.

When we had chugged at a decorous eight miles an hour back between the scalloped girders of the Victoria Bridge, I said, "My dear, you know, he *was* doing his duty. But you made an enemy of that man."

Lilian actually slammed a fist on the door top. "Damn it, Jo, the moron hinders and cumbers and thwarts *my* duty—my sacred Hippocratic duty! every time I turn around! I am sworn to salve injury and alleviate pain! How can I leave patients to suffer because I must creep at eight miles an hour for his piddling bloody *traffic regulations*?"

"Yes, dear. And it is infuriating—more than infuriating! But will it help your patients, to have a personal vendetta with Higgins, if that Bill goes through?"

"*Damn* the bloody Bill!" We wheeled summarily into George Street. By the greatest good fortune the way was for once clear. "And damn Higgins too!"

I did not reply, *Yes, dear.* Lilian turned short for our driveway; but as the car came to a stop, she shut off the engine, leant on the steering wheel, and sighed.

"You were right, Jo, as always. It was a low blow. But he vexes me beyond all bearing. Why doesn't the fool government make laws that let us both do as we've sworn?" She bit her lip and swung open the car door. "Only one thing for it, Jo. We must enlist more Parliamentarians. That bloody Bill must. Not. Pass."

◊∆◊∆◊∆◊∆◊∆◊

That night she cornered Dr Hardie in the theatre interval, during one of our rare uninterrupted treats. By the look of his protests before they parted, I gathered that "enlist more partisans" was easier said than done.

Already concerned, after that day's contretemps I came near dreading the thought of the Bill's passage, imagining Lilian torn between the compulsion to reach her patients and dread of the inevitable speeding excess. And how if the law of instant arrest was passed, and Higgins caught up with her after another incident like the Woolloongabba clash?

However pointlessly, I came near badgering Dr Hardie too. Then by pure chance, I collected an enthusiastic helper in the cause.

We had met Mrs Longman during my five-year term as secretary of the Pioneer Club. A brisk, humourful woman who came to Queensland in 1904, she was a force in the attainment of state women's suffrage in '05, though we had met seldom since. Still, when her short-clipped head popped up beside me at the Creche and Playground Association meeting, I recognised the perky grin instantly.

"Josephine!"

"Irene! How charming to meet again!"

"Indeed, indeed! Albert and I are down from Toowoomba for the entire day. Shall we have tea after this?"

An early afternoon meeting left comfortable time to visit the Shingle Inn in Edward Street. Over their excellent scones we caught up on the four year hiatus, and soon I found myself pouring out the story of the Speed War: Higgins' bloodhound propensities, Lilian's devotion to her patients, my own fears. "Imagine, Irene, what life will be like for Lilian if this wretched Bill comes in!"

"And for you, Josephine." She gave me one of her warmly sympathetic glances and patted my glove beside the Inn's solid but shining sugar bowl. "And for all the women and children who depend upon your doctor. Lilian is right, the Bill must not pass."

"But the Automobile Club cannot seem to find supporters."

"Tut, tut! Then we need other lobbyists, Josephine."

"Lilian's patients, do you mean? There are certainly plenty, but—so many of them are not important people…"

"But over half of them," Irene pointed out, calmly, but with a twinkle, "have just acquired the vote."

"Oh! Oh, Irene, of course!"

◊Δ◊Δ◊Δ◊Δ◊Δ◊

With suffrage won, Lilian and I had dropped out of electoral campaigning circles. Irene had not. Inside a week she had set her forces in motion through almost all Brisbane electorates; a good number of women responded, and many pledged to urge their husbands to join as well. "We have the perfect lever," Irene told me cheerfully. "What patient or parent that Lilian's helped will want to lose her? How many others will understand, when shown the consequences of the Bill for themselves?"

The Doctor's Protection League, as Irene wickedly termed it, was under way early in November, undeterred by a season of particularly fierce storms. In mid-November, Irene and I again took tea at the Shingle Inn. Though

Irene's neat head looked as perky as ever, I felt a qualm at the disparate expression on her face.

"Try the rock cakes this time, Josephine, they really don't live up to their name."

"Thank you, Irene, I will. How is dear Albert?"

"Busy as always, the clever man." She returned the menu to the arriving waitress. "Very willing to address his legislative member over that wretched Bill, as you might expect."

"So kind of him." I concentrated on straightening the place mat. "And how is the whole campaign, Irene?"

Irene made an all-too-graphic face. Not for the first time, I wished I felt as free to curse as Lilian.

"There *is* support, Josephine, I assure you. Unfortunately, the motor-car has such a poor overall reputation, that," she sighed and pushed her folded fan into her bag, "that even Lilian's reputation has not—yet—managed to turn the scales."

She glanced back up at me and assumed cheerfulness. "We will keep working, Josephine, I do assure you. It's not finished yet!"

◊∆◊∆◊∆◊∆◊∆◊

By the end of November, even Irene's assurance could not ease my rising qualms. As Lilian and I drove home from attending a bad fall at a building site in Windsor, I reflected wretchedly on that morning's gloat in the *Truth:* however eager, even impassioned, our supporters, the Parliamentary majority remained, by a narrow margin, in favour of the Bill.

It was a torrid afternoon, the air heavy, the whey-and-charcoal clouds already milky with oncoming storm. Glancing up and back as we turned onto Lutwyche Road, Lilian remarked, "I hope we get through consulting hours before it breaks."

I could not help adding, "I hope no one founders horses, getting home," and she gave me a warm smile.

"One thing to be said for the new motor-cabs, Jo."

Lilian had been delighted by the reception of my paper at the Society for Prevention of Cruelty to Animals, but preaching to the converted does not always bring wider change. She also knew the plight of cab-horses over-driven or under-watered distressed me almost more than any other abuse.

I produced a matching smile. Lilian transferred her attention back to the road ahead, and stiffened with a jerk.

"And here's a very bad case."

The traffic that far up Lutwyche Road is lightest between two and three o'clock, with few delivery carts or vans or workers' bicycles, only the occasional omnibus and horse or motor-cab, and rarer private cars. But from the haze of dust and fumes and glittering metal a rider was racing at near full gallop on a lathered horse.

I caught a glimpse as they flew by: a grey horse blackened with sweat and white with foam, a spatter of red from over-used spurs, some kind of bag or pack over a blue workman's shirt, hat pulled down to hide all but a flying moustache. The horse swerved past an approaching wagonette and Lilian exclaimed, "The damn fool!" I could not help crying, "That poor beast!"

"I'd go back, but..." Lilian touched my elbow lightly before she turned her attention to the road. I knew the "but": *I already have people ahead, waiting for evening surgery, also expecting my help.*

"No." *I understand.* I tried to divert my attention. "Do you imagine, an urgent telegram? A crisis at the Post Office? Some kind of telegraph breakdown? That satchel—was it mail?"

"A good question, Jo. And a good thing they don't apply speed limits to horses, or Higgins would be hot on his tracks—Good God! There he is!"

"Higgins! Surely not—good heavens! But what has happened to *him*?"

Lilian slapped on the brakes to cut behind yet another omnibus and whipping the car through a convenient gap pulled across and up behind the furious figure at the gutter edge.

Higgins was as black with sweat and dust as the unfortunate horse, and crimson enough to herald a coronary. His bicycle was crumpled at his feet; he was alternately kicking its frame out of shape and waving furiously at oncoming motor traffic, which, unable to distinguish his uniform and unnerved by his behaviour, kept swerving wildly out around him in the street.

"Constable, what's wrong?"

Lilian can make herself heard on a building site. Higgins whirled about and noticed us for the first time.

He went purple as an egg-plant fruit: rage, embarrassment, chagrin, fury churned visibly over his features. I called out before he could either expire or burst.

"Is it the man on the grey horse?"

"The—the—"

He strangled a fresh gout of profanity. "Madam—police business—" He almost choked. Another motor-cab escaped his clutches and he kicked the fallen bicycle a car length down the street. "Ah, ah, DAMN!"

Lilian suddenly pulled the handbrake on. "Jo," she said crisply, "can you get in the tonneau? And keep safe?"

I understood almost as she spoke. "Of course, my dear." Flinging my own door open, I scrambled round among the surgical impedimenta in the tonneau, even as Lilian leant out and shouted, "Constable Higgins! Over here!"

Higgins glared. Lilian used her operating theatre voice. "Get in my car. The horse went straight on up Lutwyche Road."

Higgins' jaw dropped. Then the eyes sparked blue in his scarlet face and he charged for my open door.

Lilian put the car in gear, revved hard, and before Higgins landed had catapulted us into the street.

◊∆◊∆◊∆◊∆◊∆◊

Clinging for dear life to the tonneau side I had a mad urge to declaim dear Mr Paterson's "Lay of the Motor-Car": *We're away! And the wind whistles shrewd/ In our whiskers and teeth!* For the wind was certainly whistling in Higgins' whiskers and he was clinging to the dashboard harder than I.

Lilian whipped round another slow wagonette. Higgins came as near as a grown man can to a squeak and I suddenly understood he had never driven with her at speed, maybe never driven at speed in a motor-car at all.

Lilian hit an open furlong and put her foot down. The speedometer crept round past twenty, reached for twenty-five. Higgins made a noise that might have been, "Oh, Gawd," and I shouted into the gale, "What did he do? The man on the horse?"

Higgins spluttered. I expected another cry of "Police business!" Instead he straightened half an inch and bawled, "The ba—the mongrel shot through with the whole Lennons' payroll!"

"Oh, damn!"

Higgins boggled. I knew Lilian and I were both remembering scores of cooks, maids, charwomen and washerwomen we had tended. People whose loss of a week's pay from the big hotel would mean not merely vexation but privation for them and their families. I yelled, "How did he get out here?"

Lilian threw the car down a gear behind another omnibus, revved up, swirled round the bus and cut across the bows of an approaching wagon. Higgins gurgled and seized the distraction.

"Bailed up the bank-van right at the door—arp!" Lilian had ducked round a pair of cyclists so close I saw the whites of their eyes. "Got clear up Queen Street, dodged the blokes at Brunswick corner—I was at the General, the station called—oof!" We flew across an intersection just ahead of a smartly trotting dog-cart. "Ahh…" With a wheeze Higgins regained his breath. "I cut him at the hospital crossing. Horse was lathered, reckoned to hang on him till the horse dropped—then I done the bloody bike!"

"And not a cab would stop." I could not help feeling sympathy. No wonder he had kicked the offending bicycle down the street!

"Nobody else out here, if I coulda kept him in sight—!"

"We'll get him back." Lilian said it the way she told patients' panicking relatives that their loved ones were "as bad as they could be, but I'll get them through." Higgins' shoulders shifted. Then he actually turned his head to give her one wind-teary, astonished, almost, I thought, wondering glance.

Lilian did not notice. Her eyes were slitted at the road, where ahead of us an empty space ended in another clutch of cyclists. And beyond them, the silhouette of a racing horse.

"There he is!" Higgins slammed the dashboard. "By Gawd, Doctor, you get me up with him and we'll run that beast into the ground!"

"Oh, Lilian." The protest was torn out of me. I could not bear the thought of the innocent, helpless horse destroyed, and by those on the side of the law.

"Can't run it down, Constable." Lillian accelerated across another intersection. The speedometer hit thirty and two astonished butcher-boys fell off their cart-poles. "Jo wouldn't like it. But…"

The speedometer dropped back to twenty-five. Lilian remarked into the almost conversation-level lull, "This car's supposed to be quiet as a ghost. "

"Huh?" was Higgins' contribution. But I had seen a goat-cart emerge from what must be a back-lane some quarter-mile ahead. Still well in front of the now labouring, barely trotting horse.

"Oh!" I cried thankfully. "Oh, Lilian, yes!"

"Hang on, all."

Again it was the surgeon's voice. The intervening traffic, another fruiterer's cart, sailed under Higgins' elbow. The road opened, two hundred yards perhaps to the horse, another hundred to the lane.

Lilian floored the accelerator. The car surged forward with a high version of its usual muffled roar. House-fronts whipped past, the horse's quarters suddenly loomed in the windscreen and Lilian whisked the car right up beside it and hit the brakes.

The Humber screeched its loudest and best. The man shouted, the horse tried to hurl itself sideways and blundered head-first into the alley mouth. Lilian stood on the brakes again and leant on the steering wheel so the car propped short and then shot round into the noisome alley, just as the horse stumbled over a deep rut and went down, flinging its rider out ahead.

Lilian braked us dead and rapped, "Constable?"

Your man, your business. Higgins had not needed the invitation. He was already wrenching at the door. The handle gave, he tumbled out and charged, with the weight and velocity of an angry elephant, and a veritable gorilla's roar.

Law-maker and breaker hit the alley-dirt amid a mighty dust cloud. Lilian said in satisfaction, "There you are, Jo," switched off, and got out.

I was out as fast and making for the horse. Lilian delayed only to seize the spare rope we keep under the seats, before she swept down on Higgins and his prey.

Higgins had already made his own arrangements, I found, when I had time to spare from capturing the horse's reins and soothing it to its feet. Lilian had the rope ready, but Higgins had dislodged the haversack with a knee in the middle of the prone captive's back, produced a pair of handcuffs from somewhere, and got one round a flailing wrist. Lilian was just in time to rope the other close enough for the second cuff.

Wheezing, puffing, uniform black with dust and sweat, lurid face powdered with dust like a floured oven-roast, Higgins rose to his feet, replaced the pinning knee with a foot, and in a pose like a triumphant big-game hunter, began declaiming, "I arrest you in the name of the King for armed robbery, illegal discharge of fire-arms, wilful attempt to injure police-officers, and…and…"

There he had to stop and wheeze. The prone captive was too winded to protest, but Lilian's lips suddenly twitched.

"And riding without due care and attention, Constable?"

Higgins' head whipped round. They stared for what seemed a full minute. Then, to my utter disbelief, Higgins' dust-caked countenance split in a slow, magnificent grin.

"Orright, doc." He made a dab at his temple, whence his hat had long since fled. "We'll call it quits, hey? That was, um—quite a chase. But I've—we've got him. And the money. Ain't even ruined the horse." His chest seemed to swell. "With a single-handed arrest. I reckon, you'll do me a bitta good over this." The grin subsided into sober promise. "And I reckon, I'm gonna do a bitta good for you."

Lilian's amusement had also vanished. After a moment she began to coil up the rope. Then, as soberly as Higgins had spoken, she said, "Yes, Constable. Whatever you chance to do, we'll call it quits."

A moment later shouts, police whistles and the reverberations of another over-heated car motor began to ricochet down the alleyway. Lillian stepped back, Higgins resumed his big-game hunter's pose, and we led the hobbling horse clear as the rest of the police arrived.

◊∆◊∆◊∆◊∆◊∆◊

Precisely what Higgins did and how he did it we have never been privileged to learn. What we do know is that shortly after the briefly notorious "Lennons' Payroll Robbery" arrest, he was promoted to Sergeant. We hear, via the newspapers, that as finances become available the Police Commissioner plans to expand police car numbers from two to something nearer a fleet.

Better still, Mr Feez and other reputable sources inform us that the Police Commissioner has withdrawn support for the Police Jurisdiction and Summary Offences Bill. It may never come before Parliament, and if it does, it will not pass.

The best rumour of all is talk that the city speed limit will at last be raised. Soon, Lilian may be able to drive with perfect legality at sixteen miles an hour!

The Dragon, The Terror, The Sea

Stephanie Lai

The war wearies her. At first it's a way to consolidate her power; later, it is necessary to maintain her boundaries.

She hears rumours, on the coast. Rumours of the British and the Portuguese; rumours of troubles in towns; rumours of leadership and mistakes and opportunities.

She hears rumours, and she makes plans.

◊∆◊∆◊∆◊∆◊∆◊

Ching Shih takes seventeen women and children ashore with her. Her flagship brings her into port; though large, it is dwarfed by the military ships already there. Word of the Governor is true, at least, and this comforts her as she leaves her crew behind and disembarks with her seventeen women and children.

In the distance, a third of her armada floats off the coast of Kwangchou; a promise she carries beside her into every battle.

There is a respectful silence in the ports; further into the town, as they ride, there are jeers from soldiers and whispers from imperial workers. "Children," she hears, voices scandalised. "Women," she hears, voices rough and amused. There is the clatter of horses' hooves and, in the distance, the ring of steel upon steel. She looks down at Chew Ying beside her; born to one of her pirates and an experienced deck hand, she imagines his ten year old head marked with ink; imagines 大辟 carved into his forehead; boiled alive and slowly sliced. Young Chew Ying looks up at her; flashes a grin that is all teeth and eagerness and the promise of an ankle strapped with knives.

He is not her child, but the fleet is filled with her children; even those who were pirates before she was born. They are what she has made them, and they follow where she leads.

Ching Shih sits up, her back straight. She is the dragon; she is the pirate; she is 中国南海的恐怖, the Terror of the South China Sea.

Pirates take anything they need, and this thing, she needs.

◊Δ◊Δ◊Δ◊Δ◊Δ◊

The Red Flag Fleet is 1500 vessels; banners of varying hues fly in the sea breeze. Through her fleet, Ching Shih levies taxes upon every town she comes across, and she has never heard a word of complaint.

She knows what it is to live a life on the fringes of a town that doesn't want her.

The Red Flag Fleet protects the towns under its flags, and no words of protest ever reach her ears.

◊Δ◊Δ◊Δ◊Δ◊Δ◊

Ching Shih has not brought only seventeen women and children into Kwangchou with her. She has brought many boxes of Kwangchou tael with her, and the clinking emanating from the crates as they sway behind horses is distinctive. No Kwangchouyahn will not recognise the sound; she watches the heads around her go still as they try not to follow the *clink clink clink* with anything but ears that show disinterest.

She has tried to dull their noise with ribbons and seals, but she hasn't tried that hard. She likes the sound.

Governor Lingbai looks down at her from his seat. Though Ching Shih is tall, he is taller, here in this city.

He smiles down at her: takes in her large feet and her scarred face; takes in the women and children with open faces curled around behind her. The walls of this room tower above her, with watercolours at intervals and the ornate carving into the ceiling. Ching Shih notices a rich, velvet curtain framing a window, and wonders how she missed this evidence of the British in her city.

Governor Lingbai neglects to offer her tea. After all this time, and all this effort, he doesn't take her seriously.

Well, she supposes, that's half the point.

Condescendingly, excruciatingly slowly, the negotiations begin. "You are a beautiful woman," says Governor Lingbai. "I cannot believe you are truly the Terror of the South China Seas. And who is your first mate?" Lingbai laughs as he looks down at Chew Ying beside her; the child is clearly not the formidable shape of her consort, Chang Pao.

She does not kowtow, though he implies she ought; she remains unconcerned by his demands, making minor concessions which mean nothing to her, until she has exactly what she wants. The children, as discussed, play games behind the boxes filled with taels, knocking into them occasionally to cause them to clink together. Ching Shih observes Lingbai's eyes drifting towards the boxes every time.

Her women sit and read scrolls of paper, breaking off every now and then to pass one over to Ching Shih as she comes to another agreement. If Lingbai notices, at the end, that she hands over exactly as many parchments as she brought, he doesn't mention it.

Ching Shih returns to the ship a married woman, with promises of amnesty for her flotilla and an agreement to bow to the emperor, should she ever meet him. She returns with all seventeen of her women and children, though the guardsmen's eyes had lingered on her women. She offered one single kowtow rather than the usual nine, and blinked twice to prevent herself from laughing.

Ching Shih returns with none of her boxes, but they were rather heavy, and anyway, she has more to come.

On the ship, the children yell; brush the tears from their cheeks and throw knives at one another, shrieking with delight as they show off the prizes they took from pockets and hands. Each child and each woman sits before her and tells her what information they have gleaned from their hours in the city and the palace, from their hours in the shadows shaking as if their fear is real.

They are pirates. They fear nothing but the dragon, and it is she who keeps them safe.

◊Δ◊Δ◊Δ◊Δ◊Δ◊

She is young when she meets Zheng; young when he requests she run away with him; young when he asks first before he kidnaps her, and she tells him yes.

"I will be your equal," she says, and doesn't give him a chance to laugh.

On her knees in Kwangchou, she has seen what power can do. She will take it where she can, and wield it as far as she is able.

◊Δ◊Δ◊Δ◊Δ◊Δ◊

The Red Fleet settles into Kwangdung. Though they have given their thousand ships to the emperor's tiny navy and their weapons to his armies, they are pirates, and they know how to adapt.

The Red Fleet levies taxes through its gambling dens; creates heavens in its brothels. The fleet spreads through Kwangdung with efficiency, guided by Ching Shih's directions. The taels clink into her counting house, and Chang Pao arranges men where men are needed.

She ignores a summons from Lingbai; when the second comes, she sends Ying instead. He is thirteen.

Her children grow. Her fleet grows.

She grows roots in Kwangchou, and her heart grow heavy with it.

◊Δ◊Δ◊Δ◊Δ◊Δ◊

The months pass. Ying buys a ship with the money he has earned. She smiles at him but lets him go. "Don't let the emperor find you," she says to him as he sets off, taking thirty of his brothers and sisters with him. They have grown tired, these last four years on the land, and she can't fault them for sailing away.

They are all of them from the sea, and though not all of them will return, she can't stop them from going.

Ching Shih wishes, for a moment, that she could follow them. She closes her eyes and allows herself this moment: the deck beneath her feet and the tang of salt on her tongue. She thinks of her sword by her side and Zheng, lost to the South China Seas.

She sits once more before her sums, and pushes the sea away.

◊Δ◊Δ◊Δ◊Δ◊Δ◊

There is a man early in her reign, shortly after Zheng's death. The news has come and she has shed her tears behind her closed door; before it, she is a pirate holding firm, no weak concubine crying in the face of disaster. She works with Cheng Paoyang and Cheng Qi to consolidate the fleet. The work she and Zheng have done together, as commander and second of the Red Flag Fleet, is good but remains as yet unfinished. She would not have it remain so.

She will not be a widow, unsure of her future.

She is foolish, she knows that. But she has a moment of weakness and Li Nan knows that when he knocks on her door; Chang Pao is above decks and Cheng Paoyang and Cheng Qi are off on another ship. He comes at her, snarling, and she has no moment of warning before she's knocked off her feet by the force of his lunge. It is only force of habit that keeps her from shrieking.

A pirate doesn't shriek. It was an early lesson.

She feels the indignity of it as he reaches for her ku; as he fumbles for his own. He wouldn't do this to her if he considered her truly the Commander of the Red Flag Fleet; he wouldn't do this to her if he saw her as more than just a woman. This will not do and, as she holds in her cry and her sounds of rage, it's her training, and the knowledge that she will not be defeated by a man, that pushes through her veins as she shoves him across the room. He lands with a loud thud and moves sluggishly; slowly. She leaps for him, yelling, her dagger in her hand, and he draws breath and pushes to his feet.

He does not push far.

By the time Chang Pao has rushed through the door, Li Nan is no longer a man to be feared. Ching Shih's hand, though shaking, was firm and her aim true; the dagger that never leaves her side is through his chest.

His eyes, lifeless, gaze out towards the ocean. He's most certainly dead. It's not good enough, though, and on the deck, in front of her men, she calls out her findings; calls down her judgement. It is her own arm which swings the blade; and it is her own sword which makes the cut, clean through. His head lies there, the blood sluggish as it stains the deck.

She has him cast overboard and feels nothing but the dull ache of betrayal, and the warmth of a job cleanly done.

She rests a hand on Chang Pao's arm. It is warm beneath her fingers, and she guides him belowdecks; bids him lie down beside her.

She takes him, rough and loud, and she does not care who hears her.

She will take this fleet, and they will go where she leads them. She is no woman to be stopped by some man.

But some women, she thinks. And some men.

She conceives the first of her rules.

◊Δ◊Δ◊Δ◊Δ◊Δ◊

Yi Ping finds her sitting, the tea in her water tray long gone cold. She has heard rumours of Chew Ying and his fleet of her children, maintaining her legacy the only way they have ever known.

They have tangled with the British over the growing opium problem. They knot foreign sashes to their swords and laugh about it. She shakes her head at their youth and enthusiasm for the things she never truly let them experience.

Still, it has been years, and she tires without them.

"Long Sao," he says. "Forgive me. We have a problem."

She boils the water again, and watches as Yi Ping washes the tea. "Tell me," she says, finally, and they talk of books and rumours and plots and things that make her heart ache.

She thinks of the sea.

◊Δ◊Δ◊Δ◊Δ◊Δ◊

Ching Shih is younger, but Zheng's death is not so fresh. She has battled the British Navy and the Portuguese Navy. She grows weary of running; grows weary of the ghost heads she leaves tumbling in her wake.

She hides the fleet in coastal towns; continues taking levies, and allows her children to grow again. In a small town, the emperor's messenger greets her. The messenger has been living here, waiting for a chance to speak to her.

His life is comfortable, and she wonders that he even bothers to deliver his message, this message that shakes in his hand as he speaks to her. The emperor's messenger bids her visit Kwangdung, to talk with the Governor there.

"I am not—" she begins, but the emperor's messenger interrupts her.

"Please go," he says. She considers adding a rule just for this slight, but that seems churlish. She has suffered worse, and the messenger is prostrate before her. "Commander, please return to speak with the Governor."

She is tired, but not that tired, and this is a way to grow her fleet without the constant fear of defeat; without a continuing need to set the emperor's ships on fire.

Besides, the messenger called her Commander.

"Chang Pao," she says. "Cheng Paoyang. Cheng Qi." Her captains array before her, waiting for her word.

She turns the fleet towards Kwangdung.

◊Δ◊Δ◊Δ◊Δ◊Δ◊

She counts the money again. It's not that she doesn't trust her bookkeepers; rather, when there is a problem, one must seek not to assign blame before one has tackled it oneself. Yi Ping is correct, she soon sees; there's something missing.

Together, they trace the paths. She may not be a bookkeeper, but she is used to the ways of money, and Kwangdung is her place. It has chewed her up and spat her out but it hasn't defeated her, and she will open its mysteries to her.

It is Sheng, she finds; Sheng, who has been with her since before they moved onto the land. Sheng, who beheaded three British naval men at her order. Sheng, who has couriered in the dens since they landed. Sheng has succumbed to the ghost drug, to the opium that has seeped into Kwangdung.

He bows his head when he is brought before her. "Long Sao," he begs. "Forgive me."

"My son," she says.

She beheads him herself, but has him buried as family. She doesn't need his ghost coming for her when she has so many others to deal with.

◊Δ◊Δ◊Δ◊Δ◊Δ◊

There is a rule: takings are registered within the fleet, following which it is redistributed. The capturing ship takes 20%, and the rest goes to the fleet. Withholding means ship-wide whipping. Repeated withholding, or withholding of large amounts, results in beheading.

There is a rule: theft from a village that pays its fees is punished by beheading.

There is a rule: desertion, or abstention without leave, results in ears cut off before the fleet.

There is a rule: cuckolding is illegal. Rape is illegal. Both are punished by beheading. Concubines and wives are allowed amongst the fleet, and women who are not kept on are to be released in safety upon the shore, unpenalised and unharmed.

There are no complaints. Her fleet grows.

◊∆◊∆◊∆◊∆◊∆◊

Ching Shih purges her gambling dens, her brothels, every place her fleet touches. She purges her fleet of ghosts and opium, and thinks no more of it until a man—a Chinese man, a Kwangdung man, comes for her in the night, dagger raised and gun shaking, a trail of ghost steps behind him.

"What brings you here?" she grinds out, his dagger grazing her side as she sweeps his legs out from under him.

He doesn't answer, but his gait gives him away; in her moment of distraction he draws her blood. He laughs at her, the slow, languid laugh of a Chinese man trapped by a ghost.

He coughs as she takes him for what he has, and the smell on his breath makes her gag.

No tool of the British can defeat her, she has always assumed, but her own blood cools at her neck and the stench of the opium dens fills her nostrils.

She is growing old, and she misses the sea.

◊∆◊∆◊∆◊∆◊∆◊

Ching Shih sits opposite Ying, her children arrayed along down the table. Ying begins the tea ceremony, washing the cups and rinsing the tea. Xiao Guang leans beside him, preparing a second set. "Long Sao," Ying begins, as Ching Shih takes her cup and brings it to her mouth. This set is old, now; she purchased it when she first made landfall here in Guangzhou. She remembers laughing as she brought it to Chang Pao, telling him it was their wedding set, inlaid as it was with red dragons and yellow chrysanthemums. He had laughed, too, as she had spilled the tea on her hanfu and watched it fall onto the ground, unused as she was to the firmness without a deck and the lack of sway beneath her.

The cup is smooth at her lip, and she sips the tieguanyin, a gift from her favourite son.

"Long Sao," he says, "The outsiders are coming."

This is not news to Ching Shih. Her life is rumours, now. Rumours from her servants, rumours from the employees in her gambling house. Rumours coming in from the ports. What comes next is news, though, and her heart seizes within her chest.

"There is a rot," he says, "The opium is brought by the British, and they will not stop. I don't know if we can keep it at bay."

Ching Shih presses her lips together, disappointment pooling in her gut. That her son should give up. That the emperor should give up. That this jewel, the centre of the very world, should give up to these outsiders.

"We should return the fleet to the sea," Ying says.

She puts her cup down, watches as her children do the same.

"You will stay," she says. "We will not lose all we have gained after we gave up the sea for it."

Her children don't question her.

She is the dragon, and she will keep them safe.

◊Δ◊Δ◊Δ◊Δ◊Δ◊

She is surprised on her way to port. The attackers are a mix of foreigners and Chinese men, and they fight unexpectedly well. As she shoves her dagger into the closest attacker, she hears the tear of material; another man has reached for her hanfu and torn it beneath his hand. As she ducks to punish him she hears the whistle of gunpowder overhead.

She drops to the ground, and takes another man down with her. When it is over, her hanfu is torn, her arm requires mending, and she has lost a guard in the attack.

She is slow, though, and she fears.

She is growing older.

◊Δ◊Δ◊Δ◊Δ◊Δ◊

There are new rumours, of an Imperial Commissioner, of the flow of opium, of the terror of the emperor. "The sky is high," Xiao Guang says to her when she delivers the news, and Ching Shih laughs; allows herself to complete the chengyu. "The emperor is far away." She has no faith in the Daoguang emperor, who lets the British and the opium in when it suits him and continues his attacks against the people when it does not.

She bans the smoking of opium across her organisation; Ying enforces it with banishment and fines. Her people love her, so they obey; there are other drugs in the gambling houses anyway, and it's no trouble to succumb to other pleasures.

At her request, Xiao Guang develops a list of allies.

She worries at the edges of her territory, at the future encroaching.

◊Δ◊Δ◊Δ◊Δ◊Δ◊

The Imperial Commissioner arrives with fanfare that fades into the hush of a waiting storm. He hates the opium, the wind says. He has the emperor's blessing, says the sand. He will crush the British beneath his wagons, Cheng Shih hears.

Chew Ying brings his ships and junks to bear; Chang Pao transfers his commission, belatedly, with the Governor's seal, to the Imperial Navy, and disappears into the distance.

Ching Shih sends a letter to Governor Lin, and it is no surprise to her when a reply returns immediately.

◊Δ◊Δ◊Δ◊Δ◊Δ◊

There is a rule: women are pirates.

◊Δ◊Δ◊Δ◊Δ◊Δ◊

The Red Fleet takes Hong Kong.

Not officially, of course. The Red Fleet hasn't existed in twenty-nine years. Its leader is an old woman, cowed by years on the land and kowtowing to the emperor. Her ability to command, if it ever truly existed and was not a ridiculous lie perpetuated by men, is well and truly gone.

But when Imperial Commissioner Lin bans trade into Kwangdung, and pressures Macau, held by the Portuguese ghosts, into doing the same, there is nowhere left for the British to ply their trade.

They go north instead, where there is no Red Fleet, where the emperor's hand weakens. The fleet loses track of them until word comes that Dinghaih has been occupied by the British. The opium trickles in again, softly, gently, from the north.

Ching Shih has never been frantic. In all her years of command she has planned, and reacted, and sometimes failed. She remembers ships on fire and a sudden retreat. But the opium trickle becomes a flood from Chekiang, and Ching Shih has no reach there.

She sends her fleet past Fukien, but the Governor there ignored Lin Ze Xu's words, and the British are firmly entrenched. Their opium soaks every den and every house north of Wenchow. Ching Shih is not frantic, but she cannot stop a flood upon the land.

Even after thirty-nine years, it is still not her place.

◊∆◊∆◊∆◊∆◊∆◊

She wakes one morning soon after, and the red of the regrettable British East India Company flies over the buildings. The rough sounds of English carry on the wind.

Ching Shih allows Chang Pao to begin preparing the tea as she looks over the latest missives, as she hears reports of Lin Ze Xu's banishment, as she considers the options of her fleet.

She considers the flag fluttering and her fleet, its edges tattered. She thinks of her children; of her grandchildren.

She breathes in the pu-er, fresh dried this spring, rinsed once and cooling.

She thinks about the sea.

Theodora

Barbara Robson

The great Empire of Rome is in thrall to a demon Emperor, his wife a demon whore. She is called Empress and allowed to rule as though worthy of that rank, though all know her base beginnings. None speak against her: all declare themselves, joyously or in fear, to be her humble slaves. No senator, no clergyman, no military man dares oppose this "Empress", this demon, Theodora.

— Procopius

~May 510~

The two girls moved nimbly through the crowded market. Slaves haggled over apples, birds fussed and fluttered in their cages, and merchants called out their wares. Comito, fourteen and clad in a provocatively sheer tunic that advertised her profession, led the way between the carts and temporary stalls with a confident stride. Her sister, Theodora, trotted after her, carrying a three-legged stool. While Comito did not acknowledge the appraising glances that came their way or the well-dressed ladies who swerved to avoid them, Theodora looked about, wide-eyed.

"See how they look at you, Comito! You are famous!"

Comito came to a stop under a broad olive tree near one edge of the market, then turned to face her sister, cocked her head, and raised her painted eyebrows. "The word is 'infamous', grape-child." She looked around. "This will do. Let's take a break in the shade. Did you bring the pears?"

The younger girl set down the stool that would keep Comito's fine clothes clear of the dirt, then sat on the dusty ground and fished two ripe pears from the bag that had been slung over her shoulder. She juggled the fruit from hand to hand as she waited for her sister to take her seat and arrange her skirt. The pears looked very good.

"Are you sure you want one?" asked Theodora, coyly. "You'll muss your face."

Her sister smiled. "Rogue. You can't have both. Give it here."

Sighing, Theodora tossed Comito one pear, then bit into the other, releasing a burst of sweetness into the dry afternoon air. She hurried to suck an escaping trickle of juice from her hand before it dripped onto the ground. It was good.

One of the men who had been looking at them from a distance made up his mind to approach. "You're that girl from the theatre!"

Comito held his gaze. "Yes?"

"You dance well enough. Are you going to be on again tonight?"

"Of course."

"And after? Where can I find you after your show?"

Comito's eyes flicked to her little sister, then back to the man. "I'll be mingling," she said. "You won't have any trouble finding me."

"I'll bring you a present," said the man. "Do you have many admirers, yet?"

"I've been on the stage for nearly a year. What do you think?"

Instead of answering, the man turned and sauntered off.

There was a brief silence. Theodora broke it. "I'm going to be famous one day, too," she declared. "I'll be the greatest actress the world ever saw and everyone will admire me and then I'll marry a senator and have cinnamon and dates whenever I want."

Comito pulled a face. "Don't be in such a hurry. It's not much fun, being an actress. And you won't marry a senator. It's against the law."

"Why is it against the law?"

"Actresses aren't allowed to marry."

"Why?"

Comito indicated the crowded marketplace. "See the way the citizens leer at me?"

Theodora nodded.

"See the way their wives glare?"

Biting her lip, Theodora shrugged.

"We'd be too much competition!"

Theodora huffed in consternation. Comito laughed.

"Cheer up, little sister. Maybe you'll meet a nice soldier and he'll keep you as his mistress. That's the only way to escape the stage."

◊∆◊∆◊∆◊∆◊∆◊

The Empress' nature is plain for all to see, but if you need proof, merely ask her lovers from those days in the theatre. Ask, and you'll hear how they were visited by demons in the night as they lay with her in her rooms. With these demons, the witch Theodora made her pact to gain power.

— Procopius

~January 512~

Theodora woke in the dark. She had gone to bed exhausted but happy after the sixth consecutive night of her debut performance and had dreamed of clicking fingers and applause. Why had she woken?

A shadow in front of the moonlit window…an unfamiliar, rancid smell. She sat up, confused…then saw him. An ugly, drunken soldier. A man in her room! She screamed.

The soldier recoiled, unsteady on the heels of his feet, but he quickly recovered his footing and grinned at her. His teeth were yellow in the moonlight. *I have the power here*, said that grin. Theodora screamed again.

"Eeeeeee-aaaah!" Another scream joined hers, and now there was strength in the sound; louder, more ferocious. Now the room was filled with ululating sound and billowing red muslin; filled with fury. Her friend Macedonia was there, kicking and beating the soldier with bare feet and fists! Theodora, still yelling, swept a ceramic cup from the table by the bed, and flung it at the soldier. It shattered against his chest. Frightened, he turned and fled through the open window. Macedonia screamed obscenities after him, her words as red as her chemise.

Theodora shivered, her skin clammy. Before long, she would have to be ready for men like that soldier. But not yet. Not now. Not until menarche made her a woman.

◊Δ◊Δ◊Δ◊Δ◊Δ◊

Our demon Emperor and Empress drive society to decay, delighting in overturning all solid principles of the past. Actresses are allowed to marry, and when they stray, their husbands dare not discipline them, nor even accuse them, for fear of Theodora's wrath. Widows are allowed to keep fortunes, and even to become the guardians of their children, leaving the next generation with no strong hand or guidance. Rome slides into ruin. How did this come to pass, while good men stood by and watched it happen?

— Procopius

~February 516~

Macedonia unravelled her friend's hair from the curling clips, guiding the fresh ringlets prettily down the side of Theodora's face so the dark curls offset her pale complexion. They had both scrubbed themselves head to toe in the baths this afternoon, then rubbed down with cinnamon-scented oil. Macedonia's skin still felt luxuriously clean and soft. Theodora's glowed with excitement.

"There now," said Macedonia, releasing the last ringlet with just a hint of regret. "You're beautiful."

Theodora blushed, smiling. "You too. Are you sure you don't mind filling in for me tonight?"

"Actually, I thought I might not after all. I'm tired of dancing. You've been out so many nights with Hecebolus lately, I think it's my turn."

"Oh! But... Oh!"

Macedonia leaned languorously back on the couch, saying nothing.

"You're right; I've been selfish. It is your turn. It's just..." Theodora thought she might cry, her chance with Hecebolus slipping away.

Macedonia relented, laughing. "Nimwit! Of course I don't mind! Your senator's a Governor now! Of course you must go!"

Theodora's grin returned quickly. "Appointed to Pentapolis! Oh, I wonder what Pentapolis is like! Do you think he'll take me?"

"You know he will, or you wouldn't be smiling." Macedonia took her friend's hands in her own and kissed her cheek fondly, hiding her own tears. "I'm going to miss you."

◊Δ◊Δ◊Δ◊Δ◊Δ◊

Theodora is cruel. She has never been known to be reconciled to anyone who offended her, neither during his life, nor after his death.

— Procopius

~April 520~

Theodora concentrated on putting one foot in front of the other, making steady progress along the long, hot Egyptian road.

The sun burned and the sky burned and the road burned. Except where it glistened as though wet.

Her blisters had long since hardened into callouses inside her shoes, but her feet still hurt.

One foot, then the other.

Hecebolus was supposed to have been her escape. Not a charming man, not a gentle man, but a rich man. A senator. He had said he loved her.

One foot, then the other.

From a child begging before the Hippodrome to the darling of the Byzantine stage to the mistress of the newly appointed governor of Pentapolis! That was how it was supposed to go, and how it had gone. Not more than she'd deserved.

One foot; the other foot.

In less than three years, Hecebolus had tired of her. Abandoned her. Evicted her. She was humiliated, with only her clothes and the meagre few coins in her purse.

One foot.

Theodora rolled her aching shoulders, stretched her arms behind her back, and looked back down the long, empty road. In the distance, it rippled in the heat. Why, when it had been dry all day? Perhaps, like a rainbow, the mirage was a promise from God. There would be another caravan before too long.

She turned to continue her journey. There would be another caravan, another caravan-master, and he would take her on, just like the last one had, for a while. She still had her looks. She had something to trade for passage.

Damn Hecebolus.

One foot. The other foot. Damn Hecebolus and damn all lying men. Two and a half thousand miles of good Roman roads would lead her home.

◊Δ◊Δ◊Δ◊Δ◊Δ◊

He is no descendant of divinity, this Emperor, but a farmer's son. A farmer's son, but adopted by his uncle, the Emperor Justin, at a tender age, and given a good education among honest citizens. So how can it be explained but as delight in degradation that he chose a whore for his wife? He, who could have chosen the most decorous, virginal, pious young maiden in all the Empire—a girl with a dowry as healthy as her breast—instead chose a stage wretch, discarded trollop of a provincial governor and veteran of more abortions than this Emperor has seen days in battle. There is no other explanation than that Justinian is as much a demon as his wife.

— Procopius

~December 520~

Being back in Constantinople was not so bad. Theodora had arrived, shivering and fevered, at the height of summer, her period later than it had ever been before. The tonic Antonina procured to bring on the bleeding had hit her body so hard that it had seemed she might die. But Chrysomallo had taken her in, and her friends took good care of her; Antonina, Macedonia, Chrysomallo and Indaro taking turns by her bedside until she was out of danger.

By mid-autumn, Theodora was back on the stage. Her performances grew more daring, the audiences more bawdy, her tongue sharper, both on- and off-stage. Her manager shot her worried looks as she satirised Pope Hormisdas as a clown and secret puppet of the Green faction, but she got away with it: her audience loved her.

Soldiers and magistrates still waited for her after shows, bearing silver for her, or incense, perfumes or silks. She sent most of them away with barbed witticisms. Still, they hoped. She was an actress. By definition, she was available.

It was only as a favour to Macedonia that she accompanied her friend on a rendezvous one cool winter night. The rain had stopped, but an early mist gathered about the evening as they walked together, hand in hand, dressed as beautifully as if Hecebolus and the long, cruel summer had never happened. Theodora was feeling optimistic for the first time in far too long. Macedonia was being frustratingly mysterious.

"So who is he, this prospect of yours?"

"A soldier."

"Seriously? Just a soldier?"

"He's very well connected."

"A well-connected soldier?"

"Very."

"What's his name then, this well-connected soldier?"

"John."

"And John's connections?"

"You'll see."

Theodora was silent for a moment, walking faster to warm herself up. She hoped the taverna had a good fire. But her curiosity was frustrated. "I'll see? What does that mean?"

Macedonia smiled knowingly and kept walking.

"You've set me up with one of this John's 'very good' connections? Is that what you're saying?"

If Macedonia had intended to reply, it was too late. They had reached the bar (it did have a good fire) and the men were waiting for them.

Theodora's heart sank. It was evident that both men were soldiers. The biceps were the giveaway, combined with the swagger. And the swords. She supposed the one on the left was Macedonia's John. A handsome man: Macedonia had an eye for that. The man on the right was not bad looking. For Macedonia's sake, she could be nice to him for an evening.

The soldier on the left spoke first. "Macedonia! Good to see you again, after all our letters. Theodora! Delighted to meet you at last." His voice was deep, but smooth, not gravelly, like some of the military men she had known. He had the accent of an educated man, but without the haughtiness of a senator. Where had Macedonia found him? Theodora was used to needing no introduction, but these men intrigued her. She put on her best party face and winked to the other man before turning coquettish eyes to the one with the nice voice.

"Massie didn't tell me I had such a treat in store! I can tell we're all going to get on like Leda and her swan."

The handsome man smiled. "Not shy, I see. Macedonia said that about you."

"I guess she's told you everything about me. And none of it good!"

"All of it good! Or all of it interesting, I should say. And I saw your impressive show last night."

The second man now had Macedonia in an embrace and was guiding them towards a table. So that must be John, which meant the soldier she was talking to was here for her. Theodora appraised him: he had a wide, friendly face, blond hair, blue eyes, strong chin, and broad shoulders. She could certainly do worse for company. He was an admirer, too! That helped. She smiled more sincerely as they took their seats.

"What part did you like best? The Swan?" Her most risqué performance.

He chuckled, but wouldn't admit it. "That part, too. It was all wonderful. Though I think you're wrong about the Pope."

A moment passed, while Theodora tried to bite her tongue. She'd never had that knack. The mood changed. Macedonia winced as Theodora drew an indignant breath. "Wrong," she repeated, quietly. "I'm wrong about the Pope? My goodness." She paused, then almost spat her next words. "The Pope's a shit-eating Chalcedonian. What else do you need to know?"

Macedonia looked alarmed. "Theo-dor-a! I'm sure Justinian doesn't want to talk about that!"

"On the contrary!" said the soldier (Justinian?), unfazed. "I'd like to hear this."

(Justinian? That was a very familiar name, and Macedonia had said John was well-connected. Was she getting herself into trouble? Well, what if she was? This was important.)

"If we have a disagreement," Theodora said, "then we do need to talk about it. What could be more important than talking about God?"

"How about what we'll have for dinner?" offered Macedonia, brightly. "Is the food here good? It smells good!"

"You're a Monophysite?" asked Justinian quietly, ignoring Macedonia. "I'm curious as to why."

"You're Chalcedonian? But you have only to think about it for a moment to see how wrong that is!"

"A Chalcedonian, yes!" said Justinian. "But tell me again how I'm wrong. I don't often hear that, except from my aunt."

"Mmm, that stew smells good," said Macedonia. "I think I'll order the stew. How about you, John? Theodora? Justinian?"

"Maybe later," said Theodora, without looking up. "To first principles, Justinian. God is divine. That is the central tenant of our faith!"

"Divine, but also human." He opened his strong hands, palms to the ceiling, and raised his eyes skyward as though calling on God to explain it for him. "God gave us his only son as a man."

She waited until he brought his eyes back to earth—or at least, her cleavage—before she replied. "Human, but only as an aspect of the Divine. Humans are imperfect. God's nature can never less than perfection."

"Jesus is human, and also Divine. Two natures, united in sacrifice." He spoke with his hands as much as with his voice and she replied in kind.

"One nature…" she brought her palms together with a clap, "…in two aspects!"

It wasn't enough. "If you deny Jesus' fundamental humanity," argued Justinian, "You deny His suffering. You deny His sacrifice, and God's love."

"I don't deny His humanity. The Divine is all things! But if you deny His divinity, you deny God."

Theodora caught the look on Macedonia's face. Okay. So this was *that* Justinian. She was arguing with the nephew of the Emperor. She knew she should stop, but her opponent was worthy: she was having fun. And was that a sparkle in Justinian's eye?

Justinian took a sip of wine and smiled at her, happily. "Let's get this straight. It isn't that Chalcedonians deny His divinity…"

It was a long night, and the first of many.

◊Δ◊Δ◊Δ◊Δ◊Δ◊

The Emperor is as agreeable as Theodora is disagreeable. He is a man of average size, his face pleasant, his manner disarming. He the worst kind of fool, besotted with his wife and easily led by the nose. But he is cunning: he lies as easily as he breathes, pretending always that his motives are pure.
— Procopius

~February 527~

Theodora pondered. It was time to say something. Her husband was a good man, but he was never going to act on his own. She chose her time carefully;

after dinner, when they were alone in their office and had time to talk it through. Instead of taking her seat at her own desk, she sat on the edge of his.

"Justinian. Your uncle is falling into senility."

He frowned, not looking up from his paperwork. "You think I haven't noticed?" The tension of the week's events was clear in his voice.

"I know you have noticed. You've been doing his job for months now. Isn't it time you were recognised as Emperor?"

"My uncle is Emperor."

Theodora stood and stepped behind him to stroke the soft curls at the back of his head. "I know he is, love," she said, softly. "But for how much longer?"

Now he looked up, bristling with the beginnings of anger. "Until he dies, if I have anything to do with it!"

She stole a kiss, smelling his tension. "Of course. But that can't be far off. And what then?"

He held her gaze for a moment, then shrugged as the momentary anger left. "Well, then I think I am well positioned…"

She pursed her lips. He met her eyes again, questioning. "…No?"

Theodora chose her words carefully. "We are not badly positioned, but there is no certainty. You are not without enemies. There are other contenders. Whereas, if you were named co-Emperor now…"

"…Certainly not without precedent…"

"…Then your succession would be assured…"

"…And you, of course, would be Empress beside me." Justinian leaned back in his chair, thinking hard. "You may be right that it is best to move now." He frowned, considering the obstacles. "It will have to be managed carefully."

"Then let us begin."

◊Δ◊Δ◊Δ◊Δ◊Δ◊

The arrogance of the Empress is without precedent.

— Procopius

~April 527~

Emperor Justin died naturally only a few weeks later; Theodora was grateful that her husband had seen sense. The succession, nonetheless, was having teething trouble. She was not the senate's favourite person.

"I demand to see Emperor Justinian!"

Vestiarios Calopodius, guarding the door, was not having a good day. This must be the twentieth angry man his position had forced him to face down, and he hadn't yet had a meal. He remained polite, but spoke firmly.

"That won't be possible, sir. The Emperor is not receiving visitors. The Empress, however..."

In a room above the palace courtyard, two women vied for position at the window.

"This one has gone red in the face," reported Chysomallo, her voice delighted. "I think he might be having trouble breathing!"

"Ooh, let me see!" said Indaro. The scene below had been repeated many times that day, but each new arrival brought fresh amusement.

Tired of yelling, the patrician hissed his next words. "If you think I'm going to be fobbed off with the Emperor's whore..."

"Sir!" said the guard. "I wouldn't let anyone hear you talk like that if I were you. The Empress has the full authority of her position!"

"Now you listen here...!" began the red-faced man, one hand going to the hilt of the sword at his side, the other balled in a fist near the guard's face. Calopodius didn't even need to signal to his men. Basil and Peter each took hold of one of the patrician's arms then marched him to the palace gate and threw him into the street.

The ladies at the window cheered.

◊Δ◊Δ◊Δ◊Δ◊Δ◊

Rich men are separated from their fortunes on trumped-up charges of corruption. Others are forced, unwilling, to free their slaves. Pimps are made to free prostitutes, reimbursed only the price they paid, with nothing accounted for their costs of upkeep. The brothels are closed, with no further compensation to the owners for loss of livelihood—instead, it is the corrupt women who are given alms. The army is paid scant wages, its soldiers lean, its generals forbidden from taking the profits of their conquests. Money from the palace coffers—money stolen from generals and senators, soldiers and magistrates—goes instead to unreasonable munificence to barbarian nations and ill-conceived building works that the Empire cannot afford. A seaside convent to house former prostitutes, and buttresses to hold back the sea. Grand temples are being erected for both the Monophysite heresy and the true Chalcedonian faith, mocking the church with false piety. The fortunes of an Empire are squandered on gilt mosaics, our people made destitute.

— Procopius

~May 527~

Calopodius' job was beginning to get easier. The red-face patrician was here yet again. Procopius was slow, but he was learning.

"I. Would like. To see the Empress," he said, biting off each word. "If it isn't too much trouble. The matter is important."

"Certainly, sir," replied Calopodius. "If you'd care to wait over here?" With the sweep of his arm, he indicated the crowded room beyond.

The patrician eyed the throng uncertainly. A man of his stature should not expect to wait...but then, several of his peers were already there, in the crowd, so perhaps he would not lose face. He weighed his pride against the urgency of his business. His creditors were beginning to press and if he left it any longer, the matter might become public.

"Will the wait be long?"

"Well, the Empress is rather busy..."

"And the Emperor?"

"Not seeing anyone today."

Procopius bit his tongue and took a place in the crowd.

Indaro turned away from the window, pouting. "There hasn't been a good tantrum in ages. Are you going to see any of them today?"

Theodora looked up from her bath. "Do you think they are learning? Maybe this afternoon, then."

Chrysomallo demurred. "I think you should make them wait another week. Teach them some respect."

"Oh," said Theodora, "They'll learn respect." She smiled in anticipation. "I'll have them kiss my feet before they are allowed to speak." Raising one foot from the bath-water, she inspected her toes. "Do you think I should paint my nails?"

◊Δ◊Δ◊Δ◊Δ◊Δ◊

The Basilica called Sophia is, it cannot be denied, a spectacle of indescribable beauty, overwhelming to all who see it, but altogether incredible to those who only hear it praised. Exceedingly long and unusually broad, it soars to reach the sky, towering above the city and yet glorifying it, because it is a part of it.

— Procopius

~August 531~

"I hear the building work goes well," said Theodora, joining Justinian on their favourite balcony after an invigorating day of debate in the senate. "The Brazen tower and the church."

Justinian, turning away from the view of the city, grinned. "Wait until you see the mosaics! They are going to be spectacular!"

"And well they should be, celebrating so many victories abroad. Did they take a good likeness?"

Justinian reached out to tap her nose affectionately with one finger. "Of you, of me, or of Strategos Belisarius' troops in Persia?"

"Of the troops, of course! To capture a likeness of you, they need only take the Greek gods as their models. As for me, well…"

"The Platonic Ideal of beauty."

"Aha! I've educated you well!"

"I count on it."

"That Strategos, though… He may be getting too big for his boots. You should call him to heel."

"What, back to Constantinople?"

"Else risk a mutiny. He is not quick to take direction."

Justinian frowned. "But an excellent commander." He raised one eyebrow. "Are you sure Antonina didn't put you up to this?"

"Antonina would love to see her husband safe at home, but she has diversions enough while he is away. It's Belisarius I'm worried about."

"In that case," said Justinian, "It shall be done. Now, which stonemason should we employ for the Eastern arch?"

◊Δ◊Δ◊Δ◊Δ◊Δ◊

Such is our misgovernment that the whole populace is now in disarray. In the aftermath of the plague called down by God to punish Romans for their demonic rule, bands of youths prowl the streets of Constantinople, dressed in what they called the Hunnic style and terrorising the citizens. They cut their hair short at the sides, leave it long at the back and shave the fronts of their scalps, but let their beards and moustaches grow long. They dress in richly embroidered robes, showing off their colours—the Blues are the worst of them—their sleeves tightly gathered at the wrist, but voluminous at the shoulders, as though pretending to impossibly large biceps. At night, they go about openly armed, knocking down unarmed citizens and stealing their purses. And yet, the Empress will not suffer the admonition of her favourites, blaming the Greens for every trouble.

Facing no punishment, the miscreants grow so bold that they even go openly in the day-time, decapitating innocent men with their swords to prove their manhood; outraging women. Sons overturn their fathers. Yet we are not without hope. Those who have suffered indignities and slander at the hands of the Emperor and Theodora saw the opportunity in this kindling of terror. The people, rioting, have turned their wrath at last upon the palace.

— Procopius

~January 532~

Here in the palace, it seemed strangely quiet. In this moment, the sounds of riot were oddly distant. The air caught in Justinian's throat, acrid. His head felt full of smoke, empty of blood. He should find somewhere to sit. He should find Theodora. He sat, then realised she was already there beside him.

The sky glowed red on the horizon, transformed by the burning city, but hung almost green overhead. The Praetorium burned. The Brazen House burned. The senate house burned. The Hippodrome had been set ablaze, and the Baths of Zeuxippos with their beautiful statuary, burned. Even the Hagia Sophia, his soldiers informed him, had been gutted and burned.

What did they want from him?

His advisors had told him he must take a firm hand against the gangs, and so he had. Seven felons, Blues and Greens alike, had been arrested, convicted and sentenced to death. Five had hanged quickly, but two had survived when the scaffolding broke. The Greens and the Blues had united in calling for their freedom and he had wanted to relent, but these were murderers. He had held firm.

They had chanted in the Hippodrome all day, the Blues and the Greens both, but he had held firm. Belisarius had pushed him to free the prisoners: the mob was dangerous. Mundus had urged him to send in his soldiers to slaughter the trouble-makers, all thirty thousand of them, while they trapped themselves in the Hippodrome. Perhaps he should have. But Justinian had steered a middle path, certain that they would see reason if only he continued to hold firm, for the good of the city.

All hell had broken loose. They turned against him.

They had long since freed the prisoners. What did they want from him now?

"Conquest!" he heard the shout faintly, then louder, as the blood returned to his head. In many voices: "Victory!" In a rush, the world returned, and he was breathing again. Not distant; the mob was at his gate.

"What do they want?" he asked aloud.

"They have sent another bill of demands," said Calopodius. "The prefect Eudamon to be dismissed, John the Cappadocian to be dismissed, the quaestor Tribonian to be dismissed, and all his new laws overturned."

John's name in the list was no surprise: a good man, but tax collectors were never popular. Also Eudamon: the prefect had overseen the hangings. But in calling for Tribonian's dismissal, they showed their hand. This was not the demand of youthful trouble-makers, but of his enemies in the senate. Tribonian was the author of the legal code that had cemented Theodora's plans for social reform.

Justinian saw no alternative. "Give them what they want."

"That's pointless," said Theodora, sharply. "It won't stop them."

Justinian looked at his wife, beautiful in her anger. As always, her passion balanced his mildness. "I know it won't," he said, quietly, "but it may hold them long enough for our soldiers to arrive from Thrace."

He thought, but did not say: *it may hold them long enough for a fast ship to be prepared for our escape.*

◊Δ◊Δ◊Δ◊Δ◊Δ◊

Word came that the mob had dragged Hypatius, nephew of the Emperor Anastasius, from his home, and taken him to the burnt-out Hippodrome to crown him their Emperor. More concessions would not sway them. "Load the ship," said Justinian to Calopodius. "I will break the news to Theodora."

◊Δ◊Δ◊Δ◊Δ◊Δ◊

Once, a little girl had trembled in her bed, powerless and humble in the face of an intruder. From her friends, she had learnt the power of fury.

Once, a young woman had been flattered and showered with jewels, then thrown out into the street with nothing.

She would not be thrown out again.

Theodora was magnificent in her rage.

In front of his loyal senators, in front of his Thracian soldiers, in front of the God they had argued over so many times, she talked her husband down.

Though Indara begged her to stop, though Chrysomallo begged her to flee, Theodora held the floor, dressed in her most royal attire. She spoke. People listened.

"As to the belief that a woman ought not to be daring among men, nor bold when men hold back from fear, I say that the present crisis does not permit us such niceties. When all that we hold dear is in the gravest peril, there is nothing left to be done but to make the best plan that we can to deal with the immediate danger."

She spoke loudly enough for all to hear, but held Justinian's eyes.

"For my part, I say that this is not the time to flee, not even if it costs our lives to stay. No one who has been born can escape death, but for an Emperor to become a fugitive is unendurable! May I never be separated from this purple, and may I never see the day on which those to whom I speak do not address me as Empress!"

She knew what people called her when they did not call her Empress, but she had not had to hear it for a very long time. She had thought her husband understood. She paused, willing him to understand. He met her eyes, face unreadable. She spoke more softly, her voice still clear. "If you want to save yourself, oh Emperor, then there is no difficulty. We have plenty of money, there is the sea, and here are the boats. But ask yourself whether it may not come about, after you are safely away, that you would gladly exchange that safety for death. As for myself, I will not come. Purple makes a fine burial-shroud."

And so Justinian stayed.

◊∆◊∆◊∆◊∆◊∆◊

It was the Blues who betrayed the revolution, listening too well to the promises of Justinian's spies. Thirty-five thousand died in the riots, but all in vain. Theodora and Justinian hold their power more strongly now than before. One of these days, Justinian, if he is a man, will depart this life: if he is Lord of Demons, he will set his life aside. Then all who chance to be still living will know the truth.

— Procopius

For So Great a Misdeed

Lisa L. Hannett

Gunnarr's mother won't stop crying.

She isn't sobbing or wailing; Rannveig isn't the type of person to make a spectacle of herself. She grieves quietly, the front of her kirtle splotched and spattered, the under-dress's long sleeves streaked brown-red up to the elbows. Her son's halberd—its enchanted blade famous throughout all of Iceland—is clutched like Óðinn's staff in her left hand.

The weapon's long shaft, Hallgerðr thinks, holds her stout mother-in-law upright. That and the hot steel in her gaze. Rannveig glares as Hallgerðr strides to and fro across the hall at Hlíðarendi, sorting through her husband's possessions, packing her own favourite things. Hallgerðr feigns indifference—let the hag stare!—but her traitor feet speed up as she passes the hearth. The older woman has not shifted from that red-stained spot these past two days, her fine leather boots now ruined with Gunnarr's lifeblood. Face bleached from lack of sleep, grey plaits frizzed, Rannveig waits for the blade in her grip to sing. For it to resonate with bloodlust, as it has so many times before battle. For it to shout, in its metallic voice, that Gunnarr's death will be avenged.

Rannveig scowls whenever Hallgerðr draws near. Weeping has done nothing to soften her hatred.

Hallgerðr climbs the short ladder to the loft where she, Gunnarr, and Rannveig sleep. *Slept*, she corrects. Grief catches in her throat, but Hallgerðr refuses to let it loose. She soft-steps across the platform, avoiding the short beds, the wooden boxes filled with wool blankets, the furs. Smelling the spice of pine clapboards running up to what's left of the turf roof. The clods of dirt fallen from the low ceiling, peppering mattresses and blankets.

Gunnarr's scent, once so strong, is barely present in the shirt Hallgerðr collects and presses her to face. Inhaling deeply, she breathes his absence.

"What are you up to, girl?" Rannveig calls, words clenched in the old woman's jaw. "Get what you want, and go."

What I want, Hallgerðr thinks. From an iron hook on the far wall, she takes a silk pouch: filigreed box-brooches, strings of indigo glass beads, silver rings clatter inside. Next the embroidered girdle Gunnarr gave her after their wedding. She bags the scentless shirt, and two more like it. Rannveig thumps the butt of her staff on the floor downstairs, and Hallgerðr takes a last look around. Light sparks off a single shelf in the corner. Hurrying over, she sweeps her oldest trinkets off the board and cups them in her palm.

What I want, she thinks again, looking at the delicate bronze boat, the tiny silver sheep, the golden crescent. *What I want is for things to be how they were.*

"Hallgerðr," Rannveig shouts. "Now!"

"What's the rush," she snaps, pulling Gunnarr's stringless bow out from under the furs on their once-bed. "My hurrying won't make you any younger."

Hefting the useless weapon, she wraps it in a wool cloak and stuffs the bundle under her arm.

What I want, she thinks, *is to stay.*

◊Δ◊Δ◊Δ◊Δ◊Δ◊

It is not wrong to want.

Those were the seer's words; Hallgerðr remembers precisely, though decades have rushed by since they were uttered. Generations have died. Whole families have been lost. She was ten, maybe eleven. Past thirty now, she yet remembers the tone of the seiðr-woman's voice, burred as the hand she'd pressed to little Hallgerðr's head, the edges of the witch's curse stiff and blue-limned with woad, just like her lips and eyebrows and fingernails. *It is not wrong to want*, she'd said, flashing black-stained teeth, pain in her smile. Her eyes fixed on Hallgerðr's uncle Hrút, as he watched his long-legged niece teasing the other children by the hearth, while her father, Höskuldr, crowed, "Isn't she the loveliest thing you've ever seen?"

Hallgerðr already caught warriors' and bondsmen's eyes. With thick sheets of blonde hair swaying below her slim waist, she'd abandoned her place at the witch's side. Skipping around the fire in the centre of Höskuldr's large hall, snatching bone game-pieces from her cousins' boards, she forced them to chase her. She'd laughed to see them glower, laughed even harder when at last they caught up, grubby hands tugging at her kirtle until she relinquished their toys. All gazes in the longhouse followed Hallgerðr—

from the lowliest slave to Höskuldr's most trusted retainer, from the oldest grandmother to the newest guest, this Lapplander, the fate-sealing seer. Everyone paid attention to Hallgerðr, and she had been glad. Honoured to have her father's affection. Proud to be called beautiful. She *had* been happy, for a while. Yes, she remembers being happy.

Until Hrút spoiled it. "The girl has thief's eyes," he'd said. "No good will come of her; she is headstrong and greedy. Foster her out until she learns humility. Þjóstólfr will take her, if you ask him."

Hallgerðr's heart sank at her uncle's comments. Crouching beside the children, she feigned interest in her baby brother Bárðr, while sneaking a look at Höskuldr. He'd sat, like the rest of his men, on the edge of the fur-laden bench that doubled as a bed at night. Bowl in one hand and bread in the other, he'd ruminated, chewing the strands of his drooping moustache. Hallgerðr had leaned over and slapped the baby's chubby arm to stop his babbling. Then she had scuttled back to the guest-bench at the far end of the room, where the seiðr-woman sat smirking.

Hallgerðr had waited for her father to defend her, to tell Hrút to shut up, to say there was no way he'd let her go.

Slowly, Höskuldr had frowned. Þjóstólfr came from the Hebrides; a strong warrior who had killed many men without once paying reparations. "He's hardly the type of man to improve Hallgerðr's character," he said at last, but had no chance to say anything further. Instead, the witch had made her pronouncement.

It is not wrong to want, she'd said, in that haunting voice.

Grey tendrils did not swirl dramatically around the stranger. No flames guttered, portent-filled. The afternoon was always dark in Iceland at mid-winter, but the elements were calm outside. Snow had blown in great drifts up the sides of Höskuldr's hall, adding insulation to its turf walls. Inside, all was snug and quiet. Smoke from the hearth and steam from the cook-pot billowed lazily upwards, escaping through a hole in the roof. These wisps of peat-scented air ignored the woman, much as the men did, returning to their ale and fish.

But to Hallgerðr, the foreigner's observation had been hook-sharp. *I want to stay here with father*, she remembers thinking. *What's so wrong with wanting that?* When the witch urged her closer, Hallgerðr had shifted without hesitation, though there'd been a strange smell about her: tilled soil, pine and juniper. As the woman bent to move her gloves and satchel to make extra room, there'd been a gust of fermented milk.

"It is not wrong to want," she'd repeated, staring at Hallgerðr with mismatched irises: one hazel, one green. In later years, Hallgerðr would imitate that perfect posture, that haughty tilt of the chin; she would tighten her stomach so her torso also appeared longer and stronger than it was. The seiðr-woman wore a deep red kirtle over a black wool dress, colours

Hallgerðr would forever associate with cleverness and far-travelling. An evening-blue cloak hung from her shoulders—lined with the fur of fifty white cats. From a silver chatelaine around her waist dangled a stone-tipped wand, a sheathed knife, a tiny copy of Þórr's hammer, and a leather pouch of rune-sticks that clattered every time she moved.

"Why do you keep saying that? About *wanting*," she'd asked bluntly. Then as now Hallgerðr was not one to waste time with niceties. "Why bother repeating yourself?"

"To remind you," the witch had said. "To make you understand." Licking her lips, she'd spent a moment rummaging in her sack. She'd withdrawn three small trinkets that glinted in the firelight. One by one, she placed them in the girl's hand.

A bronze open boat, with an oversized fish welded inside.

A silver sheep balanced on a cairn of stones.

A gold-plated bow fit for a tiny warrior, only lacking a string.

"You have a rich future in store," the seiðr-woman had said, and Hallgerðr's heart raced.

"Can I keep them all?"

The woman grinned, nodded. "It is not wrong to want."

◊∆◊∆◊∆◊∆◊∆◊

Of course Hallgerðr had kept the shining trinkets. Of course she'd agreed with what the stranger said. She'd agreed and in so doing—or so she has come to realise—Hallgerðr had clinched her doom. Her fate. Her *urðr*. Hers and Gunnarr's. At the time, she'd believed there *was* nothing wrong with wanting attention, affection, the precious joys in life. She remembers this last most acutely; how she'd not just wanted, but *needed* possessions.

Great lengths of fine woollen cloth. Embroideries from the East. Bedsheets from Constantinople, soft as summer water. Amber beads from Rús. Scarlet and fur cloaks, the gifts of Norwegian kings. She'd needed these treasures and more: barrels of whey, crocks of skýr, jugs of smooth buttermilk, blocks of strong cheese, enough salted herring to see ten families through the long winter. All of this, she remembers thinking, would make her attractive. Desired. Wanted. All of this would prove her worth. With this wealth in her pantry and coffers, she would be loved.

◊∆◊∆◊∆◊∆◊∆◊

"Selfish girl," Rannveig says now, eyeing everything Hallgerðr carries down from the loft. "Gunnarr's burial mound hasn't yet been dug—and you're stealing his grave-goods!"

"So says she who refused to give Njáll that halberd when he came asking for it," Hallgerðr replies. She will *not* be called a thief in her own house. "Knowing Njáll and his sons, they've worked day and night since Gunnarr's—" she won't say *defeat* "—skirmish. The mound is ready to welcome our warrior to the afterlife. How do you expect him to fight in Valhöll without his best weapon?"

"You know as well as I," Rannveig says, menace in every syllable, "that given a fair chance, no one could beat my son with a bow."

"Think what you like, old wretch." Flushed, Hallgerðr turns on her heel, still carrying her largest bundle. She retreats to the private weaving room Gunnarr had built for her, long ago, at the other end of the house. With trembling hands, she places her burden on a workbench next to the loom. In her fist, bronze grinds against gold and silver. Loosening her grip, she lets the boat, the sheep, the broken bow clunk onto the table.

What good are the seiðr-woman's predictions? What good are cheap baubles to her now?

Hallgerðr sighs. Crossing to the loom, she admires her handiwork. She takes up the wooden beater and drives home the weft, pushing threads needlessly up and up and up. A hand-span of material is all that's left to weave, but once Rannveig has her way, Hallgerðr won't be here to see it finished. The pattern has come together nicely: the colours are strong. Puffin-black lines zig and zag across a field of deep green, the hue fair as the hillsides around Hlíðarendi—or so Gunnarr had said when he came back to the farmstead, months ago now, and found Hallgerðr setting the first threads. *Fair are the hillsides*, he'd said, returning when he should have been three years in exile. Only three years...

Footsteps scuff past the door. Hallgerðr turns; behind her, the room is empty. The packed earth is swept clean, no sign of intrusion. Not footsteps, she decides. Wind rustles through the grass growing on the rooftop; the beams and turf in the hearth-room will have to be repaired and replaced, but this small corner of the house remains undamaged.

Outside, her son Högni instructs a slave in a voice so like her husband's it hurts. *Ready the horses*, he's saying. *Mother's first*. Grani, her second boy, is returning from the homefields, where Gunnarr's bondsmen are mowing hay; the scythes' rhythmic song rings across the miles.

Most likely his last harvest here, Hallgerðr thinks. Rannveig always favoured Högni over her younger grandson. "Grani's disposition is too much like *yours*," she'd sneer. "Högni, though, is a good man. Upright. Like his father." Closer to the house, a goat is griping, joined now and then by a pair of snorting steeds, impatient for the journey.

Unhooking a pair of shears from the wall, Hallgerðr removes her kerchief and grabs a thick handful of hair. Quickly, before she can change her mind, she snips close to the scalp.

In the background, persistent as a truth, comes the rush of the Grótjá. When Rannveig has her way, that dark river will separate Hallgerðr from this land she's grown to love. The farmstead that once belonged to her most beloved husband, Gunnarr Hámundarson. Gunnarr of Hlíðarendi. Gunnarr the Great.

Her Viking.

And oh, she thinks, long locks falling like water down her face: Oh, how she'd *wanted* him.

◊Δ◊Δ◊Δ◊Δ◊Δ◊

Not like that pig Þorvaldr Ósvifsson, who turned Hallgerðr's stomach before they'd even met. Her father, Höskuldr, had arranged the marriage in mere minutes, without taking an instant to ask her opinion.

"Name the conditions," Þorvaldr had apparently said, hand outstretched to shake on any deal Höskuldr offered. "Let's get this done. I'll not let Hallgerðr's temper get in the way of this bargain."

The memory of her first husband's audacity—his outright *gall*—still burns. Unbelievable that such a low-born man had such a high opinion of himself! That he thought himself a match for *her*. True, his wealth walked on many feet, and some thought him well bred, but he was no warrior. He had no honour. And his personality! She could have found better conversation with that goat bleating in the yard. No, Þorvaldr had been no Gunnarr.

But what's worst, Hallgerðr thinks, is how eager Höskuldr had been to barter her away, to be rid of her…

Tugging at her hair, Hallgerðr cuts furiously. She has outlived the cursed seer and her charms. She's outlived three husbands. She's outlived Höskuldr. She's outlived her mean uncle Hrút. They'd lived, they'd fought, they'd died, just as all men do—but not before they'd shipped her off to Þjóstólfr, her foster-father, who proved his love more than Höskuldr ever had.

The lavishness of her first wedding feast hadn't salved her wounded pride. Over a hundred guests, including her foster-father, who'd joined the newlyweds at Medalfell Strand soon as the festivities had ended. Þjóstólfr had stayed with them throughout the winter, a welcome distraction from married life.

Þorvaldr. Hallgerðr shudders. The man kept such a miserly pantry, always running out of flour and dried fish, then accusing *her* of over-indulgence.

“The supplies used to last until summer,” he’d snarled, pockmarks vivid against the ale-flush in his cheeks.

“It’s no concern of mine if you and your family tried to save money by starving yourselves,” Hallgerðr remembers replying. She still thinks it was reasonable for Þorvaldr to provide the essentials. Support the household. Support *her*. She’d intended to discuss the pauper-portions of their meals like an adult—but then the pig had slapped her.

Hallgerðr puts down the shears, feels the patch of cropped hair at her brow. Two sturdy strands are all she needs, only two, but she has cut ten times that many. *Not enough*, she thinks, taking up the clippers again.

“It’s not enough,” she’d said to Þorvaldr, and he’d struck her, struck her face so hard it drew blood. Then he sailed off to the Bear Isles, where their storehouses had stood, to get his wife more grain for bread, more salted herring.

Shivering in the cold weaving room, Hallgerðr contemplates pinning an oiled hide over the window to keep out the breeze. *No time*, she thinks, just as Rannveig bellows from out in the hall: “Dusk is falling, girl. You’re out of this house today, dark or light. Trolls take you for all I care!”

Hallgerðr plunges her hands into the kirtle’s deep pockets. She balls her fists, harder and harder, nails digging into palms. Harder still, until they cut into flesh.

Do they cut as viciously as the knife Þorvaldr had wielded, defending himself, the day he slapped her, the very day her foster-father ambushed him on the Bear Isles?

Is his loss as heavy as the two-hundreds of silver Höskuldr had been forced to pay as wergild for Þorvaldr’s shortened life?

Perhaps. Sometimes.

Höskuldr and Hrút had blamed Hallgerðr for her first husband’s death, but Þjóstólfr’s axe had done the deed. Yes, she’d been furious, jaw bleeding and sore from his attack. Yes, she’d had a quiet word with Þjóstólfr and maybe, just maybe, she had implied that none of this—none of this!—would have happened if only he’d been around at the time.

“And you would have been here,” she recalls saying, lighting a spark that had burnt Þjóstólfr’s honour, “if you cared for me at all.”

It is not wrong to want.

Yes, she had wanted the pig gone.

But *she* hadn’t been the one to butcher him.

◊Δ◊Δ◊Δ◊Δ◊Δ◊

At the other end of the house, Högni enters, the clomp of his boots less graceful than his father’s. “*Amma*,” Hallgerðr hears him say, voiced pitched low, addressing his grandmother. "*Amma*, they've built a huge mound—Njáll and his sons. They've stood a great throne in its depths, carved from the best Norwegian pine. Gunnarr sits there even now; upright, as always. The Njállsons will see him avenged. Please, *Amma*. Forsake this vigil. Clean yourself off."

Sweet Högni, always avoiding confrontation. In this, too, he is different from his father.

Half of Hallgerðr's hair is amassed on the workbench, a pool of molten red-gold, a gossamer shield. Two strands are all she needs, just two strands—but which two? Which are the strongest? The best? Tilting her head, she yanks another handful. Tears spring, but she won't let them fall. Vision blurred, she looks over at the loom. Blinks until she can see more clearly, and waits for her galloping pulse to slow.

It had taken long summer days of stringing wool, threading and rethreading, for Hallgerðr to weave *Lætrsérannarsvíti at varnaðiverða* across the top margin of her tapestry. *Let another man's woe be your warning*. How Glúmr Óleifsson, her second husband, had laughed when his brother, Þórarin, had used this same maxim to discourage him from marrying her!

But to Gunnarr—oh, to a warrior like Gunnarr—this phrase was a call to arms. A Viking's battle-cry.

Glúmr should have been Högni's father, Hallgerðr thinks. He'd been a lamb of a man, soft-eyed, curly-headed. Preferred farming to fighting. But he had understood her; he'd accepted she was a woman who knew her own mind. He'd asked *her* if she'd be willing to marry him. Dear, simple Glúmr. Honest as the flocks he'd loved tending. Plain as the fleece on their backs.

How he'd contented her, for a time.

They'd lived in fine style at Varmalœk, a large farmstead with more bondsmen than Hallgerðr knew what to do with. The larder was always full, the hearth roaring, the blankets piled high on their happy bed. Glúmr had been a sheep, but a generous one. He'd given her whatever she wanted, including a plump baby girl. Þorgerðr grew to be as beautiful as her mother.

When she was asked, Hallgerðr freely admitted how fond she was of her second husband.

"We are very much in love," she'd told her foster-father, the first and only time he visited them. In hindsight, Hallgerðr realises she shouldn't have let him stay so long. Maybe she shouldn't have sweet-talked Glúmr into taking him in after her father had evicted him from Höskuldsstead. No. That wasn't her fault. Glúmr should have grown a spine: *he* should have sent the troublemaker away. After Þjóstólfr had spent weeks nitpicking and complaining. After he'd pestered the shepherds and harassed the slaves. After he'd shown no respect for anyone other than Hallgerðr herself.

All that winter and the following summer, she'd taken no sides when Þjóstólfr quarrelled with everyone. She'd done her best to keep quiet. To not let anger consume her.

Only Þjóstólfr could have riled Glúmr into such a fury, and over something so trivial. A few lost sheep—no reason to rage and bellow! The flock was still large, the storehouses bursting with wool and dried meat. The strays would find their way home, but Glúmr took no chances. These sheep were valuable. They needed finding immediately. Supplies would run low too quickly without them. So he'd said.

In truth, Hallgerðr thinks, Glúmr wanted an excuse to get rid of Þjóstólfr. To send him into the mountains just when the weather had turned foul, when the paths would be treacherous with ice.

When Þjóstólfr refused, saying he was no herdsman, saying *You seem awfully fond of the beasts*, saying *Is my foster-daughter not enough for you, Glúmr?* saying *Does your love spill into these sheep?* the growl that tore out of Glúmr's throat woke little Þorgerðr, who'd finally—after hours of jiggling and feeding and cooing and rocking—*finally* fallen asleep on Hallgerðr's lap.

The baby's puffed eyelids had widened, as had her mouth. And oh how she'd *wailed…*

Glúmr's arm was then flailing, pointing at the door, ordering Þjóstólfr not just to the mountain but farther still, *Out! Out! Out!*

"He's not going anywhere," Hallgerðr had shouted to her husband, while the baby screeched in her ear. "Keep your voice down, sheep-lover!"

A thoughtless, heat of the moment cry. But the moment *had* been hot—hot as the thunderclap of Glúmr's palm striking her cheek. Hot as the stream of tears she'd wept afterwards, bitter and heart-broken. Hot as her conviction when she'd told Þjóstólfr—she'd *commanded* him—not to avenge the insult, not to interfere. Hot as her foster-father's axe whirling through the air, connecting with Glúmr's back and neck and head. Hot as Hallgerðr's wrath upon learning of his disobedience.

As Glúmr's corpse had cooled, so had Hallgerðr's temper. She'd been clear-headed, calm, when she'd advised Þjóstólfr to travel to her cruel uncle Hrút's farm and report the murder. To explain that she herself had had nothing to do with it. To admit it had been *his* blade that had slaughtered her lamb of a husband. To go, now, and seek Hrút's advice.

Advice she'd known would be swift, and final.

Despite everything, Hallgerðr had loved her second husband.

She had not wanted him dead.

◊∆◊∆◊∆◊∆◊∆◊

"Mother, what have you done?"

Hallgerðr's back stiffens. Gripping the shears, she presses against the table, hoping to screen what lies upon it. The wood's smooth edge bites into her thighs. Iron cuts into her fingers. The chill, late-afternoon air pricks at her newly-shorn scalp. She does not turn as her son approaches, his tone bewildered.

"Your hair," he says. Then, panicked, "You're bleeding!"

"Go away, Högni."

As always, the boy doesn't listen. The man. The leather-stink of him draws closer, the clomping boots, the high-pitched concern. "Mother, stop this nonsense. You need to come—"

"Are you deaf, child?" Hallgerðr slams her hand onto the workbench. Once, twice. Pain rattles up to her elbow, but she lashes out again. Only this—agony, anger, violence—only *this* gets their attention. "I don't *need* to do anything. Not yet. Not yet."

"Mother," Högni repeats, and there it is at last, the snarling impatience, the rumble before a Viking storm.

That's more like it, Hallgerðr thinks, giving nothing away. She could have been proud of this Gunnarsson, given the chance.

"Get out," she says, glancing over her shoulder, meeting her son's grey glare. "Go tattle to the hag. Tell her I'm being difficult."

Högni thumps down the passage like a man condemned to Niflheim. "What is she doing up there?" comes Rannveig's parched voice a moment later, but the question goes unanswered. Putting the shears aside, Hallgerðr burrows into the bundle and retrieves Gunnarr's bow as Högni's heavy footfalls traverse—and exit—the hall.

Against the evening-blue cloak, the bow's pale timber gleams. Its grip burnished from use, the curved lengths polished smooth, the ends capped with silver. Lying on its side, string cut in two, the weapon looks helpless. A viper without fangs.

Many a man had met death at her third husband's hands, when his bow had been whole.

The weapon was slung over his broad shoulder, the day they'd met, that long-ago summer at the Alþingi. Handsome, muscular Gunnarr. Striding from booth to booth, greeting friends and kin he hadn't seen since last year's two-week Assembly. Laughing easily at quips, bantering with tradesmen, play-fighting with the travellers' children. A sight to behold, a confident man in his element.

Hallgerðr had watched this proud warrior climb the Law Mount, then stand still as an idol at its grassy peak, gazing out over Þingvellir's river valley below. The tunic and breeches he wore both blue as the water's depths, the fine stitching around collar and cuffs white as rapids. Forearms gleaming with hard-won rings. Glints of red in his close-cropped beard. A broad smile that dimpled with pleasure when he'd looked down and caught Hallgerðr spying.

There had been no point in playing shy. Hallgerðr had come to the Alþingi dressed in the seiðr-woman's colours: a crimson gown adorned with silvery finery, a dark cloak that was trimmed with lace down to the skirt. Her elven tresses swung free, hanging to her waist. More than anything else, this had caught Gunnarr's eye.

Her stunning, beaten-gold hair.

◊Δ◊Δ◊Δ◊Δ◊Δ◊

How quick they'd loved each other that day! Sitting on a gentle slope, rugged cliffs rising behind them, lava-stone crumbling into the river-crossed valley. For hours they'd talked, blithe as fairies in the meadow, facing the duelling-holm below. The earth radiated warmth; they'd discarded their cloaks, plumped them like pillows. Hallgerðr remembers the crunch of grass as she shifted towards Gunnarr, blades prickling through her skirt. His beard bristling against her mouth. The peaty smell of his skin as they kissed, the salt of his tongue. How he played with her hair, running strand after strand through his fingers, and how she'd teased him, pulling away, making him *lean*. Making him embrace her again…

Stop it, Hallgerðr chided herself, but it was too late. Memory had her in its jaws and shook all her bottled tears loose.

Are you married, Gunnarr had asked late, late that night, the summer sun still five fingers above the horizon.

Before answering, Hallgerðr watched a trio of geese, their wings beating lazily against the mauve sky. "Not at the moment," she'd admitted, "and there are not many who'd risk it."

Is it because you can't find a suitable match, he'd asked—stupidly, Hallgerðr thinks even now, for how could he not know? About Þjóstólfr. About the pig and the sheep. Gunnarr wasn't *that* much younger than her, was he? Surely the news would've travelled as far as Norway. For years, everyone had paid attention to Hallgerðr's doings—here in Iceland, Hallgerðr's ill-fated marriages had *been* the news.

"Not exactly," she'd replied, separating fact from gossip. "Though I am apparently hard to please in the matter of husbands."

Gunnarr had laughed then, loud and long, as if she'd set him a challenge.

◊Δ◊Δ◊Δ◊Δ◊Δ◊

Their wedding was the largest Hallgerðr had known. Held at Bergþórsváll, Njáll and his wife Bergþóra's farm, it had hosted hundreds of guests. Höskuldr and Hrút had come with their entire households, as had the Alþingi's most prominent speakers, honourable men from each of Iceland's four quarters. All of Gunnarr's friends and family had made the short trip from Hlíðarendi, including Rannveig, who had scowled throughout the celebrations. Bergþóra herself served at the feast, an honour befitting the host, helped by Hallgerðr's daughter Þorgerðr, who was fourteen years old, and a stunning beauty. Course after course crossed the boards. Ale flowed like the Rangá river. And Gunnarr had beamed. He'd kissed his bride. Held her fair hand. Laid a wreath of forget-me-nots, an unbroken circlet of affection, upon her golden head.

This, Hallgerðr had thought, looking at the rich joy around her. *This is what I have always wanted.*

For the first time, Hallgerðr took over supervision of day-to-day proceedings at her new home. The servants grew to love her; she ran the farmstead at Hlíðarendi with a lavish hand. *Gunnarr should only have the best*, she'd thought. *We* all *should*. So the table was well laden each night, the bondsmen's clothing expensive, the slaves' huts clean and free of lice. From chests in the loft, Hallgerðr freed Rannveig's finest tapestries and hung them year-round in the hall. Guests were invited to feast the smallest occasions, Hlíðarendi's unending hospitality bordering on the crude. *Let them scoff*, Hallgerðr had thought. *As long as Gunnarr is happy, let the others whisper.* She had never hidden her desires from him. She'd never been dishonest. All of her husbands, Gunnarr included, knew what they were getting when they married her.

And yet, Gunnarr's affections had cooled as quickly as they'd first heated. After Högni's birth, his attentions were split. Once Grani arrived, they'd completely broken.

Too much time spent with Njáll and his smug kin. Njáll the all-seer who watched the future flicker in the hearth, but did nothing to prevent its unfolding—not even when it came to his own death! Wise, passive Njáll, had lain there in his bed and let life burn down around him.

"The trolls take your friends!" Hallgerðr shouted once, as Gunnarr left for the summer Assembly without her. Njáll was going with him, of course, Njáll *and* his sons; but as had happened more and more over the years, Hallgerðr had been left behind.

Left behind, but not alone. Rannveig was always close at hand, nagging and condescending. She claimed Hallgerðr wasn't a good *húsfreya*, that her only skill was in planning against men's lives.

Unfair, Hallgerðr thinks. Uncalled for. It hadn't been her fault that Þorvaldr and Glúmr had died. Those deaths had *not* been her fault.

◊∆◊∆◊∆◊∆◊∆◊

Taking up Gunnarr's bow, she sighs, weary as the coming dark. The string's eyelet is lined with bronze, the balance of metal and wood perfect. Angling it to catch the last streaks of daylight, Hallgerðr unknots the broken cord then crumples it into her pocket. She won't leave anything her husband once prized behind, not even this tangle of thread.

As their children grew to manhood, Gunnarr was so often gone, always gone. What did he expect Hallgerðr to do, left to fend for herself at Hlíðarendi with two young boys, a household to run, a harridan mother-in-law, and Njáll's arrogant wife constantly taunting?

They'd been a team, once, she and Gunnarr. After the children, their pairing had shifted. Instead of running off together during Assemblies, lying in the long grass on half-lit nights, eating honey straight from imported skeps, licking the sweet-smoky substance from fingertips and lips, Hallgerðr would start things on her own. Later, Gunnarr would sweep in to settle matters, often armed with a purse full of compensation.

"She's a hothead," Hallgerðr once overheard Njáll say, accepting a sack of silver from Gunnarr. Payment for one of his servants' deaths, another casualty in Bergþóra and Hallgerðr's ongoing feud. It was hard, nowadays, for Hallgerðr to keep track.

"You'll have a tough time," the beardless man said to Gunnarr, the two of them newly returned from the Alþingi, "atoning for your wife's continued mischief."

It had been no *real* mischief, Hallgerðr thinks now, keeping Njáll's servants from dying of old age. Gunnarr disagreed. She can still picture the way he looked when she'd inched up to the door and peered outside at him in the yard. The furrow of his brow when Njáll accused her of being sneaky. Lines deepening beside his nose as he'd pulled his lips firmly shut, the way he always had when being cautious. And he'd been cautious more often than not. Slow to anger. *Measured*. Everything had always been *equal* with Gunnarr and Njáll, everything had levelled out—and it had been profoundly annoying.

Gunnarr's passion had simmered. The wild Viking she'd loved was trapped beneath a calm, business-man's veneer.

So she'd fought back when Bergþóra taunted. She'd tricked a few slaves into stealing supplies from Bergþórsváll. Yes, there had been a few accidents, a few deaths. But through it all, her ridiculous feud with Njáll's stuck-up wife, through it all she'd only thought to entice him. Her Gunnarr. Her Viking. Lure him out of complacency with good food and spiced ale, with fire and honey-smoked kisses. She had never done more, never taken less, than what he'd deserved.

Throughout the leanest times, she had served feasts fit for a warrior. Dressed in her best red gown, her best evening-blue cloak, wearing a crown of forget-me-nots, she'd brought platter after platter to her household. She'd borne Rannveig's barbed words without snapping back, not once; though, yes, some of what she'd prepared—the cheese, the butter—had come from someone else's pantry. Like her famous forefather, Ragnarr Loðbrók, Hallgerðr pillaged to benefit her family. Surely the Viking sleeping under her husband's neatly-trimmed beard, beneath the jerkin that hadn't seen blood in far too long, beneath the muscular chest whose scars had begun to fade—surely that Viking would recognise in her a worthy, like-minded soul? Surely that Viking would be proud to know of Hallgerðr's conquests, to see others bandage the wounds she'd struck, to hear her crow?

◊Δ◊Δ◊Δ◊Δ◊Δ◊

Though cold, Hallgerðr's fingers are nimble. Gunnarr had asked her for two, but now she threads three, four, five lengths of her hair through the bow's eyelets and knots them fast. It isn't enough, she thinks, twisting the strands into thicker cords, pulling them taut.

"Hallgerðr," cries Rannveig, the halberd's shaft thunk-thunk-thunking on the floor. "Time's up! Enough is enough!"

No, she thinks, looking at the half-strung bow. *It will never be enough.*

It is not wrong to want, the witch had said and, idiot child, Hallgerðr had believed her.

Not so long ago, the entire household had wanted the provisions she'd *acquired* from Otkell Skarfsson. Iceland had suffered two seasons of great dearth; last year's harvest had failed, and every face in the local assembly-places had looked gaunt, Gunnarr's included. Even so, her husband, stupidly generous, had shared Hlíðarendi's hay and supplies until their stores were exhausted. The servants, the slaves, even his shrew of a mother, had grown so hungry at Gunnarr's farmstead, that the great man himself was forced to go begging.

He'd called it *buying*, of course, but Hallgerðr had known better.

Gunnarr had debased himself, begging at Otkell's well-stocked homestead. And what was his reward? Nothing but another mouth to feed—that slave who'd caused Hallgerðr so much trouble recently. That split-tongued, dark-browed Melkólfr.

Hallgerðr tastes bile, stomach squirming even now at the thought of the pity-goods they'd received after Otkell had refused to lend Gunnarr essential provisions. Fifteen horses had carried hay, five horses laden with cheese and dried fish and vats of whey, hand-delivered in abundance from Njáll and Bergþóra!

There would be no *charity* for her husband. A Viking *takes* what she needs…

It was *right*, what she'd done, what she'd had Melkólfr do. Otkell had refused to help, despite his wealth; he'd offered not food, but a slave. He'd deserved to be plundered. And Melkólfr had been sly as she'd expected such a liar to be; he'd slipped over to his once-master's farm at the blackest hour of winter-dark, and stolen more of Otkell's food than the folk at Hlíðarendi could eat in a season.

"Where did this come from," Gunnarr had asked, as Hallgerðr brought out the final tray for the feast. He was so thin, jerkin hanging off his lean frame, hollows collecting shadows beneath his eyes. Yet, even diminished, Gunnarr had had the nerve to sit in his hall like a king, back stiff as the table she'd just covered with abundance—creamy cheeses, pots of smooth skyr, plates of rye bread slathered with salted butter—and he'd *spat* upon what she'd provided.

"It's not men's business to be concerned with kitchen affairs," Hallgerðr had said, more sharply than she'd intended. Hunger had whetted her tongue to a point. "It makes no difference where it came from, you may as well eat it."

Uncle Hrút's vulgar words—*that girl has thief's eyes*—had echoed in Gunnarr's reply. "I will not be in league with thieves," Hallgerðr's third husband had said, right before she felt Þórvaldr and Glúmr's rough palms redoubled in his slap. Vaguely, she recalls the crack of skin on skin, the crack of the butter plate as she dropped it, the crack of her heart—but she didn't feel the impact of Gunnarr striking her, not right away. The burn came much later.

As the servants cleared the table, swept up the broken crock, and brought out the last of their home-dried meat instead, Gunnarr had stood and glared down at Hallgerðr.

Oh, what a glare.

There he was, she'd thought. Her Viking. Rage in his eyes, in the sting of his blow. Rage, a gift he'd given her, open-handed. One she promised to repay, when and if ever she could.

◊Δ◊Δ◊Δ◊Δ◊Δ◊

Winding hair after hair onto her husband's bow, Hallgerðr knows one thing to be true, deep in her marrow: Gunnarr died of pride and an overblown sense of honour. He died because his reputation had grown too large; his fame overspilled the banks of the Rangá river into the territories of proud men. Men with good reputations, but not *great* ones, nowhere near as impressive as Gunnarr's.

It was impossible to live in the shadow of perfection.

So they ambushed Gunnarr once, twice, then put him on trial for surviving. For refusing to lay down his weapons. For being so skilled with halberd and arrows. *We'll accomplish nothing*, they'd said, *as long as Gunnarr can use his bow...* They'd prosecuted him for killing Otkell's son, Þorgeirr—in self-defence!—because that jowled lug of a man, like his father, had been as popular as he'd been fat.

The trial was a farce. News and rumours, lawsuits and justifications, measures and countermeasures, rumours of who slew whom and why...all a torrent of empty words.

Words can't nullify a debt. Words can't make a person forget when she's been wronged.

Hallgerðr snorts.

Fools, all of them. Proud, vulnerable fools. Þorgeirr Otkelsson had ambushed the greatest warrior in Iceland—no matter how he'd died, Hallgerðr thinks, Gunnarr was still the best of them—and the hero was punished for striking back.

Exile. Three years, no more, no less, to be spent abroad. Banished from his district. Banished from Iceland. Banished from the home he'd loved so well.

A light sentence! Three years overseas, no more, no less. Three years, else he could be slain on sight by the kinsmen of the blubber-faced man he had killed. Three years to save his life.

"Go," Njáll had said. "A journey abroad will bring you greater honour than any you've earned before."

"Go," Rannveig had said, a crease of concern darkening her brow. "Give your enemies someone else to quarrel with for a while."

Hallgerðr had said nothing.

Was it really that hard for him to leave? No, Hallgerðr had thought then. She'd been uprooted herself, three times already. She'd travelled far from the Dales she'd known and loved, far from Höskuldr, far from Hrút. She'd been fostered and married—to a pig, a sheep, and last to this—*hero*—this warrior, this handsome Viking, who could not bring himself to take to the sea.

Pride.

Honour.

Winding and winding, Hallgerðr readies the bow, stringing it with strands of equal length and tension. They thrum when plucked, resonant as Gunnarr's halberd before a battle, singing for blood.

Storytellers claim it was the beauty of the countryside that kept him from leaving. A ship was waiting to take him a-viking with Kolskegg and four other men. He had added his wares to the hold, bid his overseer and servants farewell, paid a last visit to his dear friends at Bergþórsváll and left behind his halberd, his deepest thanks, and a household of heavy hearts.

That afternoon, he rode away while Hallgerðr was in the homefield surveying the flocks. He'd saved no kisses, no goodbyes, for her.

Almost, Hallgerðr thinks, not for the first time, *like he knew he'd be back.*

Around the hearth on winter evenings, the saga-tellers have already started making a tale of Gunnarr's devotion to Iceland. His horse stumbled, they say. The beast threw our hero just beyond the Markar River. That's why he stayed; it was the horse's fault.

But Gunnarr was an accomplished rider.

Others claim it was the landscape that held him captive. Standing, dusting himself off, he was spellbound by fields of rustling grass. By ripples on the river he'd swum as a boy. By the mountain crowned with clouds, thick and rich as Norwegian ermine. From a distance, his gaze had fallen upon the longhouse at Hlíðarendi, so they say, which he'd built with his own hands. Next to the fields of barley, the deep green turf roof had sat like fresh seaweed in a bed of golden sand.

Fair is the hillside. Fairer it seems than I have ever seen before...

That, so they say, was the clincher. A farm, no more beautiful than any other in the region, and no less. As productive as the next ones, but no more. A cluster of buildings, rectangles of peat and straw and driftwood clapboards. Nothing impressive. *That* is what convinced the exiled man to stay. To open himself to attack. To wax poetic in the face of fate.

But Hallgerðr knew her third husband better than that. It wasn't a few clumps of dirt or mangy livestock or weed-speckled hills that forced Gunnarr off his horse that day, that convinced her Viking not to spend three years plundering his way to Norway and back.

It was honour, that fickle motivator.

It was stupidity.

It was pride.

In all his life, Gunnarr had never fled from a fight.

◊Δ◊Δ◊Δ◊Δ◊Δ◊

The shine on Gunnarr's reputation dimmed, the day he returned. On that afternoon, Hallgerðr had seen him more clearly than ever before.

In the slump of his shoulders, she saw weakness. In the jut of his jaw, selfishness. In the clench of fingers on bow, revenge.

Yes, Hallgerðr had been glad to see him tethering his favourite roan in the yard. She'd relished the musk of him as he entered the hearth-room. It was wrong that he'd returned, but Hallgerðr had known—far better than sullen Rannveig ever could—that Gunnarr was where fate had deemed he should be.

Here, at Hlíðarendi, with her.

Here, where she could repay him what he was owed.

"The horses are ready, Hallgerðr," Rannveig calls now, a note of triumph in her tone. "Grani is waiting with them; hope you've packed him some rags. Högni will stay with me—won't you, child? Let those two go together, the traitor and the greed-driven boy." Hallgerðr hadn't noticed her first son's return, but she hears his faint assent. Typical. Högni hasn't the guts to challenge his elders.

Unlike his father. For months, Gunnarr had flaunted his outlawry, his bold presence at Assemblies both impressing and incensing the gathered chieftains. He'd had a Viking's nerve, her husband—and for a while folk were too afraid to attack him. But as the weeks passed, half-hearted grumblings had flared into full-blown affront. Spurred by long-simmering grudges, over a dozen men had advanced on Hlíðarendi, spears pointed at the high-day sun. The horses' hoofs tore across partly-mown fields, hastening when their riders realised Gunnarr was at home alone.

Well, he hadn't *truly* been alone.

Hallgerðr closes her eyes, prays for a half-breath of silence. Not until he is enclosed in his cairn will Gunnarr ever know what it means to be on his own.

Hallgerðr was here, at her husband's side, when Þórgrímr climbed onto Hlíðarendi's roof. She'd been here when Gunnarr had eviscerated the Norwegian, shoving the point of his spear-tipped halberd up through the soft turf above their sleeping-loft, between the rafters, then between the struts of Þórgrímr's ribs. She'd been here when Gunnarr had leapt down to the main hall, where Rannveig had hurriedly opened the windows, and he'd shot arrows through the blank squares with such skill his attackers had been forced to withdraw. Once, twice, thrice the troop had advanced, and each time they'd been beaten back. Yes, Hallgerðr had beheld it all.

Through a gap in the shutters, she'd seen frustration in the men's flushed faces, their fury, their impotence, and she'd sympathised. She'd understood.

All of them, at one time or another, loved Gunnarr as much as she did. They'd witnessed his feats in battle, his prowess, his boundless luck in horse-fighting and sailing and husbandry. They'd seen him deal incredible blows, seen him kill, heard him talk his way out of trouble. It took twelve, or twenty, or thirty of them to match Gunnarr Hámundarson. Dozens to bring him low, dozens more to serve him his due.

Dozens of men, Hallgerðr thinks, or one woman.

"Give me two strands of your hair," Gunnarr had said. Hallgerðr hears his strong voice, even now. Fearless, firm, echoing out of his grave. "Give me two strands of your hair," he said, when the attackers had finally prised the roof off the house, when they'd begun to rain dirt and arrows down on them, when Gunnarr's matchless bowstring had snapped. "Give me two strands of your hair," he'd said then, as if Hallgerðr owed him, "and twist them together to make a new string for me."

What more can I give you, she had wanted to shout. *What more than years? Two strong sons? Countless opportunities to increase your prestige and honour? A welcome bed? A full larder, even when others starved?* This last still rankled most, and though Rannveig had sneered at Hallgerðr from the corner in which she'd hid, though Gunnarr had already been bloodied from two shallow wounds, though his bow was damaged and his halberd useless against enemy missiles, Hallgerðr had raised a hand to her flushed cheek, remembering.

"My life depends on it," he'd said, panic slicing his warrior-calm. "They will never get at me as long as I can use my bow."

"In that case," Hallgerðr had replied, the words rampaging like trolls from her lips, unstoppable. "In that case, I'll remind you of the slap you gave me, which I'd promised never to forget. Consider us even."

Hallgerðr can't describe the expression on her third husband's face, though its image has kept her awake for two nights. While his mother yammered about stinginess and shame, Gunnarr's eyes had glinted—let no one say he wept!—and the mouth Hallgerðr had kissed countless times disappeared beneath the beard she'd never grown tired of touching.

"Every man has his limits," he'd had said at last. "And his pride. I won't ask again."

If only you had, Hallgerðr thinks, twisting the last tight cords of long hair into Gunnarr's bow. There would have been an apology in that asking. There would have been an acknowledgement—of what? Hallgerðr has thought on it for days, but still isn't certain. All she knows is she wishes, fervently, that he had asked again. Just once more.

"Get out of my house," Rannveig screams now, standing in a dried pool of her son's blood. Every ounce of her energy is now devoted to standing, marking her son's death, holding his weapon, screeching at his killer.

Hallgerðr gathers the bow, checks the balance. *Perfect*, she thinks, then tests the hair-string. It's flexible but tense. Powerful. Strong as her need to give it to Gunnarr. To place it whole in his callused hands. To see him use it, one more time. Yes, Hallgerðr wants that more than anything.

And it is not wrong to want.

The Pasha, the Girl and the Dagger

Havva Murat

The hulking man pulled the swaddling away from the tiny baby. "A *girl*…" The words were a whisper. He held the infant up to the slanting light coming through the window to make sure, but it was undeniable; the baby was perfectly female.

He shoved the bundle at his sister, who had attended the birthing of the infant. His wife lay unconscious in the bed behind them. The furs were soaked with blood. He couldn't bring himself to go to the woman who had been his wife for fifteen years. She had promised him this time she would give him a son. She had seen it in a dream: Saint Clement had handed her the child and proclaimed it would help them turn back the Turks. And now this. The tiny female wriggled and let out a mighty wail as her aunt Besjana wrapped her up again and cradled her against her chest.

"She's healthy and strong this one." Besjana patted the baby's back.

"I have five daughters already. I need a son. Why won't the Lord give me a son?" Grigor Kelmendi dropped his stubbled face into his hands.

"She could give you grandsons. Perhaps that was the meaning of the dream?"

"Or granddaughters." Grigor shuddered. "How am I to repel the Ottomans with an army of women? Will they talk them to death?" He threw his eagle-crested helmet against the wall. The iron rebounded with a clatter on to the stone-flagged floor.

"It is not for us to argue with the Lord, Grigor. Take your daughter and stop your roaring." She held the offending bundle towards him.

"I will not! Leave her out on the mountaintop. If the Lord loves females so much let him care for her."

"You would leave your own daughter out in the snow? What if our father had done such a thing with me?"

"He only had you, Besjana. He didn't have to bear the shame of fathering six daughters and no sons. Do you want all of Albania to laugh at me? The mountain lion who could only father lionesses."

"They will not be laughing when you draw your sword against them. You are the greatest warrior these mountains have ever produced, Grigor. Not a man of the Kelmend has ever come close to you."

"And yet the Lord shames me by sending me daughter after daughter. Do you know the Ottomans recite poems about me in the great hall at Rozafa castle?"

"Then turn your anger on them; ride to Shokdra and rip its walls down to the earth, but do not harm this child!" Besjana held the infant close.

"No one can know I have fathered another female."

"Your mother is a woman. If it wasn't for her you wouldn't be here!" Besjana clutched the child more tightly.

"I have never disrespected my mother." His eyes were burning wounds.

"The Virgin too was a woman, if it wasn't for her, our saviour would never have come."

"I am still without a son to help me repel the Ottomans! I have no use for daughters, Besjana! I cannot train them for war." He ripped one of the shutters from the window and threw it at the floor where it smashed. A freezing gust blew into the room.

"You must stop this, Grigor, please." Besjana shook as the baby's screams grew louder. "The baby needs to be suckled or she will die. Your wife is not long for this world. We must think of the child." Besjana looked down at the piteous sight on the bed and pulled another fur on top of the bloodied mess.

But Grigor was lost in his own wretched thoughts. "No one must know. Tell them mother and child died together."

"You will not leave this child out on the mountain to die—she is perfect and beautiful." Besjana kissed the child's head, her tears mixing with the fresh blood.

"I will do with her what I will!" he roared. "Give her to me, Besjana." He snatched the baby from her arms.

"Grigor, promise me you won't kill her. Swear it on your honour as a Kelmend knight."

He looked at Besjana and the haze of his anger dissipated. She was a good sister to him: loyal, fierce, protective. And he was not a murderer, though he'd killed many a man. She was right. He couldn't leave the child to die. It would be as shameful as keeping her. He must find another way.

"I will not kill her." His voice was gruff as he looked at the wailing bundle.

"Let me take her, Grigor."

"I will not have this child associated with me. If you want to help, Besjana, have my wife buried." He glanced at the pale visage of his wife. There was no time for tears. Ottoman reinforcements marched on them from Shkodra at that very moment. "I will take care of the child." He shook off his sister's pleading hands, wrapped the child in his fur cape so that no man or woman would know what lay within, and disappeared into the storm outside.

◊Δ◊Δ◊Δ◊Δ◊Δ◊

Besjana was met at the doors of the Shirgj monastery by a Benedictine monk dressed in the coarse robes of his order. She swooped past the spindly old monk into the interior. It was even colder inside than it had been without. Besjana pulled her fur cape tightly about her body.

"You are the lady Besjana?" The monk looked at her suspiciously. Everyone was a potential threat with the Ottomans breathing down their necks.

"As you see." She pulled the glove off her left hand and showed him the eagle-crest of the Kelmendi on her ring. He nodded and she walked through the vaulted entrance of the monastery. "The child?"

"The coin?" the monk responded.

Besjana untied a leather pouch from her waist and handed it to the monk, whose face split into a greedy smile.

"A true man of God," Besjana scoffed.

"Even a man of God has accounts to settle."

"Take me to the child."

"She is upstairs."

"Are you certain she is the child I seek?" Besjana asked as she was led up the stone staircase, past Byzantine murals of the Madonna and child.

"Ten months ago a baby was abandoned here in the middle of the night wrapped in the finest fur I have ever seen. A rider was seen on a great, grey warhorse emblazoned with the very crest on your ring."

"I see." Besjana felt euphoria ripple through her core. *She had found her.* "And you kept this information to yourself?"

"I am fond of having my head attached to my body, so yes, I kept the activities of your noble brother to myself, until now." As he spoke, they left the stairwell and stopped before a timber door.

"I too am quite skilled with a sword, so I suggest you continue to keep your silence." Besjana pushed the door inwards and entered. Lying in the middle of the room was a row of tiny cribs filled with infant girls. Seven little bodies slept beneath crudely knitted blankets of goat hair hardly warm enough to keep out the mountain air.

Besjana recognised, without having to ask, the visage of her niece. It had taken ten months for her to track down the baby, but the girl was the very image of her dead mother. She grabbed the child from the crib and cradled her, wrapping her fur cape around the both of them. She was so cold. It was a wonder she was alive at all.

"Where is her fur?" Besjana barked at the monk.

"We sold it to pay for provisions. Your brother left no money. We do the best we can for abandoned children."

"This is the best you can do?" Besjana grabbed the monk by the hood of his robe.

"Lady, I am the one who has cared for your niece these long months."

"She is dirty and her crib is soaked with piss. I ought to drown you in it."

"My Lady, please. You will wake the others."

Besjana looked at the other forlorn little bodies asleep in the room. She felt despair clutch at her heart; it was a curse to be born a girl in these lands, perhaps in all lands. "Where are their parents?"

"Some are dead; some are like your brother. They do not want their shame to be known to the world."

"There should be no shame in giving birth to a girl." She stared into the priest's face. "I am a woman and I could take your head off with one strike of my axe."

"Please, my lady. I am only saying what others believe."

"You are all stupid creatures." She moved towards the door. "I am taking my niece home. I will be sending a servant to care for these girls. If she writes to tell me they are ill-treated, expect to see me again."

"Yes, my lady."

"And remember, Grigor might be the best warrior in all of Albania, but he will never be more clever or cunning than me." Besjana swept from the room and back to the freezing waters of the Bojana River where her oarsmen waited.

◊Δ◊Δ◊Δ◊Δ◊Δ◊

"Nora!" Besjana's voice bounced off the rocks where the girl was playing beside one of the mountain streams that flowed in the forest around their home.

Nora caught the dragonfly between her thumb and finger and yelped in excitement. "I caught it!" She jumped up from her perch and dashed across the stream to where her aunt waited in the shadows of the trees.

"Quiet, Nora. We have company."

"But I caught the dragonfly in my fingers."

"That is very good, but do you remember what I told you about visitors?"

"What visitors?" Nora was more interested in the dragonfly.

"My brother has come with two of his men."

"I have an uncle?" The child's eyes widened and she made to run towards the cottage.

"Nora, no." Besjana grabbed her arm and yanked her backwards.

"I want to see him." The dragonfly escaped from the child's grip.

"Do you remember what you must do if we have a visitor to the cottage?" Besjana knelt to peer into Nora's face.

"I must pretend I am a boy?"

"Yes, very good, Nora." Besjana's shoulders relaxed.

"But, I'm really a girl like you, aren't I?" Nora's forehead creased as she looked up into her aunt's face.

"You are, but no one can know that. We must pretend you are a boy until you are old enough to protect yourself. Do you understand, Nora?"

"Why would anyone want to hurt me?" The child laughed.

"This is not a game, Nora." Besjana shook the child. "Your uncle must never know you are a girl. He must only know you as my son, understand?"

"But Nora is a *girl's* name. You should have given me a boy's name instead."

"Very true. You can choose a new name for yourself."

Nora's face lit up. "Can I be called Kreshnik?"

"You want your name to be 'Knight'?"

"I'd like to be either a knight or a zana, a mountain fairy. Both are strong and fierce, but Zana is a girl's name."

"Kreshnik it will have to be then." Besjana ruffled the girl's long chestnut hair that fell in waves to her waist. "Now you must go around the back to the stable and cut off your hair."

"Cut off my hair?" Nora's voice was hollow.

"It is too beautiful to belong to a knight, Nora. I shouldn't have allowed you to grow it. Imagine if your uncle had found you out here running about?"

"Must I dress like a boy too?"

"Yes. See that the stable boy gives you some of his clothes to wear. Your uncle must not suspect who you are, Nora. Your safety depends on it."

After watching the waif-like figure disappear between the trees, Besjana wound her way back through the forest and into the cottage where her brother was downing another glass of raki.

"Easy, Grigor. I've only got a few bottles left." She frowned at him as she entered.

"How can you live up here alone with only a few bottles of raki, woman? If I lived this deep in the woods I would drink all day."

"I have better things to do than drink; I have my work." Besjana looked at the spinning wheel that sat in the corner.

"You gave up the life of a noble woman to come up here and spin wool?" Grigor curled his top lip and then took another swig.

"I make clothes as well and care for my flock."

"Ha—goats and sheep, your only company." He turned to the two Knights who stood by the front door and the three whooped in laughter.

"That's where you are wrong. I have someone I want you to meet," Besjana told her brother as he downed another glass of raki

"You haven't got a man living up here with you?" All traces of mirth disappeared from Grigor's face.

"I have a son." Besjana's chin lifted proudly.

"*You* have a son." He almost laughed.

"Yes."

"How in God's kingdom did *you* get a son, sister? You've never married."

"I'm not claiming a virgin birth, Grigor. The boy's father is dead and I shall speak not another word about him, so do not ask me." She rearranged the fur that was draped around her shoulders. She needed more wood for the fire but she didn't dare ask the men to go out and get it until Nora was safely disguised. What was taking the child so long?

"If he wasn't dead I would kill him myself!" He banged on the wooden table with both his fists. "How dare any man touch my sister without my permission! What were you thinking?" His face flushed an ugly red.

"Have another drink, Grigor." Besjana got up and pulled another bottle of raki from the cupboard.

"You are an unnatural woman! You could have had any knight in Malsia." He pulled the cork from the bottle with his teeth and spat it across the table at her.

"I didn't want a knight of Malsia. I've seen the way knights treat their ladies. I was there when your wife died, remember?" She threw the cork back at him.

A shadow passed over Grigor's face and he took a long swig of his drink. "I will not speak of your past if you do not speak of mine." It was as close to an admittance of regret as she would ever get from him.

"Agreed. Now, here is my son." Besjana stood as the door was pushed inwards. "Come, Kreshnik. Come, meet your uncle."

Nora hesitated for a second in the doorway, casting wary glances at the armed men who flanked the entrance, but the strange light in Grigor's eyes drew her towards him. "Uncle." She scratched at her close-cropped hair.

"Your name is Kreshnik?" Grigor looked the child up and down.

"Yes, it is."

"Well, little knight, it is time you met a real kreshnik." A rare smile cracked his face.

"You are a real knight?" Nora couldn't hide her excitement.

"The most famous in this land; your mother has not told you of me?" Grigor cast a disapproving glance as his sister.

"Only that she doesn't like you much." Nora shrugged.

"Nor–Kreshnik!" Besjana shook her head.

"You are not afraid of me, boy?" Delight shone in Grigor's eyes.

"I'm not afraid of anyone."

"Fearless and quick. How old are you, boy?"

"He is five," Besjana lied. Nora had recently turned six.

"You are tall for a five year old but too skinny to join my knights yet. You're mother must be a terrible cook."

"And not beyond poisoning unwanted guests," Besjana sneered as she moved over to the pot she was making goat and bean stew in.

"Lucky I have brought my men to taste-test for me," Grigor laughed. "I have missed your fire, sister."

"How did you find me?" Besjana gave him a guarded stare.

"We were tracking some Ottoman spies in a nearby village when we heard a story of a beautiful woman living alone on the mountaintop. My men were eager to catch a glimpse of this zana, but instead we found you and your son."

"The villagers are simpler people than I thought if they cannot tell the difference between me and a zana."

"Well you are still beautiful enough to mesmerise my men here, so they weren't too wrong." Grigor looked her up and down. "You must marry."

"I will do no such thing!" She turned on him with her spoon.

"Be sensible, woman, you cannot raise this boy on your own. What will you teach him, to weave cloth and braid his hair?" The knights by the door laughed.

"I climb trees and catch animals and ride the horses," Nora interrupted.

"Hush, Kreshnik." Besjana pushed Nora behind her. "I will not return with you to Kelmendi."

"You would rob the child of the chance to train as one of my knights?" Grigor's brow creased.

"I could be one of your knights?" Nora ran around Besjana to stand before Grigor again.

"Out of the question." Besjana pulled Nora backwards into her arms. "Kreshnik cannot train with you."

"Why ever not? The boy wants to become a knight. I am in need of more knights to fight the Ottomans. If we do not continue to train and fight, even your remote home up here will soon be overrun by the Turkish vermin."

Besjana could not tell Grigor the real reason she didn't want Kreshnik to train with him. What would happen when Nora's body could no longer be disguised as that of a skinny boy? Short hair and a stable boy's clothes would not disguise the female figure she would one day have.

On the other hand, Nora had rare dexterity and strength. If she was trained as a Kelmendi knight, she may be able to protect herself when her true identity was revealed. Besjana knew of herbs she could give the child to delay the changes of womanhood for a few years more.

"Very well." Besjana released Nora.

"You changed your mind?" Grigor was taken aback.

"If you want to train my son I will allow it. But the child sleeps in my room and will always be within my sight, understand?"

"Knights do not have their mothers hold their hands on the battlefield, Besjana."

"None of your knights ever had me as a mother."

"So I can really do it, I can really train to become a knight?" Nora's face was suffused with ecstasy.

"Yes, you can," Grigor slapped the child on the back. "And your first task as a knight is to start eating. We need some meat on those bones if you're going to be able to carry your armour."

◊Δ◊Δ◊Δ◊Δ◊Δ◊

"How much further to Shokdra?" Nora called after her uncle. "My mother is not feeling well."

"That is the bridge ahead of us, and just behind it the castle. I told your mother this was no trip for a woman to make; this is a tournament. Go tell the old crone to stop her whining." Grigor playfully shooed Nora away from the band of Kelmendi knights where he sat in full armour astride his warhorse.

"You know she will never leave my side until one of us is dead." Nora laughed as she expertly turned her horse and galloped back to her place in the cavalcade.

In the ten years since Grigor had taken her and Besjana from their forest home, never once had he guessed that little 'Kreshnik' was in fact 'Nora'. Besjana had done well in delaying the onset of womanhood with herbs, but it could not be delayed forever. Nora, now sixteen, had to bandage her chest tightly each morning and go on solo reconnaissance missions into the mountains at least once every few months; she thanked the saints that she wasn't as regular as other girls. There would be problems explaining more frequent withdrawals from Kelmendi.

Despite Grigor's gruff manner, Nora had come to love and respect her 'uncle'. She had not wasted a minute with him over the years, learning how to fight, hunt and ride as well as any of his men. There might be stronger knights in the ranks, but her cleverness, her speed and her dexterity with a sword had drawn the notice of everyone in Malsia. Nora had learned that brute strength could never win over clever planning and intuition. She had saved her little band from many a scrape with the Ottomans over the last few years using guile rather than brawn. The heavy-footed Turks were no match for the Kelmendi who could disappear into the mountain fog as fast as the fairies they were reported to have descended from.

So it was that this band of revered knights had been invited down for a 'friendly' tournament at Rozafa Castle, in Shkoder, currently home to Vutsi Pasha, the Ottoman Pasha whose task it was to take the highlands for the Turks.

Nora had never been this close to Shkoder before. She had worried this truce was a trap, but if it was, she would take many Ottoman heads with her as she escaped. The lure of demonstrating her skill at the tournament was too great. She was famous throughout the villages of the highlands but Nora would not be happy until the entire empire flinched at the sound of her name: Kreshnik.

Nora had little time to think on it further as they cantered up the hillside, through the gates and into the ward. Nora felt her back stiffen as she looked up at where the green crescent flags of the Ottomans whipped around atop the keep and ramparts. She wanted the invaders gone from these lands as much as her uncle ever had. Albania had seen a long procession of invaders; Greeks, Macedonians, Romans, Bulgarians and now the Turks. This was her chance to take a few of them out. She felt the adrenaline dance along her veins. Grigor and his knights dismounted and were led forward to where the pasha sat, swathed in cloaks, upon a raised platform erected before the keep. He wore the giant white turban of the Ottomans but was no native Turk; his face was very white and his eyes icy blue like the snow and rivers of his Bosnian homeland just beyond the neighbouring land of Montenegro. One of his men, a janissary from the same Balkan land as his master, stepped forward to welcome them.

"In the name of Allah, the most gracious, the most merciful. We bear witness that there is no god in any land save he and that Muhammad, peace and blessings of Allah be upon him, is his final messenger. Our most honourable leader, friend of Sultan Murad IV and slave of Allah, Vutsi Pasha, welcomes you here to Rozafa castle. If Allah wills it we invite you to renounce your false religion and convert to Islam, the one true religion, so that you may be availed of Allah's mercy before it is too late." The janissary dipped his head.

Grigor puffed his chest out and laughed heartily. "I prefer my religion to slavery at the hands of the Turks. Does your master not have his own tongue?" Grigor hadn't gotten his reputation as the Lion of the mountains for nothing.

"If you wish to keep your tongue, infidel, I suggest you do not insult my master again." The janissary pulled his yatagan a few inches from its sheath.

"Mjaft." The use of the Albanian word drew smiles from all the Kelmendi as the pasha came down the stairs to stand before Grigor. Vutsi

Pasha was a good two foot taller than his Albanian foe, but this did not deter Grigor.

"You've learned our language?" Grigor did not hide his approval.

"A good pasha learns the ways of his people."

"We are not your people. The Kelmendi belong to no one but themselves."

"For now." The pasha smiled enigmatically.

"You wanted a tournament, Ottoman. Let us not disappoint the crowd. Shall the two of us begin and end it here this day?"

"You have spent too long in the mountains with the beasts, my friend. This is not how we run things in the world of men. There are rules and traditions to be observed."

"Like kidnapping our sons so you can turn them into your janissaries?"

"What you call kidnapping, I call *tribute*."

"Spoken like a true silver-tongued Turk. Do they tell you what to say as well as how to scrape your forehead across the ground?"

Vutsi Pasha smiled. "You Albanians have fire but you lack delicacy."

"My deepest apologies, great pasha, but mountain lions have no need for delicacy when they are ripping apart their prey."

Nora had watched this exchange with growing impatience. "What are the rules?" The words were out of her mouth before she realised.

An angry red flush suffused Grigor's cheeks. The pasha's face remained blank as he studied her carefully.

"How dare you speak directly to the pasha!" the janissary who still hovered closely behind his master snarled at her.

"Fall back, Kreshnik!" Grigor glared at her before angling his body between her and the janissary.

"Kreshnik? Is that your name, boy?" The pasha moved forward to where Nora stood flanked by two other Kelmendi knights. Besjana immediately pushed her way through the throng and hovered just behind Nora's shoulder. "You are well protected, Kreshnik. And who is this lovely woman with you?"

"S*he* is my mother, Besjana Kelmendi, my lord." Nora answered as she turned to glare at Besjana. It did her no favours to be publicly coddled.

"The cub does not stray far from its mother." The pasha smiled as he turned back to his janissary behind him.

"I am no cub, my lord!" Nora's voice shook with anger.

"No?" The pasha turned back to her. "But you are *very comely* for a boy." He peered into her face. "Do you have talents other than that little growl?"

Nora held his gaze without flinching. "You won't think me so attractive when I have three of your men's heads hanging from my belt."

"Pretty and fierce." The pasha erupted into laughter. "I shall enjoy watching you fight, Kreshnik. You will go first." The pasha smiled before returning to his seat.

"You can't let Kreshnik fight one of their champions, Grigor, he's not ready."

"Of course I am ready!" Nora protested Besjana's words.

"There is nothing I can do now, Besjana. Your son is as wilful as you. He will never be happy until he has his chance to outshine us all or be killed in the process—so here it is, boy."

"I'm not dying today, Uncle," Nora laughed in his face. "Not until I take out a dozen of these lounging Turks, anyway."

"Kreshnik, you are young. You have never fought in open combat like this." Besjana grabbed Nora's shoulders and tried to communicate a thousand other things with her eyes.

"This is my *chance*." Nora would not be stopped.

"Chance for what?"

Nora bent her head forward to speak for Besjana's ears only. "To prove I am as worthy as any son."

"You are better than any son could be." Besjana gripped Nora's shoulders tightly but had to let go as Nora was led away by the janissary to prepare for the opening bout.

◊Δ◊Δ◊Δ◊Δ◊Δ◊

"Kreshnik, they are waiting." Grigor had come for her.

"I am ready." Nora put her sword back into its sheath and made to walk towards the inner court.

"Wait, boy. I have something for you." Grigor took a parcel from inside his tunic, and unwrapped a glistening dagger.

Nora's mouth fell open. "But that is yours."

"Given to me by my father and passed down through every generation before from father to son."

"I am not your son."

"No, but you are fearless, as I always hoped my son would be. This belongs to you now. Know that no man who ever wielded this dagger has died from a wound inflicted by an opponent."

"I am honoured." Nora swallowed the lump that had grown in her throat.

"Do not make me regret giving it to you, Kreshnik. Go out there and show those Turkish dogs what an Albanian mountain lion can do." Grigor slapped her roughly on the back and gripped her shoulder as they walked away from the horses and into the inner court.

The pasha and his janissaries sat upon a raised dais at the northern end of the court. Groups of knights from all over Albania, Macedonia and Serbia flanked the other sides. Besjana stood amongst the Kelmendi knights as Nora pulled her helmet over her head and marched forward into the centre of the court.

The ranks of Turkish janissaries across from them opened and a tall man with shoulders twice as wide as Nora's walked forward and stopped a few feet before her. He pulled a long, curved yatagan—favoured sword of the janissaries—from his waistband that looked as if it weighed as much as Nora's entire armoured body. She felt fear rake its icy fingers up her spine but she stubbornly shook it off. She knew better then to be swayed by outward displays of brute strength. Her opponent might weigh three times what she did but she had the dagger, her speed, and her cunning. She gripped the dagger hilt tightly as the spectators began to jeer and laugh at the sight of so slight a boy up against the Turkish giant. The drums stopped.

The moment the pasha barked for the duel to begin, Nora found herself leaping sideways as the huge Turk lunged at her with his yatagan. He was quicker than she had anticipated and he only took a moment to recover his balance. He lunged for her again but she deflected his blow with her eagle-crested shield. The impact reverberated around the court and knocked her to her knees, but pulling out her dagger, she jabbed him in the side, before rolling out of the way as he went down. The Turk grabbed at his wound and growled as his hand came away bloody. He cursed in a language she couldn't understand, then pushed himself off the ground and advanced on her again.

Nora raised her shield as he swung at her but the shield, made of wood with only an iron plate attached to the front, splintered in two and the blow of his yatagan knocked her backwards onto the ground. She tried to roll but the Turk pinned her down with his boot before grabbing her about the waist and lifting her over his head. The crowd erupted into laughter as he spun around with her held up as if she were a straw puppet.

"Put me down you filthy ox!" Nora pummelled at his head with the butt of her dagger. His curved golden helmet deflected her blows at first but she found his temple and the Turk crumpled to his knees. Nora wasted no time; wrapping her legs about his neck, she squeezed as hard as she could, cutting off his air.

The Turk fell to his side but his neck was so thick and muscled that she couldn't apply enough pressure to completely cut off his breath. He reached for her again, grabbing the bottom of her tunic and flinging her across the arena, still holding her breastplate, which tore at the fastenings and came away. Nora landed on the ground, the wind knocked out of her. Her clothes had come away and she was left in nothing but the bandages she had so expertly wrapped around her chest that morning. Trying desperately to catch her breath she rolled and began crawling away from the Turk.

"Kreshnik!" Nora heard Besjana's scream from the side.

Nora could hardly focus her eyes. She felt the Turk's blade slice down her back, cutting away the bandages. He leaned down and whispered something; his tone was enough to communicate his lewd intent. She tried desperately to clasp the tattered fabric to her chest as she was plucked from the ground by her ankle and held upside down, exposing her female chest to every pair of astonished eyes in Rozafa castle.

"Enough!" the pasha yelled as he rose from his seat.

Nora's opponent froze with her still held mid-air. While his attention was levelled on his master, Nora sank her dagger into his bicep. The Turk bellowed, dropping her to the ground again.

"I commanded you to stop!" The pasha grabbed Nora by her cropped hair and dragged her across the ground. Another of the janissaries snatched the eagle-crested dagger from her hands.

"You are a woman!" The pasha's voice was a mixture of horror and awe as he took in the tight buds of her breasts.

"You knew that already, didn't you?" Nora was brazen in her reply.

"I had my suspicions." His eyes travelled the length of her dirt-covered body.

"What trick is this?" Grigor joined them in the middle of the court, his eyes bulging at the sight of Nora's exposed breasts.

"This is your daughter, Grigor!" Besjana ran forward to shield Nora's nakedness, throwing her fur cape about her. "This is the girl you abandoned at the monastery. She is a braver creature than any man within these walls."

"You did this!" Grigor's shock turned to rage as he confronted his sister. "You lied to me all this time, Besjana? This is why you hid Kreshnik in the mountains." He grabbed her and shook her roughly.

"What choice did you give us?" She tore her arm from his grip. "I turned her into a boy so that she could live."

"And live she shall. She is under my protection now," the pasha declared loudly. "No one will hurt this woman."

Grigor bristled. "She is my daughter and I will do with her as I wish." He leaned in threateningly but the janissary held him back from the pasha.

"She is much more than your daughter now, Grigor. She is my champion."

"Your champion?" Nora wheezed, still recovering from the the duel.

The Pasha nodded. He turned to the crowd. "It will be known throughout all the Ottoman Empire that Kreshnik Kelmendi—"

"Nora, my name is Nora."

"So it is." The pasha smiled upon her. "That you, Nora, a woman, have shown more courage than any man I have ever met. I honour you."

The words she longed to hear. Finally she could be her own true self.

"And as the finest woman I have ever beheld, I ask you to become my wife."

There it was. He didn't want to honour her; he wanted to own her. Always the same with men: ownership, enslavement, possession.

"You cannot have her!" Grigor erupted.

"I am the pasha and I take what I want. She is my reward from Allah for all my days spent in this place of savages and infidels."

"We do not recognise your Allah. This woman is a Catholic and my daughter. Under the laws of our land you cannot have her."

"If you do not give her to me, I will burn all of Malsia to the ground."

"I belong to no man, and I will not see Malsia burned for the sake of pride and lust," Nora interrupted.

"Then you will become my wife?" The pasha's eyes narrowed to greedy slits.

"Come to Malsia in a month's time and you will receive exactly what you deserve for all your efforts, my lord." Nora gave the pasha her most winning smile. "But I want my dagger back." She held her hand out, regal and demanding.

The pasha motioned for his janissary to return the dagger to Nora. "Anything you wish, my lady." His eyes travelled over her.

"My wish is to return home, my lord. I am injured. You must excuse me so that I can rest and prepare for your arrival." She bowed to the pasha, and without waiting for his reply, walked back towards her horse, still tethered in the outer ward.

"I will be there, Nora of Kelmendi. I look forward to our next meeting," the pasha promised.

Besjana and Grigor followed her from the inner court as the other Kelmendi knights made their horses ready to leave Rozafa.

"First you lie to me and then you defy me to marry that Turkish dog?" Grigor grabbed Nora's shoulder and spun her around to face him.

"He's not a Turk, he's a Bosnian." Nora's voice was dry.

"Which is even worse. He is a traitor to his own people."

"Let's talk about betrayal, shall we, *Father*?" She drew the word out.

His face dropped. "I am not proud of what I did, Nora. But you cannot marry my enemy to spite me."

"I am not marrying him." She laughed dryly as she pulled herself up onto her horse, refusing Besjana's assistance.

Grigor's brows knitted together. "You invited him to Malsia in a month's time to get what he deserves."

"He will." Nora winked at her father as she pulled the eagle-crested dagger from her waist and kissed the blade still wet with Turkish blood. "He will get exactly what he deserves, and that is *my* promise."

Granuaile

Dirk Flinthart

He's a sorry sight, is her hostage: skinny and sallow. Hardly more than a boy with a patchy growth of beard, his neck all adam's-apple and soggy ruff. And why's he wearing a ruff to sea anyhow? Who's to impress with court fashion on a little brig plying the coast off Connacht?

Grace sniffs, and spits, gobbing into the stinking mud they're both standing in: she in her tough sea-boots, him in his hose and fine silver-buckled shoes, the eejit. He blinks, and lifts an eyebrow, but says nothing.

"A fine morning to you," she essays in clear Irish, but his sunburned face stays blank. Does he not speak the tongue of her land? And his father no less than the Lord Deputy of all Ireland, or so says that queen of theirs, that Elizabeth in her stony britches far and away in London.

He grunts and coughs at her, then whines a little through his beak of a nose. His face is expectant, like a dog under the table. Those were words? English, then. Bastard tongue that it is. And she has none of it. But there's always the scholar's way...

"I am Grace O'Malley," she says in the Latin trained into her by old Fiach the harper. "Captain of the *Gull* and chief of the captains of Connacht. Is it the knight Philip Sidney that I address?"

Both the lad's eyebrows lift. "I am he. You speak Latin?"

Well, there's a damnfool question. She ignores it. "Does your father know where you are?"

He bridles. "I am my own man. I am a diplomat and a courtier to Her Majesty, Queen Elizabeth of England, Scotland, Wales—and Ireland," he finishes with a smirk.

Grace leaves the bait in the mud, where it belongs. "Well, diplomat," she says, "I'm pleased you accepted my invitation to come ashore."

"Invitation!" The smirk disappears. "Your blackamoor crept upon our vessel in that damnable fog, carrying a keg of powder and a lighted match! Captain Runyon nigh to threw me overboard in his hurry to appease you!"

"Oh, yes, Achmed," Grace chuckles. "He's a Mussulman, you see, and someone has told him he will go to a heaven full of willing virgins if he can just take enough infidel Christians with him. Some day he'll get to put his match to the keg, I suppose. Until then—well, he's most powerfully persuasive, isn't he?" She frowns. "Now, what are we to do with you?"

Sidney pulls himself up. "I have come to negotiate terms. Your galley is drawn up on the shore. Captain Runyon has your range with the cannon on the *Sprite*. You cannot leave this island without his permission. What are you willing to yield?"

Oh, and isn't he a lovely lad, though? So confident and full of himself. Grace pretends to glance away and tugs at her heavy jerkin so it opens a little. If the lad is anything like his father, a glimpse of her bubbies should distract him well enough. "Yield?" she says, pouring a little honey on her voice. "Your ideas are amusing, but you have the matter backwards. See, while I have the son of Sir Henry Sidney here, your Captain Runyon won't risk a single shot. So all I must do is remain in your company until my galleys come to find me. Can your Captain Runyon and his little guns destroy my entire fleet? I think not, seeing as how your father and half your English navy has been trying without success for some years now." She crosses her arms, mindful of the way she lifts her tits and there, yes, his eyes flicker down and away, and now he doesn't know where to look, does he?

"I, ahhh—" He looks at her again, then up to the blue sky above, his face reddening still more. "What proof have I that your fleet will come?"

"Proof? Well, they know I am here," says Grace. "I told the lads I would come and see this mad new island, the talk of the Connacht fisherfolk." She makes a grand gesture, sweeping her hand at the pile of mud and rock sticking up out of the grey-green sea. "But three days gone, and this was open water. Then came the mists, and then the currents that spun in a gyre, and all of a sudden this new land breasts the waves. The fisherman who braved it first spoke to me of strange lights on the hill at the centre, and swore the sun turned him in a circle when he tried to make landfall."

Sidney blinks and meets her gaze. "That's interesting," he says. "Do you have a—a lodestone of way-finding on your ship?"

Grace thinks, and realises she knows no Latin word for 'compass'. Did the Romans not have them, then? "Why would I need such a thing in my own waters?" she replies. "I could no more lose my way hereabouts than you in your lady's cunny." The jape is salty, but who cares what some little snot of an English nobleman thinks? She's Grace O'Malley. Already the English call her the Pirate Queen, the mother of all revolt and discontent in Ireland. A fig for their goodwill. She looks slyly at Sidney. "You...have known the company of a lady by now, have you not?"

"Mother!" It's probably not the word he meant, but she has him off-balance, and he's struggling with his Latin. "I have one-and-twenty years. I am a member of the English Parliament!"

Grace laughs.

Sidney adjusts himself. "Our lodestone spun in circles when we came through the mists, chasing after you." It's a stab at returning to the original subject, then. "When the fog grew light, we thought we were escaping. Finding this island and your galley was a surprise."

"And to us," Grace admits. "We thought you would break off when we entered the fog. Only a madman would chase Grace O'Malley through a Connacht sea-fog. Is your Captain Runyon a madman?"

"Nothing of the kind," said Sidney. "We meant to break off, truly. The currents hereabouts are..."

Grace nods. "It is true," she agrees. "We found them likewise. Yet here we now are. What next?" She turns, and looks up the island towards the low peak in the centre, somehow still wreathed in the mysterious fog that surrounds the island, yet leaves most of it uncovered. "Look there!" she says, as a greenish light flickers from somewhere within the little cloud, like summer lightning.

"I've never seen the like," says Sidney. "This—this stinks of witchcraft."

Grace allows herself a real belly laugh. "I've met witches by the dozen, and not one could raise so much as a fart on demand, let alone lift an island from the waters." She sniffs loudly, and hauls one foot from the muck. "Stinks of sea-bottom to me." She glances at Sidney. "Nevertheless, I came here to learn what I could, and it seems to me that yon hill is likely the place for an answer. Best you stay here with my lads, Philip Sidney. I'd not like to tell your father I lost you to some magic cloud of lightnings." He won't leave her, though. She knows that already. She turns to the hilltop, slogging her way through the mud and sure enough, there's the sloppy sound of young Sidney hobbling after.

"Captain Grace!" It's Owain, slick-tongued Owain whose badgering brought her to this miserable mudhole in the first place. "The bet was that you'd climb the hill alone!"

Without looking back, she calls: "He's an Englishman, Owain. How much more alone must I be?" The chorus of guffaws from the rest of the crew is answer enough.

The hill is steep, and the footing is treacherous. Everywhere it's black slime and dead kelp, festering in the sun. Fog around the island, fog at the centre, yet not so much as a breeze in this open space in between? She looks upwards, catches sight of another flicker of light in the curling grey mists, and suppresses a shiver. It wouldn't do to let the lads see that, oh no. Hard enough to be their captain and a woman. Her reputation is worth more than gold. As long as people tell stories of mad, bad Grace O'Malley, the merchantmen she overtakes pay their tithes meek and quiet, just the way she likes. It's a lot easier to win battles when your enemies are too scared to fight. But sometimes you have to remind folk why they should be scared. And so here she is: walking all but alone into the mysterious fog. They will watch, and they will remember, and when they talk of this day the scariest thing on the whole island in their stories will be she, Grace.

The blue-green light in the cloud is close, now, and the mists are cold and yes, she is almost grateful for the company of the English idiot. Who is close behind her, she can hear. Perhaps those lightweight shoes carry less mud than her big, sturdy sea-boots?

"Is it true what they say of you?" Sidney is panting, a little out of breath.

"How should I know?" says Grace, trying to keep her own voice even. "What do they say?"

"That you hunted and killed the murderers of your lover, Hugh de Lacey, for one," Sidney says. "Personally, I mean."

"They say that, do they?" That isn't how she recalls it. She had something like six-score bravoes with her when she attacked the MacMahons. And sure, they'd murdered her Hugh—but didn't she get her fine castle at Doona in the bargain? Folk liked to remember romance and revenge, not good tactics and strong sense. "Anything else?"

"That you rose from your birthing-bed at sea and drove a score of Turk raiders from your ship with your sword, laying a curse on each as you went."

Almost right. "I had an arquebus full of nails and broken pottery," she says. "Most wonderful for discouraging a boarding party. But the only curse I laid was upon the man serving as captain on my ship, lazy bastard that he was." Couldn't even do without her long enough to let her drop a baby in peace!

Breathing hard, Sidney falls into step beside her. "Why do you support the rebels here?" he says. "You, a good member of the English Church!"

She stops so quickly her foot skids in the mud. "The English Church? What nonsense is that?"

"'Tis well known," says Sidney, stopping a few paces ahead. "You divorced Richard Bourke! The Irish Church does not countenance divorce, but the English Church permits—"

"The English Church permits me *nothing*," says Grace. "I married Iron Dick under the old law, the *Brehon* law of my land and I dismissed him under the same law. Your English Church means no more to me than the Church of Rome." He wants to know about her? Let him learn! "You English—all of you can rot. The old ways of Ireland will live on long after your England is nothing more than another province of the Spanish Empire." She thrusts her thumb between her first and second fingers and raises her fist at Sidney. "*That* for your English Church, and that for your queen!"

His face goes pale under the sunburn, and his hand drops to the little pigsticker of a sword at his side. Grace shows him a smile, and puts her hand to the hilt of her heavy cutlass. Let him draw against her. Let him try his fancy footwork and his clever French fencing in this mud!

Slowly, Sidney's hand lifts from his sword. His eyes narrow, and he takes a deep breath. "I see I have offended you," he says. "I cry your pardon, lady."

Diplomat indeed. And perhaps not so stupid as his soggy ruff makes him look. Grace makes him wait, her hand still on the cutlass, until she sees real fear in his eyes. Only then does she sniff, and nod. "Rough words are no more than foul air," she says. "I give you my pardon if you will give me yours."

"Gladly," says Sidney, and makes to keep going up the hill. Only now they are surrounded by the cold grey of the mist, and it's hard to tell even which way 'up' might be.

Something looms ahead; Grace stretches out her hand to touch a wall. It is like no other: a little rough, like stone beneath her fingers, yet seamless. Unlike the rest of the island, the wall has no mud on it at all. It has the grey-white colour of limestone on its sides, but on the top—which is no higher than her waist—the thickness of the wall glows with the uncanny light of sea phosphor. Sidney lumbers up to stand beside her, and drags his finger across the top of the wall. It comes away glowing, and he sniffs at it with distaste.

"Slimy," he says, shaking his hand. "And it smells of the sea. What is this?"

Grace points. "There," she says. A gap in the wall perhaps the width of a door. She moves closer and sees beyond a wide, flat, open place, clean and free of mud. More of the mysterious wall-stone, except here it has become a floor. How can this be?

There is a hum in the air, a strange, wordless music made by what must be a voice. But is it human? The timbre is all wrong, throaty, broken, like the sea-wind through the rigging of a ship. It comes and goes like a song half-forgotten. Grace pauses. Sidney moves close to her once more, and this time she is truly grateful not to be alone. They leave trails of mud behind them as they move farther into the walled space and the mists that fill it. Grace draws her cutlass, as much for the comfort of its weight in her hand as anything else. Sidney looks at her, and wordlessly draws his own blade.

And now the voice changes, forming—are they words? It's a deep voice, a man's voice, and it almost seems to echo here where there is no roof and the walls are only half-built. Grace looks around, but there's nothing to see except the swirling grey of the fog, and the strange blue-green light of the walls.

"Who's there?" she calls.

And yes: words. She can hear them clearly, almost understand them. They sound familiar, as though she knew them a long time ago. The taste of them is Irish, but not the way she knows it—maybe an older, more pure kind of Irish. Why does she think that?

"Speak up," she cries, this time in Latin. "Make yourself known."

"Oh," says the deep voice, close enough now that she shies back. "It is the tongue of the Roman traders. This I have." A shadow moves in the mist, coming near. The greyness swirls and parts, and the blue-green light grows in streaks across the floor until Grace can see a tall, lean man in some kind of robes. "A sword?" the voice is amused. "Ah, but it is iron. I cannot have that."

The tall man waves his hand gently, and the air moves. Grace glances at her sword, and the blue-green light has flared along the blade. A new light at her side and a distinctly English curse tells her Sidney's blade is likewise afflicted. The light is eating her blade, pitting it, turning it to rust before her very eyes. In a very few heartbeats the good steel blade decays to nothing, leaving her with a brass handguard and a couple of pieces of wood wrapped in leather.

"That's a fine trick," Grace breathes. "I'd be keen to know how that was done."

"The sea eats iron," says the man. "Ask the sea how it is done." He gestures again, and the blue-green light creeps up the half-finished walls, filling the place with an eerie radiance. It's enough to see clearly, even with the damnable fog, and Grace studies the tall man with interest.

He looks back at her, calm and unflustered, out of eyes so dark as to be nigh black. His skin is pale, as is his long hair that is caught up with a fillet of gold at his neck. There's a strange look about him: drawn, lean...*fey*. The word wells up from her memory, and Grace tries not to tremble.

The tall man—and is he a man, or is there more to this story?—cocks his head and nods. Evidently he's seen enough of Grace, for he turns away. "Off with you," he says. "You may return when I have raised my hall. I will send for you presently."

"Your pardon, gentle sire," says Sidney, and damn him but his voice is firm and steady. "I am the knight Philip Sidney of the court of Elizabeth, Queen of England, Scotland, Wales and Ireland. Will you give me your name?"

The tall creature—there's a queer certainty in Grace's belly now; it's not a man before her, no—turns its head and regards Sidney. "You know me not? How can you mistake the King Below the Sea?"

Grace draws a breath, and sidles back. Suddenly she misses the darkness of the fog.

Sidney shakes his head. "I know of no such title. I have met the kings of France and Spain, and travelled the continent, but never have I heard of the King Below The Sea."

"The Argives called me Poseidon, the earth-shaker," says the tall one. "The little men whose tongue we share; to them I was Neptune, and they gave me a great three-pointed spear." He turns his gaze on Grace. "And you, with your hair of copper and fire. You have forgotten the old tongue of your people, who called me Manannan mac Lir."

"Tales for the nursery," snaps Grace before Sidney can speak. She wills her voice to be bold, but in her belly there is a weight of fear such as she has not known. "You can make pretty lights, and you can rust a blade. So much I have seen, and no more. You are no god, no Child of Danu come back from forgotten times."

The thing that calls itself by ancient names looks deep into Grace's eyes. She can't turn away. Is she looking at it? Is it looking into her? She can't tell where one begins and the other ends, and who knows what may have come of it save that Sidney's hand falls on her arm and she wakes with a start, averting her gaze.

"Are you all right?" Sidney's grip is firm and warm, a wonder and a marvel after the cold depths in which she has swum. She wants to drag him closer, warm herself against him, but instead she pushes him gently back, and takes a deep breath.

"I'm well enough," she says. "But that one…" she gestures without looking at the tall creature. "He is more than he seems."

"He seems a great deal to me already," says Sidney. "How shall I call you?" he calls to the thing. "What name do you prefer?"

"How do you style a king in this tongue?" says the other. His tone is gentle, almost ruminative. "No. Titles are for courts and battlefields. Here I will be as I was: call me Manannan mac Lir, returned to reclaim for the Tuatha de Danann all that is properly theirs."

"And what is that?" says Sidney, unease in his voice. Grace is already moving, backing towards the gap in the walls. Are those walls higher? They are! This creature and his blue-green light—he's building a palace around them, even as they speak.

Manannan mac Lir inclines his head slowly. "Everything. We will rule over these lands as we ruled before. When I have raised these walls and rebuilt the gate once more, the others will come: the Lord of the Lightnings, the Master of the Silver Hand, the Greatsmith, the Lady of Sorrows—all the High Ones." He raises one long-fingered hand, and sketches figures that glow briefly in the dense mist. His angular face is softened now, lost in memory. "Even as time flows in my world, it has been long since I walked in this place. It is...good." He glances sideways at Grace and Sidney. "You doubt me," he says. "You, woman—you would destroy me, if you could." His chuckle is deep, like the thunder of waves on a distant shore. "Behold! Here is the power of the King Below The Sea."

Doesn't he just fancy himself, with all his wonderful titles? Grace bites her tongue, holding back the words she wants to throw in his hateful face. But what is he doing now? He opens his arms, and just like throwing back a curtain the mists part and the sun streams in all golden. They're high on the hill in the centre of the island, and below Grace can see the muddy tracks she and Sidney left, all the way down to her galley on the new shoreline. And beyond it, in the little bay—there's the *Sprite*, with Captain Runyon and his damnable cannon, waiting for word of his borrowed diplomat. Beyond that, the wall of the mists, thickening now, drawing together, spinning and reaching and rising to the sky—

"Waterspout," Grace cries in her own tongue, forgetting that her lads cannot possibly hear her from this distance. "Ware the waterspout!" She turns to Manannan mac Lir, and in her finest Latin she begs: "Please! Those men have done nothing to you! Spare them!"

But the creature seems lost in some kind of ecstasy, his face turned to the sun, his hands upraised as he sings in that broken, half-wild voice, crying words that tug at the far edges of Grace's understanding. The waterspout rises, curving and dancing like a great grey serpent, a beast of obscene appetite ready to eat her little boat and the men who depend on her, and without a sword, without a gun, Grace readies herself to leap at Manannan mac Lir, to claw the eyes from his face and sink her teeth into his throat though the doing of it be her end...

"My lord," says Sidney, his voice cool but sharp as he steps between Grace and the master of the sea-spout. "There is no need." A desperate edge creeps into his voice. "If you destroy our ships, you will lose the gifts I have brought from distant lands across the great ocean. Gifts fit even for a king of such power and might as yourself."

Slowly, mac Lir turns his head. "Gifts?" he rumbles. "You said nothing of gifts."

"Oh yes, my lord," Sidney says. "My queen's astrologer John Dee foresaw your coming. Great Elizabeth herself bid me bear gifts as tribute, that you might look with favour upon her English rule." He moves closer, and settles his half-cloak more neatly upon his shoulders. And is he suddenly taller? Grace can't fathom the change in the man. Where's the spindly boy she mocked? Who is this calm, assured courtier? Where did he come from?

"If you will but give me permission to return to my vessel," Sidney continues, "I will bring here treasures such as even you have not seen, O

King. And you will judge the truth of my words, and see for yourself the value of the good will of Queen Elizabeth and her kingdom of England."

For a long moment, the King Under The Sea is still, as though listening, and Grace holds her breath. The great waterspout curves and sways like a Turkish dancer, and she can see the lads running this way and that on the muddy shore, seeking shelter. Then mac Lir's arms fall, and the waterspout melts away in a heartbeat, leaving nothing but ragged edges of cloud.

The sun is bright and hot.

"Yes," says mac Lir. "You may bring your gifts. But be swift. Soon enough the gate will be open once more. I would show the others the bounty of these distant lands of which you speak."

"I thank you, O King," says Sidney, and damned if he doesn't kneel there on the stone floor, bowing his head. Grace watches him, and then realises that mac Lir is watching her, not the diplomat.

What does he want?

Mac Lir frowns. Grace feels her belly turn cold. "Ah," she says. "Gifts." She drops to one knee in imitation of Sidney. "Oh, yes," she says. "I too bear gifts for you, great king. Here in Ireland, naturally, we knew of your coming even before the English, and so the bounty I bring is all the greater." Her mouth keeps moving. What is it saying? She has absolutely no idea how to carry this off. Gifts? What does she have on her little galley that can match whatever this rich nobleman has brought from across the seas?

She'll think of something.

"Go, then," says mac Lir. "I have much to do." He turns away from them, resuming his weird and tuneless song, and once more the mists enclose the new, half-grown walls.

Grace goes, and Sidney goes with her.

◊∆◊∆◊∆◊∆◊∆◊

All the way down the hill, sliding through the filth, he wants to know about Manannan mac Lir and the Tuatha de Danann. Grace wants to save her breath, to think, but there's no other way to shut him up, so she tells him stories. Fragments. Pieces of childhood tales. Nuada of the Silver Arm. Lugh of the Bright Spear. The Morrigan, raven-queen of war.

When she was small, she loved the old songs and stories. She remembers begging Fiach the Harper to sing of Cuchulainn and his battle at the river ford. She recalls the long chants, the beautiful, intricate lays of poetry, and she shudders. Now she has seen one of her childhood stories in the flesh, how many more might there be? Were there really Fomorians, flesh-eating giants? Balor of the Evil Eye? And all their bickering, their battles and their vengeance-taking. How do simple, mortal humans fare when gods make war on each other? The stories are full of heroes, sure, but they say little about the smaller folk, and Grace is increasingly sure that she's likely to be smaller folk in the eyes of a creature like Manannan mac Lir.

Sidney, though—he's cock-a-whoop. So sure of himself, he is, and why not? The *Sprite* was taking him to see his father before Captain Runyon changed course to chase Grace in her galley. Like a dutiful son, not seeing his father for some years, young Sidney has brought gifts. Wonders of the new world: tobacco, the red man's weed. Something called coca, bought from Spanish merchants—a marvellous tonic to health and digestion. Another thing, a bitter powder called chocolatl, used as a restorative drink. And fine French Brandy, and pepper and spice from the Orient, and silks... oh, yes, the boy has planned well for his father. Only now he's the more excited, seeing his chance to make an alliance with a supernatural being and save all England from foreigners everywhere.

Grace is less excited. Her galley—the *Gull*—is not so well supplied. She has fine whiskey, of course, and plenty of it, but none of the exotic marvels Sidney can offer. Perhaps she should just brain the lad when they're halfway back up the hill? Say he ran away, pretend his gifts are hers? She shoots a glance at Sidney, babbling happily to himself about the Spaniards meeting their doom in the teeth of mighty English waterspouts, and sighs.

It would be like kicking a puppy.

◊Δ◊Δ◊Δ◊Δ◊Δ◊

The return trip is, if anything, worse. Sidney has two men with him now, each carrying a heavy trunk. Grace has only Lars, the mad Icelander who is afraid of nothing except earwigs creeping into his head while he sleeps, and Lars carries her single trunk with ease, despite the mud. None of the others would come, for now the walls of Manannan mac Lir's new palace rise high amidst the fog, and the ghostly blue-green glow is all too clear in the evening twilight.

Sidney is full of plans and excitement. He will show the Tuatha de Danann the wisdom of a partnership with England. They will want the rich Continental lands for themselves, of course, but in exchange, they will grant freedom to the English isles. And Ireland, he's quick to add. Then together, the allies will wrest power from Spain and France and Rome, and a golden age will follow with de Danann power and English acumen working together.

"So you do not think them gods?" says Grace. They are nearly at the palace by now, and it is indeed a grand thing, all curves and arches and white spires aflame with the sea-glow. A marvel in the near-darkness. Sidney's sailors mutter to one another in their horrible language, and Grace thinks they are unhappy to be here. Lars, though, marches stolidly onward, her trunk on his broad shoulder. As long as there are no earwigs, Lars is as happy as a gloomy Icelander ever can be.

"Not so," says Sidney. "'Tis true this Mack Leer has much power, but what of it? Have we not powers the ancients would have marvelled at? The compass? The telescope? Our clocks? Our cannons and guns?" He nods confidently. "We have wise men and astrologers, alchemists and mathematical philosophers. What this Mack Leer knows, we can learn. In time we will deal with him and his people as equals."

His accent is horrible. Grace tries not to wince. "Make sure you keep calling him 'king'," she says. "We don't want him angry enough to raise another of those waterspouts."

At the foot of the walls, Sidney's men put down their two trunks. They will go no farther, the pair of them, no matter what he says. Grace watches as he waves his arms and grunts at them, enjoying Sidney's discomfort and embarrassment. Then she signals Lars, and they enter the cavernous building.

Within, the light is brighter than before, strong enough that she cannot see the stars though there is yet no roof overhead. The walls pulse with brilliant colour, like an aurora caught in stone. From the corner of her eye, Grace can see mac Lir watching her, and she sets her chin. She won't show this creature her amazement, like some shoeless savage out of Africa.

"Gifts, O King," she says, and gestures to Lars to put down the trunk.

Mac Lir ignores her offering. "Where is the other?" he demands in that uncanny voice. "What of his promised gifts?"

"Here," calls Sidney from the doorway. He's entering without dignity, arse-first, bent in the middle, dragging a muddy sea-chest behind him. It squeals and scrapes across the smooth stone of the floor as he hauls it closer. "Wait," Sidney says. "I will fetch the second chest." He darts out again.

Grace shrugs. "If it's all the same, O King, I'll be on my way now." She averts her eyes. "Truth is, I am frightened by you and the other great ones. I have given you great tribute. I beg you please—spare me and my vessel."

Mac Lir stares at her from those dark, dark eyes. "Return to your ship, then," he says. "Bide there. Soon I will open the gate. I will send for you when you are required."

Required? For what? Grace wonders to ask, but in that moment Sidney returns, dragging his second chest. Once he settles it by the first, Grace catches his arm. "Come," she says. "The King Under the Sea has dismissed us."

"What?" Sidney straightens, and tries to throw off her arm. Grace tightens her hand around his skinny forearm, digging her fingers in where it will hurt. He winces and pulls at her hand, but she has a strong grip and she knows how to use it. "Let go of me," he snaps.

"Best leave now," she says. "Don't want to displease His Majesty with his guests on their way, eh?"

"What?" Sidney frowns.

Oh, now the boy is suddenly deaf? "We are leaving," Grace hisses.

The boy sets himself to make a contest of strength, and Grace has half a mind to abandon the pup. Mac Lir himself intervenes with a slow, imperious nod.

"You will leave now," he says. "The Opening of the Gate is not for your eyes. Your gifts will be safe. I will show them to the others when they come, and we will send for you." The dark eyes gleam. "You will speak for us to this queen of yours, Philip Sidney."

"My King," Sidney says, "I would be honoured—"

Grace makes a sign to Lars. The Icelander grabs the boy's other arm, covers his mouth with his free hand, and together they drag him out of the palace of light into the clean Irish summer night.

"What was all that about?" snaps Sidney, once Lars lets go of his face. "Release me, the pair of you!"

"Shut up," suggests Grace. "We can talk about this at the bottom of the hill."

"But—I want to see," says Sidney, looking back over his shoulder as Lars and Grace haul him downhill through the drying mud. "And the gifts! I must explain the gifts! How will he know what to do with the tobacco? The chocolatl? These things must be done properly!"

"It will wait, lad," Grace says. "Now pick your feet up, you're slowing us down!" She yanks the lad's feet free of the mud and Lars does the same on the other side. Staggering, puffing, sliding in places where the mud is still loose and wet, they wrestle Sidney down the hill like a cranky child between its parents.

Near the bottom, Grace's strength gives way and she simply lets the boy go. She finds a great stone, and puts it between her and the marvellous, terrible light of the palace on the hillside. Breathing heavily, she glares at Sidney. "Idiot," she says. "What were you thinking?"

Sidney is shaking with rage. "You lay hands on me!" he snarls. "You—dragged me! You and your beast-man! I will have your heads, I swear it!"

"Maybe," says Grace. "But it won't be tonight." She heaves in another great, gasping breath, and settles herself in the muck. There's no question about it. She's getting old. She looks up at Sidney. "You didn't ask me what gifts I brought in my trunk."

There's a pause.

"Why should I?" says Sidney. "You will have done your best."

"My best," says Grace. "Yes." She looks to the stars, and tries to guess the time. "You talked about freedom before," she says, to cover the silence.

"You said you'd strike a bargain: our freedom in exchange for the nations of the Continent."

"A thought. A plan," says Sidney. "There were other possibilities, of course."

Grace shakes her head. She beckons to Lars, who blinks, and nods, and sits down next to her in the mud. "You should probably sit down here too," she tells Sidney. "Put some good stone betwixt you and that thing on the hilltop."

When the boy doesn't move, Grace sighs, and signals Lars again. The big Icelander stands, glowering. Hastily, Sidney sits down next to Grace. She moves over, making space for Lars to rejoin them. "Freedom isn't a thing that can be granted," she says, catching Sidney's eye. She wants him to understand. "If it can be given to you, it can be taken away again, you see? It's not freedom unless you can take it for yourself, and none can take it back."

Sidney shifts uncomfortably. Something squelches, down near his arse. "I suppose I see your point," he admits. "But they are few, and we are many. And in time, as I said, we will master their arts." He turns a little, and looks at her directly. "What has this to do with your gifts? What did you bear in that trunk?"

"Your freedom and mine," she says. "Achmed's keg, and a slow match."

Thunder smites the world, and the darkness turns red-white with a roar. A rain of stones splatters mud in all directions. A piece of rock the size of a man's head lands almost between Sidney's feet. He stares at it in horror as the earth shudders underfoot, shaking and roaring and growling like the island itself is being beaten.

Then the noise dies away, but in its place is a gurgling, rushing noise, and Grace can hear the cries of her lads as they scramble for the galley. "Up, boy," she says, and pulls herself out of the muck. "Looks as though mac Lir's island is returning whence it came. Like as not your Captain Runyon will have his hands full. I'll take you back to Galway town my own self."

"What have you done?" Sidney says in a half whisper. He rises, and looks back up the hill. "What have you done?" he says again.

Grace observes the still-smoking wreckage of Manannan mac Lir's palace, and enjoys the warmth it makes in her belly. "I showed him a marvel of our age, boy. Cheer up," she says, and punches him in the shoulder. "How many people do you know as can say they helped to blow up a god?"

Then the first rivulets of returning water crawl over her sea-boots, and laughing, Grace O'Malley, the Pirate Queen of Connacht runs for her boat.

Little Battles

L.M. Myles

Was God so very reluctant to meet her? How old could a person grow, anyway?

Eleanor, by the Grace of God, queen of the English, stared down at her hands. Thin, wrinkled skin was speckled with liver spots, and pain throbbed through her stiff fingers. Still, they held the reins well enough.

She looked at the young woman riding beside her: Blanche, yet another of her grandchildren now old enough to be wed. She had so many grandchildren, and she found them a comfort, when they did not take up arms against her sons, at least. They were so young: she could not possibly outlive them all.

The drizzle of rain thickened. A young oak, growing close to the road, shivered in the wind. Eleanor's joints ached, and her muscles. It was the cold; it was no good for her. John knew that, and he *certainly* knew how old she was, and yet he had sent her to Castile anyway. She had not gone because her son had asked her, but because she knew that he had been right to do so. She had ruled Aquitaine and England, and seen more than most of the world; what was one more journey to choose the next queen of France? The septuagenarian English queen leading her small expedition over the Pyrenees to see which of her Castilian granddaughters would be most suited to the French throne. Why not?

Eleanor had held it herself, once, long ago. She knew what was needed in France, what was needed in a queen, and she had chosen the younger princess. The French wouldn't like that; they would consider it an insult. She was doing them a favour, giving them a girl more suited to their court's sensibilities, but God knew Philip wouldn't listen to reason when he could infer a slight.

"We should stop soon, her grace is tired." Sir William of Hovedon. An ugly lump of a man, but he had a sound mind even if he did mistake age for fragility.

"Am I indeed?" said Eleanor. The man had sharp eyes that turned away swiftly at her anger. What had he seen, anyway? Her expression was carefully neutral, she was certain of that. Had she slumped or sighed? Was he simply assuming, knowing that she was an old woman?

"*I* am tired, grandmother," said Blanche. "I'm not used to such great journeys as you." Eleanor almost smiled. A nice bit of diplomacy that. Shame that Blanche's Spanish accent was so strong. The French wouldn't like it, any more than the Saxon English took to Eleanor's own French one.

"There's a campsite clearing a mile or so ahead," said Mercadier. "I've used it often when I've been on this road." He looked up at the darkening sky. "Might be the best we can hope for, if this storm breaks."

Eleanor's heart lightened at his words. Mercadier unsettled her knights; he was a mercenary, and they were suspicious of loyalty plainly bought. But he had been beloved by her Richard, had fought alongside him. He had bloodied his sword at her own call when John's inheritance was at stake.

There was a murmur among her men-at-arms, and Eleanor felt sure that Sir William was going to make some objection. "Well," she said, settling the matter, "if we must spend a night in the rain, I shall appreciate Ombrière Palace all the more when we reach it."

◊∆◊∆◊∆◊∆◊∆◊

There were deer in these woods, and Blanche had gone with the hunting party. Did the dauphin hunt? Eleanor wasn't sure. If so it would be something he could share with his wife. If not, Blanche could encourage him to take up the diversion. Always good for a king to hunt; that, at least, never changed.

In her tent, Eleanor closed her eyes and listened to the bustle of activity outside, letting it drown her thoughts. Sleep came in awkward starts, failing to ease the aches in her body. A queen required constant energy, but hers refused to co-operate, waxing and waning with an irritating capriciousness.

It was Sir William who came to break her rest. She blinked her tiredness away as she took in his expression, and noted how far down the candles had burned. "Whatever is the matter?" she asked.

"Your grace…" His eyes darted to the tent flap; his neck and shoulders were stiff with tension.

"Spit it out, man." Eleanor had the distinct feeling this was what the man looked like just as battle became inevitable.

"Your grace, the hunting party has returned. They were attacked. Men are dead. The princess has been taken."

Eleanor's breath came sharply. Hot, fierce anger rose in her chest, but she did not let it enter her voice. "How did this happen?"

"They were outnumbered by their attackers. Many hours were spent searching for the princess, but they could find no trace of her."

Many hours. Eleanor looked at the candle again. They had been too afraid to return to her, she realised. "Mercadier knows these lands," she said. "Bring him to me."

A few minutes later, the mercenary bowed as he entered her tent. "Your grace, how can I be of service?"

"Whose lands are these?" she demanded. "Have we stumbled into the domain of some feckless baron who cannot keep the peace?"

"I don't know who took your granddaughter, but I believe we are only a few leagues from a castle owned by Hugh le Brun."

Sir William huffed. "These were brutes, not knights."

Mercadier shrugged. "As you say. I can seldom tell the difference."

"The Lusignans," muttered Eleanor. "I don't doubt that family is capable of carrying a grudge through the generations. Hugh le Brun is by all accounts a tedious man incapable of reason. I would not put this past him." She looked at the two men before her. "Outlaws, knights, or mercenaries, it matters not. I want my granddaughter back."

"I am as familiar with this county as any, your grace," said Mercadier. "We will find her."

◊∆◊∆◊∆◊∆◊∆◊

Eleanor did not sleep. Patience came to her much more easily than dreams. She sat in the centre of the camp, staring at the flames of a modest fire. It was getting harder to stay warm; each day the sun grew colder.

Time burnt away in the flicker of red and orange.

"We have found her, your grace."

Eleanor looked up. She could see only the outline of Sir William's face in the darkness. Another figure stood a little behind him; Mercadier, she assumed.

"Where is she?" she asked.

"We do not have her."

"Where *is* she?"

"The men who took the princess hold her near an old ruin of a fortress some miles north. Along with a few of your knights. I imagine they wish to trade them for ransom..."

She turned back to the flames. "Ransom? I've paid enough ransoms for one lifetime. Bad enough to pay one to a king, but to some brutish outlaws? I think not."

"I don't believe they are outlaws, your grace," said Mercadier, stepping forward. "Their armour is well-cared for, and they have good swords. These are not desperate men."

"Do we have the men and arms to take them?" she asked.

"With surprise and the night to cover our approach, I say it can be done," Mercadier told her. Eleanor believed him. He was skilled in battle and not a man for false optimism.

"Should we not be more cautious, your grace? If we send to Bordeaux for aid…" said Sir William.

"I will not have my granddaughter's journey delayed. I want an attack ready for first light. See to it."

Her voice held no doubt but as they left her, she allowed herself a moment to imagine what could happen if she was wrong. She knew how fragile life could be, how easy it was to step too close to a castle wall and into the eye-line of a lucky bowman…but what good was regret?

Her imaginings came to a hard conclusion, cold as an English winter: if Blanche died, there were other princesses in the Castilian court.

◊Δ◊Δ◊Δ◊Δ◊Δ◊

She had wrapped herself in thick layers but away from the comfort of the fire, the night air stung her throat. Around her, men crept forward through the forest, their weapons drawn. Someone stumbled, and muffled a gasp of pain. Eleanor looked up. Dawn would break within the hour, and she would know which way the dice had landed.

Until then, she refused to let herself worry.

Two men stayed behind with her. Youths, really. One was too young to even have a beard. "Your names?" she asked them.

"Harry, your grace," said the elder.

She smiled. "A good name."

"I'm Thomas, your grace." He couldn't have been older than fifteen.

"Be brave now, Thomas. It's a hard thing to fight, but harder still to do nothing while others fight for you."

"Yes, your grace."

"Patience is a great virtue, for a soldier, and a man," she said. Patience had become her greatest strength.

The forest lightened moment by moment. Small animals rustled in the undergrowth; waking birds called out, but her men were too far away to be heard.

A strange urge to laugh rose within her. She felt as though she was rising up and up, above the trees, reaching for the clouds. Looking down, she saw the frail figure of an old woman, the tapestry of her life stretching behind her, threads reaching out to mark every corner of Christendom.

It started quietly: cries of pain and warning shouts. Eleanor closed her eyes, and prayed.

◊Δ◊Δ◊Δ◊Δ◊Δ◊

They took her to Blanche as soon as the camp was secured.

"She's unharmed?" Eleanor asked, striding through the mulch of the forest floor.

"Yes, your grace," said her escort.

"Her captors?"

"Most are dead."

The fortress ruins were a filthy mess, decorated with broken and bloodied corpses. Sir William had taken charge of Blanche, and moved her away from the carnage. The girl was wrapped in a fresh blanket and there were dark circles beneath her eyes.

Eleanor embraced her granddaughter and thanked God she had come through her ordeal safely. She looked down at the girl's face: pale but no tears.

"Weren't you frightened?" she asked.

Blanche held her grandmother's hand tightly. "I knew you were nearby," she said.

Eleanor laughed. "Such faith in an old woman: I commend you for your good sense. Can you ride? William, find her a horse. Where is Mercadier?"

Sir William bowed, a frown etching his forehead. "I'm so sorry."

Eleanor insisted on seeing his body.

Her stomach twisted at the sight: he had been shot by arrows several times, and taken a blade in his shoulder. Quick, she hoped, it must have been quick.

"He fought well," Sir William told her. Of course he had. He always did. As fierce and brilliant a warrior as her own dear son.

As Eleanor stared down at Mercadier, she felt the stillness within her deepen. Richard's brother-in-arms, her protector, her weapon: dead. Another thread of her life cut away.

She realised that Blanche had followed her, and beckoned the girl over.

"Have you seen anyone die before?" Eleanor asked.

Blanche shook her head.

Eleanor spoke to her quietly: "Don't be afraid to look at them, the bodies. The men will not want you to, but being a woman will not protect you from violence or death. You will be a queen. You will have castles and armies and you must not flinch from doing what you must to protect your husband, or your children. Look. See what death is."

◊∆◊∆◊∆◊∆◊∆◊

As they made ready to leave, Sir William alerted her to the sound of horsemen approaching on a trail from the east. Moments later, a great black destrier burst into the forest clearing, followed by a dozen or more palfreys ridden by armoured men. The rider of the destrier lifted his helm and looked across the fortress remains, a hard scowl on his face.

"What devilry is this?" His dark eyes turned to Sir William, but Eleanor stepped forward.

"I am Eleanor, by the Wrath of God, Queen of England. Were these black-hearted creatures yours, sir?" She jerked her chin towards the ruins.

He smiled thinly. "They were, your grace." He dismounted and bowed. "Hugh Lusignan, Seigneur of Lusignan, Couhe and Chateau-Larcher. This is a great honour."

"Is it?" said Eleanor icily.

"Of course," said Hugh. "Why, it's almost enough to make me forget that my men appear to have been slaughtered by yours."

"Your men, my lord, were kidnappers and traitors."

"Were they indeed?"

"They stole my granddaughter. That is why they are dead."

His eyes fell on Blanche, flanked by two men-at-arms. "You have my deepest apologies, your grace. I gave no orders for my men to waylay a young girl." His eyes flicked back to Eleanor. "I sent them to offer you my humble greetings and invite you for a brief stay at my castle."

Eleanor took two short steps forward. "I am on my way to Normandy to see my granddaughter wed."

"A great occasion. And a great journey. I'm sure you can spare a day or two, perhaps longer, to rest and recover your strength. I assure you I'm a most cordial host."

"As is my son, your king."

"Who is not here."

Eleanor had more men, but they were worn out with little sleep and a fight just behind him. Hugh le Brun's were fresh, mounted, and would run them down easily, even on the uneven ground. Her gamble had been won; she would not risk more lives on another.

Eleanor clasped her hands together and gave Hugh an even mask of a smile. "Very well, as you are so insistent—"

"I am."

"We should be delighted to accept your hospitality. I look forward to sampling the food and wine at your table. Sir William, have a man show the good Seigneur's men where our baggage is. I have no doubt he will wish to see it safely escorted to his castle. And I shall require a horse, my lord, as will my granddaughter. I'm sure that will be no trouble for you."

◊∆◊∆◊∆◊∆◊∆◊

"Is this wise, grandmother?" Blanche asked as they were escorted into the castle courtyard. Stable hands ran to take care of the horses as Eleanor ran a discerning eye over the castle battlements. They were in good order, and the keep had its own portcullis, but the outer walls lacked a moat.

"Wiser than provoking a fight that we would have lost," said Eleanor. "Much power is an illusion. Don't ever give up even the pretence of being in control. Often that is more than enough."

As promised, Hugh offered Eleanor's party a fine meal, and she made sure that all of her men-at-arms and servants ate well too. She could hardly eat the man out of house and home at one sitting, but she saw no harm in giving it her best shot.

It didn't take the Seigneur long to make clear what he wanted.

"La Marche," he told Eleanor. He took a mouthful of wine.

Eleanor gave him a look of the blandest disinterest. "I beg your pardon?"

"Your late husband stole the province of La Marche from my father, and your son refused to return it; now I ask you for justice. I would have been pleased to have brought this to your notice when you toured the Aquitaine last month, but you neglected to visit my lands."

"A most unfortunate oversight," said Eleanor. The tour had raised much goodwill amongst the people, but her cheer had been drowned out by the long dead ghosts in the places she had visited, the fading memories, and the tombs of those she had loved.

"Indeed. Of course, I am more than happy to host you and your party here for as long as you need to consider the matter."

"Very considerate." She picked at her food, finding she had little appetite. There was a chicken bone on her trencher and she wondered what would happen if she were to choke on it. What an upset it would be for poor Hugh if she were to drop dead in the middle of his banquet.

Hugh le Brun inclined his head. "I would never detain you any longer than necessary."

"No?" said Eleanor, raising an eyebrow.

"Of course not. And you need have no fear while you tarry here; this castle is well provisioned and well defended."

"How gratifying to know you have such resources." She glanced at Blanche, noting she was taking a great interest in their conversation.

"I'm always ready to defend the interests of my king and country," said Hugh.

Eleanor held his eye, and waited until he looked away. "The county of La Marche, you say? Very well, it is yours. I give you my word." She spoke carelessly, as though she'd given away no more than an enamel brooch. She stood, and Hugh quickly got to his feet. "Now I shall be on my way. Good day to you, my lord."

Eleanor savoured the seconds the man struggled for words at her abrupt acquiescence.

◊∆◊∆◊∆◊∆◊∆◊

By mid-afternoon, Eleanor was back on the road, the party pushing on towards Bordeaux, with extra provisions and horses supplied by Hugh le Brun.

"Why did you give him La Marche?" asked Blanche. "Why did you not bargain with him?"

"Did you want to spend any more time in the company of the slimy little man?" asked Eleanor. Blanche shook her head. "Neither did I. I'm old, I'm tired, and I've been caged by giants. I will not be held against my will by Hugh le Brun. He will find it more trouble than it's worth in the end: John will not forget the insult, or the loss of taxes from the county." She didn't give voice to the other thought that gnawed at her: how much trouble would John bring upon himself responding to the slight?

Once, she had overseen such grand schemes and designed the intricate plots of a consummate politician. Once, land and people had wrapped themselves around each other until she could not tell one from the other. "Besides," she said, "land is dirt, and my time is precious."

"I heard a story once," said Blanche, "about my great-grandmother, the Empress Maud."

"I wouldn't trust any stories you hear about her, child. Men are minded to conjure the most extraordinary tales about women who would question their place in the world."

"It was about her escape from Oxford Castle."

"Ah," said Eleanor approvingly, "well, that one is more or less true."

"When you were imprisoned by the king, why did you never try to escape?"

"The Empress was besieged by a great army intent on doing her harm; I was in no danger." She cast her mind back to those long sixteen years Henry had kept her captive. "Where would I have escaped to? I needed to be there, for my sons, for when they needed me. I loved Henry; I loved my sons more. My conscience doesn't bother me on the matter, but I've often asked God to forgive me if it was indeed a sin for a wife to betray her husband for love of her sons." She laughed, lightly. "My confessor certainly thinks so." Her expression sobered as she looked at Blanche. "Best not to follow that path; not all kings are as kind as Henry."

"I hadn't planned to," said Blanche, in such a way that she made her grandmother smile again.

"Be vigilant, Blanche. Even when not locked in a tower a queen is bound: to her husband, her children, her country, past and present, and her people. It's a tangled mess of loyalties that your enemies will seek to use against you, and you will have enemies. Armour yourself in charm, arm yourself with words. Cultivate patience, if you can."

"I can be patient."

"Then you're wiser than I was at your age. I'm almost reassured."

Eleanor felt the ache of exhaustion in her bones. The energy reserves she had called upon during the last few days had ebbed away. God felt very close.

"Grandmother?"

Eleanor's eyes snapped open. "Nothing. It's nothing." She took a deep breath and straightened her back. Her hands still held her horse's reins, but the cold had numbed her fingers. Above, the clouds were darker than ever. The storm had not yet broken, but it was close.

Enough of this. She had done enough. Her thoughts turned to Fontevrault Abbey; the peace of its cloisters, and the kindness of its veiled nuns. Yes, she would go there soon, and she would rest. No one could deny her a little peace.

How many more storms? Eleanor asked that night, in her prayers. *How many more until you see fit to call me to you?*

Another Week in the Future, an excerpt

Kaaron Warren

(writing in the style of Catherine Helen Spence)

CONTENTS:

In 1888, seven years before H.G. Wells published *The Time Machine,* Catherine Helen Spence published an SF novel called *A Week in the Future.* You can read the story online at Gutenberg [http://gutenberg.net.au/ebooks06/0603381h.html].

In all honesty, although well-meaning, it isn't a very good novel. It is Catherine Spence's idea of Utopia; equality, no crime, every child cared for, family a strong unit, no advertising, no gambling, no horse-racing.

I wondered how she would imagine 2088, and have written the story with this in mind: she had not actually seen any of the developments of the 20th and 21st centuries. In the novel about 1988, for example, she couldn't imagine a world without hats, aprons and slaves.

I wondered, though, if she wrote this near the end of her life in 1910, when perhaps none of her dreams of Utopia seemed possible, would she see a darker future?

1988 ends this way:

My week has come to an end. Short though it has been, it has been full of interest, full of all that I have accounted life. A good exchange for a year or two of mere existence.

"Now, Lord, let Thy servant depart in peace, now that I have seen the salvation wrought by brotherhood for the families of the earth."

I. Introductory.

The idea of returning to 1888 filled me with dread. All that awaited me was a hospital bed with the sheets so tight and binding I could hardly breathe. And what good could I do then?

So very, very little.

With the tug of my true time pulling at me, the memory of the pain gnawing, I resolved that I would not go back.

I would go forward.

I would take another week in the future, whether or not it meant a lessening of my time on Earth. 1988 was so ordered, so well sorted, I could only imagine what 2088 would be like.

If Doctor Brown were here, I'm sure he would have said my heart would not take it. That I was sixty-two and beyond adventure. He would sit me in his waiting room with the large piles of *Scientific American* and ask me to calm myself. Fortunately, he was not here.

How to obtain the vehicle of my travel, a potion of mandragora, though? It did not seem possible that the plant still existed. I knew that the path in Doctor Brown's back garden was lined with it, but I was far from there in time and space.

Still, needs must, and as ever, anything needed can be found, this time at the hand of a young man I caught loitering. Will there ever be a time when young men are not useful? Perhaps the future will tell. I believe the world would end at such a time. Before he departed, I said to him, "I am Emily Bethel." I felt he needed to know my name or, more truly, I needed him to know it. He nodded, the dear young man, and left me to my travels.

I poured the contents into a wine glass (a little wine, a little water) and I drank, sinking into a sense of peace, so sweet. All illness gone, all weariness, dismay, tiredness. Such calm. I knew what was to come, though.

A spasm, so great I thought my soul would shake loose, then darkness, then…

◊Δ◊Δ◊Δ◊Δ◊Δ◊

II. Monday: Nailsworth. Formerly Australia.
(Excerpt)

I hoped to arrive in Adelaide, South Australia. I had thought to visit my beloved home town and expected to find blue skies over our glorious buildings, with the voices of the familiar, and wide streets and a place to purchase a new hat.

Instead, I awoke sitting in a stationary train. The carriage was filthy, the floor covered with I dare guess not. Across from me, I thought a child slept, from the size, but as she woke I saw she was a grown woman, but small.

She stretched and yawned. "What is the time?" she asked me, as if I were a great clock. "Oh, no, we must rush."

She gathered me along, much strength in her arms.

"Are we in Adelaide?" I asked.

"Adelaide? Adelaide drowned ninety years ago, along with the rest of it."

"The rest of what?"

"The coast," she said, looking at me sidelong. "And most of the inland. All we have left is Central Australia. Why do you think we are so crowded?"

As she spoke we stepped down into red dirt and I saw the truth. There was a mass of people thronging to and fro with purpose. The stench grew and I covered my nose.

I was to discover that this smell was 'petrol' from one direction, 'coal' from another. And 'beer' from a third.

Electric lights powered the streets and electric machines hummed to keep people moving.

Our beautiful country Australia was now called Nailsworth, after the place where coal was found near Adelaide.

I would find many name changes in this time.

Were we still British-run, I wondered? Or had Asia come to the fore, or Russia? I thought perhaps the churches would tell me. Religion is a clear indicator of who rules. I hoped that perhaps religion was not sectarian and very much separate from state. I found instead there was no religion at all, unless you consider worship of the coin, and of alcohol, a religion.

While 1988 had seemed almost familiar, 2088 was as strange to me as my world would seem to a creature from the beginning of time.

In 1988, families had shared large homes.

Now, families were so displaced by all the distillation factories for coal, petrol, and beer that they lived in enormous buildings, one family to a room. In 1988 such things existed but they were pleasantly communal. With a three-child limit then, there had been no chance of overcrowding.

Here, the country half drowned by the surrounding oceans, with millions moved here to work in the mines and the distillation factories, they were literally on top of each other. The children were kept inside, I supposed, because I had not seen a single one, boy or girl.

I travelled to the very edge of the remaining country only to find it edged in steel wire. "For Your Safety, signed the Examiner of Interferences". In my day, this role considered inventions and their uses; I supposed this at least had not changed.

I walked along the steel wire, hoping to find somebody real.

I saw no one. I wondered where the children were. I saw none.

I have some contempt for deserting fathers, but here, too, it seemed, were abandoning mothers. Children who become orphans no longer have protection; too many have died showing this.

I came to a large railway station and asked to where they travelled.

"New Zealand."

I must admit I laughed, thinking this a fine jest. New Zealand was many days by sea voyage! And yet they sold me a ticket (somehow I had money in my pocket) and I settled down for the journey.

It seemed that differences amongst the nations had become so extreme that each island (because they were all such now) had its own purpose.

Australia was a distillation plant.

New Zealand, it seemed, a floating laboratory.

What else would I discover?

◊Δ◊Δ◊Δ◊Δ◊Δ◊

III. Tuesday: Blake. Formerly New Zealand.
(Excerpt)

It was a long journey, but I spent the time talking to my fellow passengers to ascertain the nature of this world we now lived in. I found them, on the whole, uninformed dullards.

They knew nothing of developments with the incandescent lamp, nor of the journey to the North Pole of Besancon and Hermitt. In the end, I allowed them to tell me odd little stories that amused them greatly, while we ate ever more curious and yet tasty foods.

As we approached New Zealand, I saw massive metal cranes, dozens of them. "The anchors," my companions told me. The North Island drowned and the South floats. So they keep it anchored, until they want to move it."

"Why would they want to move it?"

"It is a laboratory. It travels the ocean making tests, seeking answers."

The *Good Ship Blake* was a Floating Laboratory in 1888 and thus came the name of this country.

"To what?" I asked, but they did not seem to know.

To the future, I ventured, but that was not something they cared to consider. All they cared about was tabling their results, with little analysis. They were blind to all else.

All who lived here were involved with science. I admit I found it difficult to fathom. They lived in cubicles, alone, isolated socially for the most part, communicating little.

"Where are the schools", I asked. "Where are the children?"

"We are sterile, here. All of us asexual and sterile. How else would we get our work done? Children are nothing but time drains."

"But they are your future," I said, appalled.

Again, the concept of the future seemed to hold little meaning for them.

◊Δ◊Δ◊Δ◊Δ◊Δ◊

IV. Wednesday: Brail. Formerly Fiji.
(Excerpt)

Another train journey, this time to Brail (Fiji).

I think Louis Braille may be pleased in some ways but saddened in others.

On this island, all are blind. There is not one sighted person amongst them. My fellow passengers were all blind, and chattered excitedly about their new life ahead. Certainly it seemed idyllic.

They did not use electricity so there was none of that awful hum. There was no sin, no violence, no crime. All were married (but children? Where were the children?) and there was no disease. The early vaccinators were right.

I only say Braille would be saddened because none read here in this place named for him.

Still, they seemed very happy and I would have liked to stay but the train beckoned, a new destination.

◊Δ◊Δ◊Δ◊Δ◊Δ◊

V. Thursday: Campbell. Formerly the United Kingdom.
(Excerpt)

On the journey to Campbell (Dr Campbell was a well-known vegetarian advocate) I wondered if the deadly war between labour and capital had ended, or if the cutthroat competition for cheapness had led to catastrophe. It was not hard to imagine.

In this place, gambling had a frightening presence. Horse racing! As vile a sport as any devised, and yet they were obsessed. I spoke to an anxious man, who said that his family relied on his winnings. I must have tutted, because he said, "Your family?"

"My mother passed over." I felt a sudden chill to realise my mother had been dead some 200 years. That there would be nothing left of her physical self.

And yet still I struggled at times to find a life of my own.

"My mother needed care, so I didn't find the time for my own family." I found no trace of my family. My dear niece Florrie most certainly had children, but I found no trace of them, nor of their children, nor of their children's children. I would need half a year to find anyone at all.

"A shame," he said, and I realised that he was being overly pleasant with me. I supposed him to be over fifty, although it is so difficult to tell in this time when facial preservation has come far. I must look ancient beyond all measure to them.

I knew that in 1988, the process of early marriage for all and protection of family and child had minimised greatly crime, vice, poverty and illegitimacy. I see that now, all this is gone. I can only imagine what will come. The degradations of old: cannibalism, infanticide, war, pestilence, prostitution; all fail if we fail to care for our children properly.

My deepest regret should be that I had none of my own, but truly, I found no man with whom I would spend a life. Am I at fault in that? Perhaps.

Every girl in my time knew that if she was tolerably pleasant, she could be married.

I did not choose to be tolerably pleasant.

Here, I discovered all citizens to be vegetarian. At least they imagined they were. Instead, they ate meat by-products made to appear as vegetable matter.

I was summarily ejected from the island on raising this point.

As I waited at the train station, a carload of young people arrived. The citizens cheered, greatly welcoming. "New blood!" they said.

This gives me hope.

◊Δ◊Δ◊Δ◊Δ◊Δ◊

VI. Friday: Maxwell. Formerly Africa.
(Excerpt)

When once this vast land made up many countries, now it is only one, with the coastline shrinking until only Tanzania, with Kilimanjaro, and some surrounding lands remain.

What exists here is a massive sorting demon, which appears to manipulate most of the world's movements.

James Clark Maxwell invented this machine. What strangeness! A sorting demon so large it displaces an entire country!

It is in control of everything from the underground electric railway, which connects all, to the clothing industry. How different it is to the South Australian Co Operative clothing company!

Vanity has risen.

◊Δ◊Δ◊Δ◊Δ◊Δ◊

VII. Saturday: Tientsin. Formerly Europe.
(Excerpt)

Chomage still weighs on my mind as it ever did. Only with employment do we find self-esteem, self-worth and self-improvement. Who would choose to be a beggar?

On the once-great continent of Europe I found little employment of any kind. I can barely speak of what I did find

Beggars everywhere, yet no one to beg from.

An opium haze from border to border. The Treaty of Tientsin 1838 saw a large amount of cocaine imported to the UK.

I thought of the mandrake that facilitated my journey here and wondered if perhaps it might be a better substance for them.

Still no children. "They are at home," I was told time and time again.

I could not bear the smell of the place.

◊Δ◊Δ◊Δ◊Δ◊Δ◊

VIII. Sunday: Diamantina. Formerly North America.

We travelled so quickly it was like a trip from Adelaide to Melbourne.

I remembered this: my friends saying, "You caught cold on the journey (Adelaide, from Melbourne)."

I said, "I have done nothing of the sort. I am hoarse because there were people in the carriage I am not likely to see again. I had important things to tell them."

At last: children! The train was full of infants. The youngest were mere weeks old, cared for by a number of nurses.

There were some sullen-faced adults, and I could not establish a rapport with any of them, much as I tried.

Instead, I helped out with the babies, to the nurses' silent gratitude.

As I travelled, I reflected on all I had seen. This was not the happy world of 1988. It had none of the potential.

There was a terrible screeching of brakes on the other track and we witnessed the most horrendous accident. Our train paused momentarily. I could only hope that lessons could be learnt, because nothing in this life comes without benefit. Not even the very, very worst. I tried to exit the train in order to help, but it seemed the doors would not open.

All I could do was watch helplessly as the carriages burned. We all sat with our faces pressed to the window. Some were weeping; others seemed distant, as if they could not bear to watch.

Three people escaped; we watched them climb through the roof. We cheered, all of us, watching these three young people, while clearly burnt and injured, run along the top of the train. They carried nothing. And there was nowhere to go but along the tracks, because we were in the middle of the ocean.

Our train departed again and I did not see what happened to them.

We arrived in Diamantina, and any hopes I had for the future were dashed.

This country was a mockery of all I had believed in. It was nothing but a poorly run, un-caring orphanage, named for Diamantina, a cruel orphanage in Brisbane.

Was the barbarous practice of war responsible? I asked a sensible-seeming girl how they came to be here.

"We are all orphans. No one can be expected to care for us, so we come here to make a life of our own."

"Was it war?"

She looked at me sidelong. "There is no war anymore. Each of the seven countries has its role and each is happy to fulfil it."

There was that, at least. "And where will you go? Once you are grown?"

"I won't know what train I'm on. I could end up anywhere."

It seemed that when they reached seventeen, they were placed on the first train, regardless of destination. They could end up in Nailsworth, in Blake, in Campbell, in Tientsin or in Maxwell or Brail.

I could think of nothing more to say to her.

In 1988 I had felt convinced that we were on the brink of a great social and industrial revolution, which would alleviate suffering, better mankind and improve our very planet Earth.

I could see now that the revolution had taken place, but, sadly, I saw little betterment at all.

In 1988 the Associated Homes with their gentle but continued pressure all but extinguished the awful and addictive habits of old.

So devastating to see this lost.

I was delighted to see the youngsters in school, although the teachers left something to be desired. It is my understanding they are sent here as an alternative to prison. Only the best of them saw this as a chance for redemption. There are teachers whose classes are a joy.

The rest of them seemed to treat the job as punishment itself.

I met one good teacher, a Miss Tosh, and we got along famously, sharing many a meal. I was not yet used to all the stares I received and she kindly explained, "They are unused to the sight of older people. Even the teachers must depart by the age of twenty-eight."

She took me into her classroom and had me talk of history. I do believe those children were on the edge of their seats.

"Were you there when the comets landed?" one asked.

"2015," the teacher whispered.

"No, I was not." They did not ask me how I had missed that, given my birthdate, and none of them thought to question me further.

They excitedly explained the damage done; the tides rising, the plates shifting.

I am forthright and it shows in my eyes and face. Here, amongst the children, with their honest, if sometimes vile or unpleasant or unintelligent reactions, it was refreshing. Honesty is the way forward. I hoped they wouldn't lose it but I was fairly sure they would.

Children went to school, and they worked to keep the basic facilities open. The drone-like adults fortunately managed most of the work.

There was little 'good' play, though. No gentle games. All of it wild. The young girls dressed like boys so there was no difference in the way they played or ran.

I believe that games, rhythmical, musical and orderly, which the little ones learned, with the avoidance of all horseplay, and all humiliating possibilities, are the beginnings of social, helpful intercourse.

At first glance, you might think that with proper care, these children, these apparent orphans, could grow. We have been so awful to our orphans in the past. Without a family, they have no one to care for them.

How was this not considered in establishing this hellish place? Were no lessons learnt from the past?

I came across a group of young girls. One was crying; the others appeared to have turned their backs on her.

"What is it?" I asked, hoping to comfort her. I thought again that without kind adult intervention, children would not learn kindness.

"Ah, don't mind her. She is a very annoying girl. She is crying because her brother is a murderer and everyone knows it."

"Not true!" the girl said. "He did not cause that accident!"

On further questioning, I understood that three young people (in fact, the ones I had seen escaping the terrible train accident I had witnessed) had been charged with causing that accident. There was no court case; as survivors, they were held to blame. One hundred and eighty-two people had died in the crash and 'someone had to pay', the authorities said.

"What level of insanity is this?" I said. No one would listen.

To my utter devastation, these children were charged with mass murder and sentenced to death. They were brought back to Diamantina, as if the children needed to be terrified into behaving themselves. I tried to push them to act, but not even the young men would respond. I thought, "You are weak and useless," and I thought, "This, perhaps, is the end of the world."

I tried and failed to stop their execution. How is such a thing even considered?

I collapsed. It seemed hopeless, and I was drained of all energy.

All health.

The children left me there in the dust. Some came to poke at me. One burnt me with a match. One tried to steal from me but I mustered a snarl that scared her off.

This was our future.

I felt destroyed.

◊Δ◊Δ◊Δ◊Δ◊Δ◊

IX. The return

I think that I will keep travelling into the future until my past catches up with me.

When there was still hope in my heart of survival (because we do know of our own passing) I thought the world a good place. But now I am dying, the world seems dark and bent on destruction. Have I imagined it all? And yet here is the bare patch of skin burnt by that child. And I can feel the texture of these new clothes, tight and binding.

Tight

And

Binding.

The Lioness

Laura Lam

~The English Channel, 1349~

The lioness and her pride closed in on their prey.

Jeanne de Clisson, known to many as the Lioness of Brittany, pirate queen and sworn enemy of King Philip VI The Fortunate, bared her teeth. "Attack!" she screamed, holding her axe aloft.

Jeanne's son, Guillame, turned the wheel, and the cog swung in the dark waters, heading towards the fat-bellied merchant ship, *La Gracedieux*, which attempted desperately to escape. The three ships of the Lioness's Black Fleet, painted dark and with crimson sails, were far quicker than the smaller craft.

One soul on board would be particularly sweet for Jeanne de Clisson to hunt. Elyas de Blois was a minor noble but cousin and former foster son to her sworn enemy, Charles de Blois, Duke of Brittany. When she killed the boy, word would reach that son of a pig even as he rotted as an English prisoner of war. Her smile grew wider.

"Arrows!" she called, and the archers at the forecastle of the cog began the attack, the slim arrows flying through the air to burrow in the wood of the merchant ship or to pierce flesh. Above them, the sky that had threatened rain all morning released its promise, drenching the decks. Jeanne pushed the wet ropes of hair from her face, moving to the railing.

"Javelins!" she called, and the crew switched weapons, the thicker shafts able to do more damage. She scowled at the rain. She wished she could attack with pots of unslaked lime, but in weather like this, it was far too dangerous, as like to burn her men as her enemy.

La Gracedieux fired arrows back at the Black Fleet, but many missed the ship entirely and were lost to the ocean. The wind was against her prey, who were not as practiced in warfare as the Lioness and her sailors.

"Board!" she cried. Her men were already swinging the grappling hooks over their heads, letting them sail to skid along the other ship's deck before catching in the railing. They were close enough now that Jeanne could see the fear on the sailors' faces on the other ship. She thrummed with the anticipation of blood.

Her sailors pulled the grappling hooks closer, until they could jump onto *La Gracedieux* with ease. Jeanne hoped the crew would not surrender. If they did, there would be no thrill of a fight, only silent slaughter.

Her crew made quick work of most of the merchant sailors. Blood mixed with the rain to stain the decks. She waited until the situation was in hand before she jumped across the gap to the other ship. The smell of iron, salt, and wet wood filled the air. Her axe at the ready, she made her way to the captain, whose arms were pinned by two of her crew.

"Captain," she said, giving him a courtly bow. "I thank you for your ship and your cargo."

He spat at her. His aim was good—the spittle hit her cheek and slid down her neck, the rain already rinsing it clean. She raised her eyebrow at him. Around her the melee continued, men screaming as they were cut down.

She raised her axe and, without ceremony, hit him in the gut with its blade. The captain was not brave in the face of his death. He screamed, high-pitched and terrified, and then bowed forward, gasping with the pain. Red bloomed on his jacket. Jeanne slit his throat with the knife from her belt and he fell to the deck, crimson pooling on the planks.

At her nod, the men dragged the captain's corpse to the side and threw him over.

"Where is he?" she asked her first mate, Sancius.

He knew of whom she spoke. "Below deck. We put him in the brig at the beginning of the fight."

"Excellent. Bring him up. I'd like to have a look at him."

He nodded and went down to fetch the prisoner himself. Jeanne liked that about Sancius. Even with his rank, he didn't mind going down and grabbing the prisoner he knew she was anxious to see. He'd been the first man she'd hired for his brawn and the jagged scars on his forearms and on his cheek. Sancius struck fear into the hearts of the men she was about to attack. They looked at him and forgot about the diminutive woman at his side, at least until she cut their lives short with her sabre or axe.

Sancius dragged the nobleman onto the deck. Elyas de Blois was little older than Jeanne's sons. His deep red hair was dark with rainwater and hung limply in his eyes. He had a pretty face: fine-boned, almost delicate, and a slight build. His green eyes were full of fear yet he held his shoulders back defiantly.

"What a pretty prize," Jeanne said, eying him up and down. Every other person from the merchant ship was now dead but for the two crewmen she'd leave at the next port to take word that the Lioness of Brittany had struck again. She lay down her axe and stepped closer to him. Elyas had been raised under Charles de Blois's roof. Probably loved the evil son-of-a-bitch. Jeanne had heard that Charles thought fondly of the boy, and had toyed with giving him one of his estates in Brittany. That would never do.

When Elyas de Blois's eyes met hers, his face bloomed with something like triumph. He began to mutter, too low for her to hear. A green fire surrounded him in a halo, and the two crew members holding Elyas dropped to the ground, dead. Elyas's eyes glowed bright chartreuse as the words reached a crescendo.

"*Volez, magie, et vaincrez le mal devant moi!*" he cried at the top of his lungs.

The green fire blazed about the boy, crackling like lightning. It left his body and made straight for her.

Green fire surrounded her. Jeanne's eyes streamed tears. She almost wished it would work and take her so she could re-join her husband, Olivier.

Life was not so kind.

The fires extinguished and she was left standing, unhurt.

Elyas's face fell with dismay.

Jeanne smiled at him, pushing the now-dry mane of her hair back from her face. "You underestimated the Lioness, *mon garçon*."

Elyas waited for his death.

"Take him to my quarters and ensure he's well-bound," Jeanne said instead, picking up her axe again and jumping back to her black and red ship. She left her crew behind to clean up the mess.

She'd play with her prey before she ate it.

◊Δ◊Δ◊Δ◊Δ◊Δ◊

Elyas de Blois had been imprisoned in the captain's quarters for hours, but the Lioness was nowhere to be seen. Every creak of the ship made him start in fear. The quarters were spacious for a ship, sumptuous and lavish. He was tied to a post against one wall, his legs bound in front of him. The bonds were tight enough that his fingers and toes tingled. He watched through the porthole as the sun set and the light in the room dimmed. Why had the spell not worked? The king himself had given it to him. Elyas had been at court the previous summer, and in the middle of the night he'd been woken by a servant and brought to the king's bedchambers. Elyas at first wondered if he were to be the king's new lover. But that was not why the king had called for him.

Another man was in the room as well, dressed in a hooded black robe. Elyas learned who he was later: Guichard de Troyes, a powerful bishop who had been tried for sorcery, maleficia and poisoning. He was accused of killing Queen Jeanne de Navarre, invoking the Devil with other priests and a sorceress who later turned against him. De Troyes' chamberlain was tortured until he confirmed the story, and then dozens of other voices also spoke up against de Troyes.

Yet after a few years, de Troyes was released, and rebuilt his reputation. He offered to be the king's personal sorcerer. Though Philip VI was said to loathe magic in all its forms, he recognized the need for the power and protection it could provide. Guichard de Troyes became a spider in the web of the court

If Elyas had known all that when he first met the sorcerer, he might have screamed and run from the king's suite. Instead, he was told a tale of a vengeful woman who took to the seas and left death in her wake. Her piracy had long been a thorn in the king's side. His health was failing, and one of his wishes was for the Lioness of Brittany to die before he did.

Elyas learned that Charles de Blois had assured the king he was trustworthy. Elyas still did not know whether to be grateful to his cousin or curse his name. Charles would never have agreed to sorcery. He was the most pious man Elyas had ever met: he wore hair shirts beneath his clothes, flagellated himself until blood ran down his back, and wrapped coarse ropes about his body so that they chafed.

Elyas had no choice but to agree to be the bait in a trap for the Lioness of Brittany. He was given a locket to wear around his neck. Within it were magical herbs and animal parts to focus power. The gold of the metal was embedded with magic. All he had to do to unleash the spell was speak the incantation while looking the Lioness in the eye.

He'd done all they asked of him. The magic of the strongest wizard in France had not worked. Jeanne de Clisson did not have so much as a singed eyebrow.

How had this happened?

He had hoped, so badly, to kill the Lioness. The king would reward him. Elyas would, finally, no longer be terrified of Charles de Blois.

Instead, Elyas would not live to see the dawn.

The door opened and the Lioness entered. Elays forced himself not to flinch. He'd die as a man, not as the simpering, frightened boy he'd always been.

Jeanne de Clisson stared at him silently, arms crossed below her bosom. He'd built her up in his mind over the last few months as a fearsome witch. Out there on the deck, she had been.

Now, her hair had dried into messy brown curls about her face. She was nearly fifty, her face lined with time and tanned from the sun, her strong-boned face attractive. She wore no paints or perfumes like the ladies at court, nor did Elyas expect she'd worn a dress since she took to the sea. She was clad in men's clothing; loose trousers, a white shirt and coat, a sword belt slung low on her hips. She'd borne seven children, yet she was trim and muscular from life on a ship. Jeanne de Clisson, with her calm stare, did not seem mad with revenge, yet she must be, to give up everything she'd known, all her possessions, to have sold her very body, to become a pirate and cause as much woe to France as she could.

"Elyas de Blois," she said, coming closer and sitting down, crossing her legs. Elyas stared at her leather boots, no longer wishing to meet her gaze.

"How did you survive that spell?" he asked, helplessly.

He glanced up at her, and saw the glimmer of madness lurking behind her eyes. "Who sent you?" she countered rather than answering. "The king or Charles? Both?"

Elyas hunched his shoulders. He felt bruised and battered, and he could only hope he wouldn't give everything up when she began to torture him.

"Charles probably would have trouble arranging a meeting with a wizard, what with his faith to the Lord," her mouth twisted with irony, "and being a prisoner of war in England. So, the king. Let me guess: he told you this spell was infallible. You would receive the bounty on my head, a title, perhaps an estate given to you by Charles once he's released. You would live the rest of your life in luxury, find a pretty, well-born girl to marry, and have the perfect life until you died an old man in your sleep."

She made his desires sound so pathetic.

"Charles and Philip are not in the business of making people's lives easier."

Elyas gaped at her informality. Though a breach in etiquette was nothing compared to murdering her way across the English Channel.

"You know what they did to me," Jeanne said. "You know why they deserve to suffer."

He had studied every detail of her life. He'd learned about her long-departed husband, Olivier de Clisson. He had been friends with Charles de Blois for years, but was persuaded to side with Edward III when the English king decided he had a clearer claim to the Breton throne than Philip VI. When King Philip learned of Olivier's deal, he invited him to a joust on French soil, and promptly had him arrested. Many believed that it was Charles de Blois who told the king about Olivier's defection, and Elyas thought that was likely true.

There was only one course of action imaginable—once the other lords of the region learned of Olivier's leanings, many others would have followed suit, and Philip VI might have a civil war on his hands. So on August 2nd 1343, Olivier de Clisson was found guilty of treason and beheaded. His headless corpse swung from Montfaucon in Paris, and his head was impaled on a lance over the Sauvetout gate in Nantes in Brittany.

Jeanne de Clisson had brought her sons to stare up at the rotting head of their father. That was when the madness took hold, according to legend. She swore she would stop at nothing to have her revenge on the king and Charles. She sold all her lands and belongings. Some swore she also sold her body to the highest bidder.

For six years, she had attacked ship after ship, selling their cargo to the English. Judging by the gold and treasures here in the captain's quarters, she was a rich woman now. Three of her sons, all youths, served with her, witness to every brutality.

Her revenge would not stop until Philip VI or Charles de Blois was dead.

King Philip had plenty to contend with. The war with England, and France's recent defeat at the Battle of Crécy. The death count was high, and rationing had pinched the populace hard. The Black Death spread across the land, killing subject after subject.

But the king was fixated on this woman who had smuggled goods to the English during the Battle of Crécy, who took weapons and stores meant for his soldiers, who beheaded noblemen and prominent merchants.

Elyas had been sent here to end her, and he had failed.

Would she claw out his eyes, disembowel him, or inflict some other evil he could not imagine? She had to be a witch, the way the green flames had not harmed her.

"I know that the king's justice can be harsh…" he began, and winced as Jeanne cut him off with a rough laugh.

"That was not justice. My husband fought for the French, but your cousin decided he was a traitor and convinced the king. Olivier is dead because of Charles and your king."

Elyas had never been a silver-tongued diplomat like many members of his family. Especially Charles. His cousin could have talked Jesus into committing sin, if he didn't consider such a thing unspeakably blasphemous. "It was not justice," he agreed, though his stomach twisted to be speaking treason against his sovereign. "But is this—what you are doing—any better?"

Jeanne looked him over with a new intensity. Her lips tightened, deepening the small lines by her mouth. "Everyone whose life I've taken has committed crimes."

"You don't know that," he said. His imminent death made him bolder. "There was a boy on *La Gracedieux*, just a cabin boy. Fourteen years old. Is he dead?"

Jeanne shook her head. "He's one of the survivors. I usually keep the youths alive. He'll be dropped off at the next port."

Anger flared within him. "He'll never recover from the death he's seen at your hands. He'll never be the same person he was."

"I'll never be the woman I was before Olivier was murdered."

"You don't know the deeds of every man you've killed, unless you've powers greater than any I've ever heard of. Who are you to enact justice any more than the king?" Jeanne blinked in surprise. Elyas guessed that no one spoke to her so bluntly. Truth might be his only chance. "I know as well as you how cruel and how heartless Charles de Blois can be."

Jeanne considered him. Elyas's heartbeat thundered in his ears, but he didn't look away from her, not even to blink. "Yes," she said, quietly. "Perhaps you do." She came towards him, slinking like her lioness namesake. Elyas pressed himself back against the post as she untied his bonds. "Let us speak properly before I decide what to do with you."

He stood up. She was a head and shoulders shorter than him. She motioned for him to sit across from her at the table. His muscles had cramped from hours in the same position, and he did not move gracefully. He stifled a groan as his muscles loosened, blood returning to his fingers and toes.

Jeanne rested her elbows on the table, interlacing her fingers.

"I saw you once, you know," he said. "You and your husband came to visit my cousin. I was eleven." She was a completely different woman. Still strong, but a different kind of strength hidden by fancy dresses and hand-stitched lace.

"I don't remember you."

"I was hiding behind the curtains. I wasn't allowed to dinner that night."

He'd had scraps thrown to him like a dog, and not enough to fill his belly. Back then, Elyas was always being punished for one infraction or another. Sometimes real, sometimes imagined.

"You seemed happy," he said, remembering her easy smile, the way she held her husband's hand under the table. Olivier was Jeanne's second husband. She'd first been married when she was twelve, to Geoffrey de Châteaubriant. They had two children before he died. But Olivier and Jeanne…even at eleven, Elyas had seen the love that sparked between them. Charles de Blois had no love for his own wife. Had he been jealous?

"How did Charles treat you?" she asked, her eyes bright with curiosity.

"You know what kind of man he is. It drove you to piracy. What do you think living under his roof for five years did to me?"

Elyas had to prove to her that he was as much a victim of Charles de Blois and the king as she was. It was his only chance.

"Tell me," she commanded.

He managed to raise an eyebrow at her. "All the grisly details?"

"*Oui*. Everything."

And so he told her of the whippings, the starving, the nights left out in the cold. Charles de Blois found so many ways to harm him without anyone else finding out. In front of others, he was the doting uncle, the generous man who had taken his brother's youngest son onto his estate for education and care. But he received little of either. Elyas had always known what kind of man his uncle could be, but he never told anyone, for fear of being disbelieved. He should have tried; he knew the laws now. Charles shouldn't have harmed a hair on his head, for it would mean forfeiting his fostering fee and broken the alliance between the branches of the Blois family. But as a frightened child, he thought that was the only life for him. That pain was the only path to salvation.

"So you agreed to the spell to give yourself freedom over your own life."

"If I refused, the king would have killed me."

"That, too." Her eyes held no pity, but she regarded him differently than when she first entered the room. Elyas did not know if that meant she would spare him.

"Why didn't it work?" he asked. "They said that it was foolproof. I said the spell correctly."

"All men are fools, and it was made by a man. So it could not have been foolproof." She reached into her pocket and pulled out the amulet that had once contained the spell. The gold was warped, and when she opened it, Elyas smelled singed dried plants and animal fur.

"On anyone else, it would have worked." She reached into her blouse and pulled out another amulet. It looked like a large, ancient coin, marked with occult symbols. Once, it may have been bright copper, but now it was caked with verdigris. He could sense the power radiating from it. The air smelled like a stormy night, with lightning about to strike. She held it in her hands and it glowed violet. Her curls rippled in an unseen wind. She slipped the amulet back against her skin, and the room seemed to brighten.

"I was a pirate on land before I took to sea," she said.

"Yes." Elyas knew this, as he knew so much else about her. She had raised a force of men, but soon decided it was safer on the water.

"You know of Thébaut, *n'est-ce pas*?"

"*Bien sûr*." One of her most famous crimes was sacking the garrison at the Chateau Thébaut.

"There was a wizard there, hiding from your king. He gave me this in return for sparing him and his family, if I promised to do as much harm to the king as I could. It seemed a fair trade. While I wear this, no magic can harm me."

He debated lunging at her and plucking the amulet from her neck, leaving her vulnerable. But for what? The spell was spent, and she'd have her axe in his gut before he could leave the room. "Then why would he part with it? Wouldn't it leave him vulnerable?"

She laughed. "Not when he was the only man on Earth who could conjure them. I'm sure he had others. I was sceptical at first, thinking it was a trick, but it has saved my life more times than I can count. You're not the first assassin sent my way. You're unlikely to be the last."

"You may as well kill me," Elyas said. "If I go back without your head in a bag, they'll impale mine on the Sauvetout gate in Nantes."

One side of her mouth quirked. "That's true enough."

He didn't let her see his fear. "All I ask, *madame*, is that the death be quick and painless."

"Painless until you wake up in hell for dabbling with witchcraft?"

He swallowed. She was cruel to tease him before she killed him. "Yes, until I do penance for my sins in the next life."

She leaned close to him, pushed the hair back from his face. She did not look insane, or angry. Only sad. She kissed his forehead, and Elyas closed his eyes, tears falling down his face.

"I can do that," she whispered. She went to a cabinet and brought out a bottle of wine, pouring it into a silver goblet. From another cupboard, she took a twist of paper and emptied powder into the wine. She held it out to him. "Here," she said. "A little alchemy of my own."

He took the goblet in hands that shook. "Will it hurt?"

"Not a bit."

He took a deep breath. "*Merci*. I'd…I'd rather drink poisoned wine than have my head struck off with an axe." It was her preferred method of executing the French noblemen she came across.

"Drink, Elyas."

He lifted his glass to her. "To the Lioness of Brittany, the most feared pirate on the seas." He couldn't help but admire her. She did not bow when tragedy struck her, but fought tooth and nail. His life, by contrast, was failure after failure. Had he ever made a decision that was all his own?

Too late for regrets.

He drank the wine quickly. She waited with him, holding his hand until his eyes closed.

◊∆◊∆◊∆◊∆◊∆◊

Jeanne de Clisson looked out at the dark smudge of land on the horizon, sipping a glass of dark red wine. The sea was quiet, the sky clear, the wind perfectly guiding them towards the shore. The Black Fleet sailed, holds full of cargo from the scuttled *La Gracedieux* and other ships fallen prey to the Lioness. As the men and women around her worked, Jeanne allowed herself a brief moment to rest her feet and let her thoughts drift as she finished her wine.

When they reached shore, her crew unloaded the cargo with practiced motions, passing the chests to the Englishmen who stood with the merchant she always worked with, Sir John Archer, as well as the lieutenant of the English Army, Walter Bentley. The gentlemen doffed their hats to her, and she nodded her head at them.

"I've a favour to ask," she said in their barbaric English.

Walter Bentley spread his hands. "What does the Lioness require?"

Jeanne motioned to Sancius. He disappeared for a moment and then came onto the deck carrying a slumped form. The merchant and the soldier looked at the body in consternation. Jeanne took her bottle of water and splashed some on the boy's face.

Elyas de Blois groaned and his eyes opened. The first thing he saw was the Lioness of Brittany.

"I'm not dead?" he asked, confused.

"Not yet," she said. She looked to Walter Bentley. "I need you to help this cub. Find him somewhere he won't come to harm. A monastery, or a small town where he can learn a trade. He can't go back to France."

"Certainly," Walter said. "It would be my pleasure."

Sancius helped the unsteady Elyas to his feet. Jeanne took the boy's arm and led him away from the others so they could speak privately. "Go with him," she said, nodding to Walter. "He'll find you somewhere safe."

"Where am I?"

"England."

He blinked at her. "So you are helping the English."

"Don't make me regret not killing you," she said. "The country across the water may as well not exist for you. Do you understand? You must not send word that you live."

He gazed out across the water, seeming very young. "I understand. France is gone."

"*Bien.*"

"Why are you doing this?" he asked.

She shrugged. "I don't know."

"Are you still going to enforce your justice on others?" he asked. "Kill everyone in your way?"

Her face was hard as she gazed out to sea. "Don't think one act of kindness stops me from being the Lioness. Don't think you've saved me from myself. Philip VI and Charles de Blois are out there. I still need to make them bleed."

Elyas de Blois was still woozy from the drugs and from the shock that he was not dead. "I hope you find the peace you search for, my lady. I'll do my best to find some of my own."

"See that you do. *Adieu*, Elyas."

"*Adieu*, Jeanne."

He walked unsteadily back to Walter Bentley. Jeanne raised her arm in farewell and climbed back onto her ship, its red sails slack.

"We sail tomorrow, my lady?" Sancius asked.

"Yes. Back to the sea. There's still more prey to catch."

Cora Crane and the Trouble With Me

Sandra McDonald

Her first marriage ends in violence and divorce. At least he teaches her how to run a gambling house. The second marriage is to an esteemed British officer. Off he goes to colonial service in India, leaving her with the quaint title of "Empire widow." Her third husband, common law if not properly contracted, dies tragically young after an exhausting and painful illness. His death burdens her with debts and the weight of broken literary promises. Her fourth husband kills her lover but is acquitted by a jury for a crime of passion. Her last lover would marry her in an instant but he can't get a divorce from his wife.

Cora's love life is complicated.

Was complicated. She's dead now, buried in an unremarkable grave in the very beautiful Evergreen Cemetery in Jacksonville, Florida. All things die, sooner or later. They flare for a brief moment, nothing more than yellow candle glow in the long dark night of eternity. They flicker out and everyone forgets their name.

Cora's marble headstone omits most of her names—the ones she was born with, the others she took through marriage, the pseudonyms she adopted for her writing and for her complicated business transactions. The establishments she owned in Jacksonville seaport and further east along the beach have long been ground down to dust. The husband she loved most is buried a thousand miles away. She had no heirs. She only had me.

What am I? Her undiscovered autobiography, trapped in an unmarked box in a forgotten room in Jacksonville's library archives. Hundreds of brittle pages she typewrote in those last few months of her life, listening to horse-drawn carriages and newfangled motorcars while the dark blue ocean rolled in and off the continent's edge.

I am the culmination of Cora Crane's travels, travails, ruminations, and regrets.

The title page says, "The Trouble with Me".

Let's start this story with the whores, shall we?

◊Δ◊Δ◊Δ◊Δ◊Δ◊

They call it the line: a row of brothels and parlour houses that cater to tourists or local men seeking sex away from their fancy or boring or steadfast wives. The year is 1896 and prostitution is so popular in Jacksonville that hotel desk clerks distribute maps and guide books free of charge.

The girls on the line know all sorts of pleasure tricks. They know how to use their fingers and mouths, how to take a man front or back, how to keep a baby from happening, how to treat themselves for lice and other unpleasant venereal diseases. They know to be coy and how to smile through a bad night. They know how to cat fight with one another and ignore the town folk who call them jezebels. They know many things except how to stop the passing years from grinding away their beauty and young faces, turning them to wrinkled middle-aged women with few prospects in the world.

Cora's not much older than they are, but they call her Ma.

As for herself, Cora knows she's not beautiful. But she is stylish and confident, and educated, too. She reads voraciously. She can calculate losses and revenue. By the age of thirty-one she has bought the Hotel de Dream, a rooming house near the line, and turned it into one of the city's most exciting destinations. She has competition: Lyda de Camp runs a popular bawdyhouse, as does the fierce woman they call Russian Belle. Cora, however, takes the best care of her girls. She feeds them good food, encourages dental hygiene, and forgives them when they run off owing her money.

Money's a sore spot for Cora. Husband One's funds diminished long ago, and Husband Two won't answer her letters from his post in India. After a good night, she banks large wads of cash while ignoring the cold stares of the proper women in town. On slow nights, as the River City settles to sleep around her, she sits by the yellow light of a lamp and writes about men, manners, love and adventure.

Ideas burn in Cora's blood. Words float through her dreams. The only thing better than a wealthy man in her parlour is a rich sentence in her head. She aspires to worldwide travel and journalism like that intrepid female journalist Nellie Bly, who famously had herself committed so that she could report on the madness of asylums.

One day Cora too will be celebrated for her writing. She promises herself that. Her books will be in the finest bookstores and libraries, so lauded worldwide for their insight and wit that no one will care about brothels and scandal.

Until then, she buys beer cheap and sells it at for exorbitant profit. She gathers painted girls to her side and deploys them to the sailors, merchants, bankers, travelers, and railroad men who have money to spare. She puts on fine blue hats and walks the wooden sidewalks with her head held high, ignoring the whispers of scandal that trail her like the morning mist.

One cold night in November, and by cold I mean temperatures positively tropical when compared to the frigid North, a young journalist named Steve Crane steps off a train, takes up lodging at the fine St. James Hotel, and heads out into the darkness seeking pleasure. He knows where to go. He's been to town before. Fumble-mouthed with women, already wasting his good looks and health with alcohol and tobacco and opium, he has enough money to pay for some good times before he ships off to cover the rebellion in Cuba.

He and Cora meet. She's read and admired his book about a poor girl in the city, and the other one about a soldier in the Civil War. He enjoys her flattery, her direct gaze, her vision of a future filled with mutual prosperity and success. After his boat founders on the way to Cuba, she takes him home and helps him write the tale for newspapers and later Scribner's. He asks her to close the Hotel de Dream and come with him to Europe.

She is in love. She makes mistakes.

They journey to Greece to cover the war and then take up residence in verdant England, making friends with fellow refugees from proper society. In a rented country estate they entertain Henry James and H.G. Wells and Joseph Conrad, along with assorted wives, lovers, children, dogs, and eccentric visitors. Viva la vie Bohème! That Cora and Steve are not officially wed is the matter of some gossip, especially among those who know of Cora's still-binding marriage to the British man in India who will not respond to her letters. She ignores what she can't change.

They run up debt. Steve runs away. To Havana, to New York, to distant whorehouses, to hotels where he can sit without distraction and pen his stories in black ink. He doesn't write to her. Cora's temper grows short as she tries to juggle payments to grocers, butchers, landlords, and servants. She tells invented stories about Steve to anyone who will listen and lend her money.

"Full of deceit and cruel to others," Cora writes in her diary. "That's the trouble with me."

Only after Steve begins coughing up traces of scarlet blood does he return to her caring embrace. She forgives his escapades. What else can she do? After his candle flickers out in a sanitorium in the Black Forest, his American family refuses her financial support.

She returns to Jacksonville and slides back into the pleasure business with a lavish new parlour house that becomes the best bordello in town. We don't need to talk about her next husband, who persuades a jury to acquit him of murder but gets his just reward when his next wife shoots him dead.

Meanwhile, the intrepid Nellie Bly has married a millionaire manufacturer. Now she has fame and fortune both. Cora has a lonely bed that she fills with entirely unsuitable men.

◊∆◊∆◊∆◊∆◊∆◊

Because Nellie is only a year older than Cora, Cora imagines them as spiritual sisters separated at birth. The socialite Jennie Jerome is a decade older than Cora, but they are both daughters of America who prefer the streets and sights of London.

Just as bad with money, just as in love with life, witty and beautiful Jennie makes every wise decision that Cora does not. She marries an Englishman with good prospects and doesn't divorce him. Of course there are dalliances with handsome lovers and one future king, but she waits for her Lord Randolph to die before moving onward to new and dubious marriages. Jennie writes plays, but doesn't let literary daydreams derail her considerable charity work and duties to society. Jennie makes and keeps a wide variety of influential friends and associates, many of whom help her political ambitions.

Jennie's family owns an enormous palace. Cora and Steve don't have modern plumbing or electricity, but their country estate is at least rumored to be haunted. Jennie marries for love and money. Cora can't marry Steve thanks to that stubborn man in India, but throughout her life she chases love across continents and lavish rooms filled with the smoke of men's cigars.

They are friends, Jennie and Cora, charming their fellow members of Society of American Women in London. Witness this black and white photo from a summertime dinner, hundreds of women in corsets, hats and frills. Jennie and Cora sit in the center of them all, united and resolute. On the topic of feminism, however, they disagree. Jennie fights for a woman's right to vote and captain her own destiny. Cora has no quarrel with the power of men in society until her Stevie dies and she finds little support from creditors, solicitors and publishers.

Their lives differ in one other crucial way. Jennie bears two children. Her oldest son Winston becomes prime minister of England. Cora has no children, although she helps bury one or two after her girls succumb to pregnancy.

I'm Cora's legacy, and my letters fade more each day.

◊Δ◊Δ◊Δ◊Δ◊Δ◊

This is their best year. 1899. Steve has returned from his flings in Cuba. The tuberculosis has not yet begun to waste him into the shriveled man of his final days. Money is tight, distractions too plentiful, but Steve has a new book coming out and Cora's essays are blossoming in print as well. She is known as a gracious hostess, if eccentric and lofty. She cooks doughnuts that delight her guests. She imagines the bright future unfolding.

Steve's novel is not well received. The debts continue to grow. Scarlet blood stains his lips and cigarettes. Every day brings new bills demanding payment. Each week Steve sends out letters beseeching publishers for advances on books and stories he will never write. Cora prods and pushes him, as she does herself, and they argue until he storms off to go sleep with his favourite dog.

"Harsh speech that cuts too deep," Cora writes in her diary. "That's the trouble with me."

Winter comes with bitter air, but nothing prevents Cora and Steve from hosting a lavish holiday party for sixty of their closest friends. They invite the ghost who lives in the house and write him into a romp complete with music and song. They do the two-step and then a waltz by firelight, such a loving couple. The next day, Steve collapses with a lung hemorrhage that begins his long sad decline to death.

He dies in June, huddled in a clean white bed and holding the damn dog.

◊Δ◊Δ◊Δ◊Δ◊Δ◊

An alternate history: Steve Crane comes to Jacksonville and makes his way down the line, stopping at Lyda de Camp's house to dally with some soiled doves who've never read his work. He sails to Cuba, survives the sinking, writes his story "The Open Boat" without help, and eventually reaches Havana. He covers a near-fatal ambush of Teddy Roosevelt's Rough Riders in the dangerous hills. Returning to his family in New Jersey, he succumbs to their concerns over his health and seeks medical treatment with the very best doctors. He dies not at aged twenty-eight but instead the age of fifty, having published several more successful novels.

Cora Taylor, as she is then known, never has reason to close the Hotel de Dream. She remains one of Jacksonville's most popular madams. She enters into a long relationship with a local businessman, Ernest Budd, and never moves to England, never meets Jennie Jerome, never dines on midnight snacks with H.G. Wells and Henry James in a haunted English castle. Ernest eventually wins a divorce from his shrewish wife, and he and Cora move to the seaside happily ever after.

Cora and Steve could have been ships that passed unnoticed in the night. Instead, as Steve observed in poetry, their love was full of the water's turmoil, passing yellow lights, and then the silence of the dark sea.

◊Δ◊Δ◊Δ◊Δ◊Δ◊

This is Cora's life in the spring of 1900: Steve is dying. Since Christmas, his mind and pen have faltered to the point he can barely read his correspondence, can't pull together a story, can't be bothered to worry about the crushing debt weighing more heavily with each passing day. The tuberculosis he caught while young in New York City, the malaria he suffered in Cuba, the fistula that has bothered him since summer—who can say for sure why he is diminishing, but his thin body won't last much longer.

Cora is frantic, exhausted, desperate. Her only hope is a trip to specialists in the Black Forest of Germany, but the journey is exorbitantly expensive and Steve is so tired, so frail. She begs for money from every available source, hires nurses, arranges for train tickets and coaches, and even brings along Steve's favorite dog Sponge.

She will do anything to keep him, but he leaves her anyway.

And here is Cora in the summer of 1910: she lives mostly at the beach these days, watching the ocean while managing the Court from afar. Forty-five years old, no longer slim and fashionable, she is trying to recuperate from a slight stroke that turned the left side of her face numb. Ernest spends as much time with her as he can hide from his cruel wife. It's a relief, really, to call most her time her own. Perhaps, like Steve in his bed at Christmastime, she has a premonition that her days are dwindling. Certainly some low feeling in her gut drives her to type late into each night, detailing long-ago soirees and long-lost friends and old failures. She can almost hear Steve's voice in her ear, cataloging the disappointments of his career and hers.

"Hold too tight to soured dreams," she writes. "That's the trouble with me."

What of Jennie Jerome? She's still in England, and now married to a man the same age as her son Winston. That union will soon end in divorce. She'll have one more mismatched marriage before high heels and a bad fall lead to gangrene and death in 1921. She's buried next to her first husband, Lord Randolph, who proved that a fortuitous marriage early in a woman's life can make all the difference to her lasting success.

And what of Nellie Bly? She is widowed now, and the company she inherited from her millionaire husband will collapse into bankruptcy in 1911. Her story is far from over, for World War I will open up another chapter for her that Cora will never read about. Even that good fortune fades. In 1922, Nellie dies alone and poor in a New York City hospital.

Pneumonia, they say. She is buried in the Bronx under her pseudonym and real name, Elizabeth Cochrane Seaman. Although during her lifetime she made much more money at writing than Stephen Crane, she is far less remembered.

On this last day of her life in September 1910, Cora doesn't think about Nellie or Jennie. She's doesn't even think about Steve. She rises late, eats a breakfast of hot tea and cold cheese, and watches the yellow sun reflect on the Atlantic. Bathers frolic in the surf, water soaking their wool swim dresses and suits. Cora thinks about her girls back at the Court, and how she should redecorate their rooms to keep the place fresh, and who she'll hire to play the piano now that the regular man is moving on to Gainesville. She's planning to balance the accounting ledgers. She's hoping Ernest comes on the noon train from Jacksonville with some of those gourmet chocolates he knows she adores, and later maybe they'll travel up to Mayport for some fresh crabs.

It's noon, but Ernest doesn't arrive. Instead, Cora helps a female motorist free her car from the tricky beach sand nearby and then, struck by a headache, retires to her bed to listen to seagulls and shrieks of laughter from the surf. She slips into a coma and dies alone, covered by thin quilt and slants of yellow sunlight, an open book strewn in her lap.

◊Δ◊Δ◊Δ◊Δ◊Δ◊

Not an alternate history, but instead a true story lost in time. The year is 1886, and a giddy Cora accepts a marriage proposal from a dashing rogue named Tommy who lives in the same boarding house as she does on Fifth Avenue in New York City. Surely marriage will set them both on a successful course through life. Although Cora dreams of becoming a Broadway actress, the closest she usually gets are the cheap seats to afternoon matinees. The night after they become engaged, Tommy treats her to good tickets for a now-forgotten play at the Herald Square Theater on Broadway. Holding hands in the dark with Tommy's warm whispers in her ear, young Cora has no way of knowing her marriage will only last two rocky years.

Seated in the most expensive seats that night are Lady Randolph and the cousins she has come to visit from London. Sitting five rows behind Cora and Tommy is Elizabeth Cochrane, an ambitious reporter from Pittsburgh who is thinking of moving to New York City.

After the show, on the short walk home, Cora's gaze flickers for a moment over a teenage boy playing hooky from his seminary school in Trenton. He's got dark hair and a thin face and gleam in his eye that promises trouble. Then Tommy laughs at something, tugs at Cora's arm, and the boy is forgotten.

Impossible, you say. Why would I lie? We are all of us ships that pass in the darkness and sail on. Yet sometimes we drop anchor together, however briefly, in ports foreign and domestic.

◊Δ◊Δ◊Δ◊Δ◊Δ◊

One last note to these notes: I am not forgotten after all.

An adjunct professor with a passion for history and a librarian boyfriend has rescued me from my shelf, carefully dusted off my pages, and is digitising me for future generations. Cora's autobiography will be available for the entire world to see. A story can't ask for a finer fate.

During her labours, the professor realizes Cora's typewriter had a worn-away "n" key that barely nudged ribbon ink onto the paper. This autobiography's title: *The Trouble with Men*. Her original passages:

"Full of deceit and cruel to others. That's the trouble with men."

"Harsh speech that cuts too deep. That's the trouble with men."

"Hold too tight to soured dreams. That's the trouble with men."

At the end was she truly bitter? Wounded? Certainly many men treated her wrong, and she had a penchant for picking the worst among them. I couldn't blame her for any cynicism or disappointment. But she never finished typing my pages to share her final disposition on the matter.

Know this much: on the last sunny afternoon of her life, in that bedroom by the sea, she took with her to bed a worn copy of *Maggie: A Girl of the Streets*. It was the first novel Steve published, and the first of his works she fell in love with. Maggie the prostitute makes some bad choices and dies tragically young. Cora made many bad choices, but here at middle age she has the Court and her girls, this house aside the pale sand and blue waves, and a lover who might be arriving later bearing a box of sweets.

The inscription in the book reads, "To my beloved wife/Two ships in the night/Love always/your Steve."

Vintana

Thoraiya Dyer

~I. Madagascar, April 1828~

A cow will never starve to please a god.

Yet there he is, Radama, my blundering bull of a husband, refusing to partake of the zebu sacrifice to honour his ancestors.

From the shaded corner of the palace courtyard, a fan held in front of my face, I quiver with rage and shame to see him, calling foolishly for fish as though the long-horned royal herds were not a sacred channel for communication with the blessed dead. As though the Lenten fast should mean anything to a king of the Merina.

And if the dead should curse him? If he should lose all that our father gained, the rule of the whole island, from sea to sea? Is he already cursed? Is that why demons of drink keep him from my bed, when I am the only one of his twelve Great Wives sanctified to bear the royal heir?

Three servants wait on me in the courtyard. The Royal Cook, the Royal Ombiasy and the Royal Weaver. All three of them have been loyal since the day, almost twenty years ago, that I was adopted by the old king and betrothed to Radama. They expected, as I did, that I would fall pregnant quickly, that my position would be secured. We were all mistaken.

My womb remains empty. Even Andrianmihaja, my valiant young officer, my true love, has not been able to fill it. He fills my heart but a full heart is not enough. Only greater piety can win the ancestors' favour. Only greater respect for tradition can win a child for Radama and for me.

The king refuses the red meat a second time. He refuses to see he is leading us to disaster.

"Shall I fetch some fish for him, Great Wife?" the Royal Cook whispers. A tall and wide-hipped woman with big, scarred hands, she squats on her heels in her lamba wrap to keep her slave's head lower than mine. Her teeth are very white and her cheeks dimpled.

"It is one thing to serve fish to foreigners," the Royal Ombiasy mutters. "Quite another for the king to insult the very bloodline that brought him to the throne."

The Royal Ombiasy wields supernatural powers. He is a wearer of crocodile teeth, a selector of suitably marked zebu for sacrifice and a guardian of one of the twelve royal sampy. The sampy are exceptionally powerful talismans, sometimes worn, sometimes paraded, always respected and feared, which grant victory to armed forces, warn of danger and foretell the future.

He is also a skinny old man with a round, bald head and conspicuously protruding ears. When he grows too bossy with me, I rub his head to ignite his temper. I am not afraid of the Ombiasy. The sampy Ingahibe, though he seems no more than several ornamented wood-sections to an outsider, is another matter.

"Fetch the king some blackfish from the west," the Royal Weaver suggests salaciously. "Radama will lick the bones clean."

My anger abruptly alters direction. I find it difficult not to strike her. The Royal Weaver was born a princess, as I was, and sometimes forgets how far she is fallen. She dares to speak to me of Radama's favourite wife, she of the ebony skin from the Sakalava tribe in the west. He licks her clean. That is certain. She has birthed his child, but that child will never rule.

"Do not irk me," I say, fluttering the fan, "unless you wish to begin weaving your own funeral shroud."

"Forgive me, Great Wife." The Royal Weaver bows her grey head.

"Fetch my husband what he asks for," I tell the Royal Cook.

"At once, Great Wife." The Cook backs carefully away from me, turning the corner before she straightens to her full height.

"Fish!" I seethe in the hot stillness. "It is not fit for a king."

In my mind, I beg the ancestors for their forgiveness.

~II~

What do you see
Keeper of the Sampy
through a god's eyes?
Through a god's eyes?

Interpret the vintana
the inexorable destiny
look to the east
along the axis
between living and dead.

Healer, astrologer,
mpanandro,
maker of the day.
What does
the sampy say?

Death comes!
Death desires him!
Death will not be denied!

But he will go alone
long before his queen.
She was born on a Friday
a red day
the day of kings.

~III~

The Royal Cook was born on a Thursday.

Thursday is the black day. It is the day of slaves. As she stands in the great kitchen where the zebu meat is being cooked without spices or adornments, where none will comment on the delicious smell for fear of implying that the sacrifice is mere food, she sees the runner girl crying in her corner cot and feels the unluckiness of her vintana, her inherited destiny, twisting the world around her.

"What is wrong with her?" she asks the water-fetcher.

"The wound in her foot. It turns black. They do not want her in the slave hut. If she dies there, they will have to burn it down."

The Royal Cook understands. If the runner girl dies in the kitchen, her cot-corner will simply be blessed by the Royal Ombiasy. There can be no burning down of palaces, not even to satisfy taboo.

"Then I must go to the lowlands for fresh fish."

The water-fetcher says nothing. She has a clubfoot and is slow. The capital in its glorious seat on the high plateau is three days from the closest port. No roads have been built to Antananarivo. King Radama proclaims that paved highways invite invasion.

And yet he wishes to dine on fish when the high lakes have been emptied by Christian converts.

"Get me water for my journey."

The Royal Cook hides her overwhelming fear as the water-fetcher scurries away. A long, slow march through the lowlands is how royalty disposes of royalty without the taboo of shedding royal blood. One bite from the wrong mosquito in that dark, wet forest or mud-legged in the suffocating, sweaty swamps will send her on the path her parents took many years ago.

On the plateau, it is windy, cool and clean. It is safe. She is only a servant but she is a servant of the Merina and does not wish to die of the dreaded disease. As she begins her run through the maze of square huts and terraced paddies that cover the hillside, she thinks of the cattle herder with the sun-kissed streak in his black hair. She thinks of how she has not bled this month and begs her ancestors for protection.

They hear her. Before noon the next day, she meets a zebu-cheese merchant half way down the slope to the sea, returning from the coast where he has traded cheese for trepang and sea turtle meat. He gives her a woven basket of salt-packed golden trevally and takes two-sixteenths of a silver coin cut into pieces.

He tells her that fishermen are blessed, because Jesus chose them for his disciples, and the Royal Cook tries not to think of the snarl that would form on the Great Wife's face if she could hear the merchant speaking.

It takes another night and morning for her to return to the palace. Without sleeping, without stopping, she goes to the great kitchen to prepare the fish. Great pots of rice simmer there for the midday meal. The runner girl moans and turns but has not yet died. The water-fetcher tells her that the king has drunk rum for two days and, though he has eaten rice, he still bellows for fish.

Even curried, the fish smells nauseating to the Royal Cook. Perhaps it is the child she suspects she carries, or the half-delirium of exhaustion. She scratches a new itch on the back of her calf and allows herself to be soothed by the burning-rice aroma as the water-fetcher readies fresh ranonapango to accompany the King's meal.

Servants take the dishes from the kitchen. The Royal Cook sighs, leans against the preparation table and touches her belly.

She smiles. She has survived; they have survived. Soon, ancestors-willing, she may have a lychee-smeared little face to wipe with the corner of her lamba. The Great Wife will not care that the Royal Cook is unwed. It is proper, and profitable, that slaves should breed.

But what if the king is displeased with the lateness of his meal? What if he should order some brutal punishment?

Her eyes feel filled with sand, but she cannot resist slinking towards the dark servant's hallway with its concealed spyhole, to make sure that her monarch is satisfied with his meal.

The Great Wife lurks at the spyhole. Her shape is unmistakeable, even in the gloom. She grows old but her curling tresses remain black as night, her angled eyes ever more piercing with pink spots of anger blooming, as always, in her pale cheeks.

The Royal Cook flinches but she's been seen. She bends her shaking knees.

"You might as well take a look," the Great Wife says. She steps back from the hole.

The Royal Cook crawls forward until she faces the place in the wall, then straightens enough to put her eye to it.

The dining room blazes with the light of naked flame. Instead of eating on floor-mats, the glassy-eyed, soppily-smiling king and his pair of rice-faced foreign visitors sit on wooden chairs at a long table draped in lace. Radama wears French clothing and sits between them, to the apparent displeasure of the Royal Ombiasy and other advisors who cluster well back from the table.

One of the London missionaries reaches for the serving spoon as the servant sets the dish on the table, and as he ladles some onto his plate, left-handed, the Royal Cook gasps. The missionary serves his companion second and the king third. The king's plate is wooden like the plate of a beggar.

"Wait, my child," the companion says to Radama. "You forget. We must say grace."

The Royal Cook slides down the wall and away from the spyhole, clutching at her palpitating heart. She turns to the Great Wife in speechless horror.

"Yes," the Great Wife says viciously. "They dare to occupy the northeast corner, the noble corner. The chairs are of equal height. One serves himself first and calls the king a child. Clearly, they do not accept Radama's divinity. If I were king, I would put them to death."

She sweeps away, pausing to spare a glance over her shoulder for the Royal Cook, still slumped on the floor.

"Go and rest," she says, frowning. "You do not look well."

In nine days, the chills begin, and the fever.

The Royal Cook moans and turns.

"Come," the water-bearer says gently, taking her hand, trying to lead her away from the wattle-and-daub slave quarters and toward the Great Kitchen, but the Royal Cook will not go.

If it is her destiny to die, let everything burn.

~IV. Madagascar, July, 1828~

Radama is one of them, now.

The ancestors have heard me and have called my husband to be one of them. They have proven their great power and I am afraid.

What if I should fail them, too? How should I proceed?

I summon the Royal Ombiasy. He hears their voices. He understands the visions they kindle before his bloodshot eyes. When he arrives, roused from his bed, rubbing his swollen-knuckled hands, he is baffled to see my handsome, faithful Andrianmihaja beside me in the lamplight.

"Great Wife to the king. What is happening?" The old man's voice is tremulous. In his shuffle through the moonlit corridors, he must have heard something over the ring of crickets and songs of frogs. Maybe the rattle of weapons. The whisper of conspirators.

Andrianmihaja answers him, his eyes shining.

"You are speaking not with a Great Wife but with the Great Glory, Ranavalona Manjaka, Queen of Madagascar."

I lift my chin. Manjaka. Majesty. Yes. I am Queen. Let those who do not acknowledge my divinity tremble.

"The king is dead?"

The Ombiasy has not used my new title a second time. I do not let my anger show. I have no choice but to forgive his lapse. I need him. The ancestors speak through him.

"He is dead. As you predicted," I say, inclining my head. "Now I must know which of my colonels still come to you. Which of them still visit the shrines and kneel before the sampy. Tell me which of them honours the ancestors with his whole heart. He will be the one to defend me against false claimants."

False claimants. Rakotoba. My husband's sister's oldest son. He is popular with some of the traditionalists, but favour with the living, with the great true-blooded web of interconnected kin, is meaningless. Only the will of the dead matters now, and my adopted father is one of them, the closest in the chain but one to this red earth. *Let the sea be the borders of your rice field*, had been his final command to Radama in life. He unified my kingdom, he raised me up and his desires shall come to pass; nothing can prevent it.

The sense of my glorious vintana surges through me, drowning out all fears of a misstep.

"I can think of two colonels from your home village, Manjaka," the Ombiasy says, naming them.

I turn to Andrianmihaja. His bearing is so regal, his sober features so fine. Years have passed since he killed a scorpion on my windowsill, ate it without hesitation when I ordered him to on a whim, and looked on me with lust I had never seen in the king's eyes. Andrianmihaja admires French warfare, studies their tactics while refusing their rum. He will be my proper husband, should we survive the night.

"My heart," I say, "go to fetch these colonels at once."

"I will go," he says. "I will not be seen." It was his eyes that first captured my interest but his fidelity that maintains it. Andrianmihaja has never taken any woman but me. He will never betray me.

I kiss him deeply, tasting the herbs that burned at Radama's bedside in the last hours of his wretched life. It was the ancestors that placed my young officer on duty this night, so that he could come to warn me that Radama's closest confidants were keeping the king's death a secret.

That secret will work in my favour, not Rakotoba's. They are all traitors. They would gift the Red Island to the foreigners. I will use the troops under the command of my faithful colonels to secure the palace. When the sun rises and the courtiers come, it will be to hear the declaration of my succession.

As for the missionaries, let them carry the news back to London.

There will be no fish at the table of Ranavalona Manjaka.

~V~

The Royal Ombiasy was born on a Sunday.

Sunday is the white day, the day of sacrifices and power, adoration and danger. All his life, the Royal Ombiasy has dreamed of horrors to come.

Now, he wakes from a dream, the same gods-cursed dream, of fire consuming the sampy. It is just before dawn, the time when his oracular powers are most true; it is why they call him maker of the day.

He refuses to believe that the vision of fire will come to pass. Even though Radama, poor, dead Radama, at the suggestion of the London missionaries, had all but agreed to destroy the great talismans that protect the Kingdom.

"He is gone," the Royal Ombiasy says hoarsely to himself in the darkness. Ranavalona is queen, she who has been like a daughter to him. Before her adoption, he visited her village. The child gazed at him with impudent black eyes from the doorway of the palm-frond hut.

Sorcerer, she chirped. *I wish to see him! I wish to see Ingahibe, the sampy who is second in power only to the great sampy Rakelimalaza.*

Go from here, piglet, he admonished her. *The Old Gentleman is not a trinket for your eyes to see.*

She stamped her little foot.

I order you to open the box. I am a princess, not a piglet!

Her family apologetically dragged her away, terrified of the sampy guardian's retribution, but he had smiled behind his hand when she was gone. She was swift, curious and full of fire, and when he first saw her in his dreams, he dared to hope that French ships, taking flight from her menacing red silhouette like frightened guinea-fowl, would be driven back in the waking world by her many sons.

Ranavalona Manjaka has no sons, but perhaps, like no woman who has lived before, she can drive the foreigners away with her own dispersal of hasina, the divine quality that is granted by a monarch to the armies.

The Royal Ombiasy crawls out of his bed as daylight creeps under the door. He dresses and performs a ritual over the sampy before leaving the shrine. Staying within the palace complex, he walks over beaten earth to the private stone hut provided for the manufacture of potions and cures.

There, he arranges cooked rice and chicken skin on many small platters. The Royal Cook is dead, but had she lived, she could not have prepared these deadly meals for Ranavalona's day of judgement. The ancestors showed their displeasure by killing the Cook soon after she fetched the fish for Radama, but Radama is gone, now. His mistakes are paid for.

The Royal Ombiasy resolves that the sampy will not burn.

His mouth flattens grimly as he opens the pottery jar where he keeps the palm-sized, oval-shaped fruit of the small and fragrant tanguena tree. Cutting the fruit and cracking the seed, he extracts the kernel and crushes a little of the poisonous oily seed over each meal. Those fasting men and women awaiting judgement will eat the meal. They will be forced to drink water, and more water, until they begin vomiting. Those who bring up all three pieces of chicken skin are innocent in the eyes of the ancestors.

Those who bring up two or less pieces are guilty and will be put to death. The palace servants were tested yesterday. Officers are on trial today. So soon after the queen's succession, all must prove their loyalty by tanguena trial if they are to continue to serve. Even if they have shown loyalty in the past, evil curses may have been placed on them by the queen's enemies. This is the only way.

The Royal Ombiasy must, of course, abide by the wishes of the ancestors, but there are ways to ensure that certain ordeal subjects survive. Especially Andrianmihaja; the queen must not be deprived of her lover.

Only a small amount of poison, then, for some of these meals. And the Royal Ombiasy will add salt to the water that the queen's lover will drink, to ensure that he vomits as quickly and violently as possible. Even then, the Royal Ombiasy will hide spare chicken skin on his person.

Just in case. The queen needs her loyal colonels to survive, also.

The second batch of meals, destined for the disloyal officers that the Queen wishes to purge, is prepared just as carefully. The Royal Ombiasy carries the meals in a basket across the courtyard himself. In one corner, silversmiths labour in the construction of the dead king's casket. Quarried stone is carted past, toward the site where Radama's mausoleum, foreign in style but with Malagasy mirrors and a west-facing door, is partly constructed.

Inside the palace, the Royal Ombiasy steps over the threshold of the throne room with his right foot. Officers kneel in three long lines before the queen. She stands, hair braided, in a sumptuous gown, but this is no betrayal; the Royal Ombiasy admires her instinct for appropriating the status symbols of the aggressors while still wearing, in their red silk pouch, the carved-figure royal talismans Fataka and Manjakatsir, along with crocodile teeth, falcon feathers and inherited cloth-patterns of power.

As he draws closer, he sees a drawing on the desk beside her, a crown she has ordered to be made in France of Malagasy-mined gold. It mingles the arches and glittering stones of foreign monarchs with the seven spearheads of the traditional Malagasy warrior. The falcon of Merina royalty will replace the Christian cross and the interior cap will be red velvet in place of purple.

The Royal Ombiasy smiles to himself as he sets the basket beside the drawing. The daughter of his dreams will reign well.

Andrianmihaja does not sweat or tremble like the soldiers kneeling to either side of him. It is not because the queen has guaranteed his safety. She has not. She is innocent of the Royal Ombiasy's manipulations and must remain so, lest the ancestors choose to punish her. Andrianmihaja must be afraid. Many died yesterday. Many will die today.

But not him. The ancestors cannot object to the Royal Ombiasy's actions, otherwise they would have warned him in a dream.

"Begin," Ranavalona instructs tonelessly, and he wishes to carry out her order but is abruptly petrified by his last thought. What if the ancestors have warned him in a dream? What if the burning sampy is a consequence of his actions today?

What if they are a consequence of his previous actions?

For the tanguena fruit in the stone hut are not fresh from his most recent forest-wander. They have been there ever since the Royal Ombiasy poisoned Radama.

Radama would not die, the Ombiasy had reasoned to himself, unless it was the will of the ancestors. But Radama had died, and now that his spirit had found its way to the twelve hills, and not to heaven as the King had come to believe, would he not now be pleased by the Ombiasy's actions?

"Manjaka, as you wish," he says, dry-mouthed.

He takes a poisoned meal to Andrianmihaja and looks directly into the young man's calm, brown eyes. He whispers the ritual words to invoke the ancestors. They surround him. Radama's spirit is here, with them.

Are you not pleased? His silent question can only be answered by the rise or fall of the queen he would die to protect.

~VI. August, 1829~

The pregnancy is difficult. I am forty-one years old.

There are false labour pains. The feeling of boulders grinding my bones from the inside. On one occasion, a few months earlier, there was blood. Andrianmihaja, my Prime Minister, personal adviser and Commander in Chief of my army, swallowed it to keep it from the earth. Royal blood must never be spilled.

Lately, I have sent Andrianmihaja away. Intercourse is painful. My head pounds and my feet swell. Perhaps I will die in the birthing.

What price, a son? asks the imagined voice of my dead first husband. By our laws, any child born to a widow after the husband's death is the legitimate offspring of the dead man, with full rights of inheritance. The ancestors are pleased with my suspension of the treaty with the British and the profits that flow with the resumption of trade in slaves. That is why they have given me a child at last.

"The ancestors," I say, "will make sure you are born safe, my son."

I can hardly hear myself with the racket that Rainiharo and his two brothers are making beyond the ornate, three-sided screen that shields me from their eyes. My maids, jewelled, unclothed and obedient, entertain the three young men. Kitchen slaves bring a constant supply of food and drink.

Rainiharo is a prince, but more importantly, he is the guardian of the most powerful royal sampy, Rakelimalaza, bringer of victories. His branch of the family must be brought closer. I must control the three brothers if I am to keep winning battles.

Rainiharo's face, startling through the steam, grins like a demon.

"Great Glory, will you not drink with us?"

He brandishes a bottle of rum.

"How dare you approach me?"

"Your women say you have been in pain. Try this. It will help."

"I am taking medicines prescribed by my Royal Ombiasy," I snap, but my abdomen chooses that moment to ripple. Pain lances through my pelvis.

"Manjaka, I beg you to believe me."

"That foul drink helped my husband into his tomb! I will not touch it!"

"I have seen your death," Rainiharo says drunkenly. "My sampy has shown it to me. You are an old woman. Much older than you are now."

I feel the blood drain from my face.

"Why have you never told this to me before?"

"The time was not right. All must be as the great talisman wills. Take the bottle, Manjaka."

I take it. The fire-throated drinking of it is too much, at first; I rise from the bath and stand, desperate for cooling, under the exquisite marquetry and painted ceilings of the main palace hall where my waist-deep, honey-smelling tun has been filled with water and scented oils.

The pains continue. I bite my cheek to keep from crying out. I take another swallow of the liquor, and another.

After a while, the pains stop. My head feels cotton-stuffed. I sink languidly back into the water. The frescoes are now blurred, bright colours, like spirits dancing at the turning of the dead, and the booming laughter of Rainiharo and his brothers, mingled with the giggles and groans of the fornicating women, seems the divine music of life, fit music for my son, who turns within me as if dancing with the spirits, too.

"Are you well, Great Glory?" Rainiharo's steam-wreathed face begs to know.

"I am well, Rainiharo," I say. "You are wise."

"You should make me your personal adviser."

"Andrianmihaja is my personal adviser."

"Is he, still? Forgive me, Great Glory, but I assumed that when he exchanged your bed for the bed of the girl-child, the young black princess, you must simply be taking your time deciding on the best way to have him killed."

I can't think. I can't breathe.

"What did you say?" I shriek.

Rainiharo repeats himself. He is too stupid to be afraid. No, not stupid. He knows I cannot kill him, for the sake of the sampy that his bloodline holds.

Andrianmihaja. My beautiful, loyal, Andrianmihaja. I told him not to come to me.

"Could he not wait?" I scream. "Could he not wait until the child was born? Not even so long as that? And why, why did it have to be the only child of Radama's that I let live?"

"He is repositioning." Rainiharo answers promptly, though I had not been speaking to him. "Great Glory, you severed our ties with Britain. Commander Andrianmihaja realigns himself with the Christians."

"He is loyal to me."

"He is a traitor. Let him take the tanguena test again."

"No!" I sit up too suddenly. My head spins. Flashes of Andrianmihaja's hunched body, wracked with regurgitation, the bile on his lips and the fear in his eyes, return to me. I cannot stand to watch that again. I grip the edges of the tub to keep from drowning. Rainiharo's face is splashed with water but he does not blink. He stares at my breasts in the flickering light of low-burning torches. "Andrianmihaja went through the ordeal when I was raised, barely a year past."

And he is the father of my son, I do not say. Radama is the true, spiritual father of my unborn child. The giver of the seed is irrelevant.

"If Commander Andrianmihaja is innocent," Rainiharo insists, "he cannot be harmed by taking the test again. It need not be public. Send for the Royal Ombiasy right now. Send one of these slave girls for Andrianmihaja. I know where he is. He is in the girl-child's quarters, spreading her legs as we speak."

Pain and rage bring me staggering to my feet.

"He is not!"

"If he is, Great Glory, will you put him on trial?"

"Yes," I say. "But he will not be there. He will be in his room, here in the palace. Send a slave there, first, to fetch him!"

Maids rush behind the screen to dry my flushed, bulging body and wrap me in red silk. The screens are removed. Rainiharo nods to his brothers. One of the women is already leaving. Dimly, I wonder why they abruptly seem less drunk than before, but I am distracted by a whirlwind of maids picking up and replacing their discarded clothes, the clink of empty bottles and the whisking away of bone-covered trays.

All too soon, the slave girl returns, flattening herself in obeisance.

"The Commander is not in his room, Great Glory."

It cannot be. It cannot be. First one husband, then the next.

"Leave the palace," Rainiharo tells the slave. He gives her directions to Radama's old harem, where the wives that were spared by my mercy still reside. "I will send two soldiers with you, as witnesses."

Everything happens so quickly. I gasp for air. I thrust women away from me. Their faces do not come into focus.

When the slave girl and the soldiers return, they speak to Rainiharo and not to me.

"My prince," the kneeling soldier says, leaning on his serrated spear, his musket slung over his back and his feet bare beneath his lamba, "I have spoken with Commander Andrianmihaja. After sending the girl-child back to her mother, I informed the commander that the queen wished him to be subjected to the tanguena trial to prove his innocence of treason."

"And his reply?"

"My prince, the commander bade me tell the Queen that he will not subject himself to the trial again. She must take his word that he is loyal to her, or she must condemn him to death."

My body sways as though Andrianmihaja has dealt me a physical blow. Who is he, to force my hand? Who is he, to say "must" to the Great Glory, the Queen of Madagascar, Ranavalona Manjaka?

He is no better than Radama. A Christian-loving traitor. A man who used me to gain power but does not love me. Not any more.

He will die while she still smells of his sweat and semen.

~VII. October 1830~

The Royal Weaver was born on a Wednesday.

It is the brown day, the eldest of all days. A day for women and a day for evil.

Her voice joins the joyous voices of the others, singing the songs of homage by the river, under the sky, as they wrap the washed bones of Andrianmihaja in his new burial shroud. The polluting wet matter has leached away, leaving the sacred dry matter behind. It is over a year since he received a silver spear through his bravely bared throat.

Though the famadihana is ordinarily raucous and unrestrained, the women are wary, owing to the circumstances surrounding the former army commander's execution. Those that came in the morning, relatives of the deceased, danced with the shrouded remains, and passed them from hand to hand, but only where the agents of the queen would not see.

"Your son is well, Andrianmihaja," murmurs the Royal Weaver, who was the commander's great-aunt while he lived. "He is almost walking. He has a great and wondrous vintana. You know why he could not come today."

The queen and her son must not ever be polluted by the presence of death. They are not permitted to weep in public, to tear their hair or mourn in any way. They do not even look in the direction of Radama's mausoleum when they cross the courtyard. The dead king in his silver coffin has not and will not be exhumed. Royalty is the exception to the annual turning of the dead.

These bones, however, the pure and insoluble parts of Andrianmihaja which reflect his pure spirit, have been feted through villages during the day. They have enjoyed a tour of the new fields, new additions to the zebu herds, and new firearms produced by the queen's White Slave. Warriors triumphantly told to them the tale of the French defeat at Foule Point, where the foreigners, crippled by chain shot from Merina cannons at the fort, tried to escape back to their ships but were overrun and cut down. French heads now rot on spears set into the sand along the beach.

The cloud-screened sun sinks low in the sky. Now, it is time for the bones to be re-wrapped and returned to the family tomb at Namehana. The Royal Weaver has made for her great-nephew a great many fresh silk, weft-patterned burial shrouds, each with the prestigious family geometry repeated around the edges. For days, the heddle was lashed to the rafters of the royal weaving hut while the Royal Weaver bent her aching back over the loom, separating the two sets of warp elements with a wooden stick from a baobab tree selected for its auspicious qualities by the Royal Ombiasy.

Rebelliously, the Royal Weaver incorporated royal red and silver thread in the innermost shroud. The others grow restless and uneasy when she produces it, but the Royal Weaver knows she can trust them to say nothing.

Before the Merina came to dominate all the tribes of Madagascar, the Royal Weaver and all her family in the east had a right to these colours.

The bones are wrapped again, and again. The final, outer silk shroud is white as the clouds which obscure the white sun; white as the clothes of the crowd of mourners that surround the bier, waiting to take Andrianmihaja home. The women's hair is loose. The men's feet are white with dust from the thin trail that winds through the grassy hills.

The Royal Weaver cradles the package of bones. She remembers Andrianmihaja as a swaddled child. She kisses him, now, as she did then, with the same affection, and places him on the bier, joining the procession back to the excavated earth tomb, where he must be reinterred and the tomb sealed before daylight fades.

Birds twitter. Grasses sigh in the wind. The Royal Weaver sighs with them. She is the last to leave. She will close the west-facing door in the hillside.

The others are already distant, returning to the river to wash their feet in running water to cleanse themselves of the pollution of death, when the Royal Weaver notices the shadow by the east side of the hill.

"Who is there?" she calls sharply. The white-wrapped figure has the edge of its worn, rafia-palm lamba pulled up and over the face. Only the wet, weepy eyes are showing.

"There is daylight, still," croaks a voice that is unmistakeably the queen's. "Please, let me enter."

The Royal Weaver falls to her knees, stricken. She can summon no protest as the disguised, amorphous shape of Ranavalona enters the hill, reaches for Andrianmihaja's bundled bones and whispers something to them in the gloom.

There is daylight, still, but now the very life and light of the Sacred Red Island has been mingled with the darkness of the dead. Who can say what will happen?

On her old knees with her head bent, the Royal Weaver senses blood and pain running into the molten gold of the Great Glory's royal vintana as the queen walks in stiff silence away from the tomb.

~VIII~

What do I see,
Queen of the Merina
with a god's eyes?
With a god's eyes?

I have done as you bade
my late husband to do,

O Andrianampoinimerina,
my father.

The borders of my rice field
are the seas.

Yet, the French come!
The French desire my rice field!
French oak slices red coral waters!

Let them come
in their winged villain's ships.
I have eaten their god.
I was born on a Friday.

Hallowed Ground

Juliet Marillier

~Year of Our Lord 1178: Autumn~

I am digging a grave. Not my own, though I am eighty years old and my joints ache. Not, indeed, a resting place for the mortal remains of any man or woman. If it were necessary to bury the departed, I would call upon one of the younger, fitter sisters, or upon one of our lay assistants. Berthe, for instance, has the brawny arms of a countrywoman and can carry a pair of milk pails as if they weighed no more than a couple of breviaries.

I am digging to hide the grave of a repentant sinner. Matthias was his name. Yes, he was excommunicated for his wrongdoing. But he died repentant. He received absolution. So he lies, as he should, in hallowed ground within our convent walls at Rupertsberg. We laid him to rest in the shade of a yew and sang a psalm.

May God rest his soul. If the church authorities in Mainz have their way, his bones will not lie tranquil long.

My blood boils at the thought. I pause in my labours to pray for a quiet heart, for self-discipline, for humility. Around me the garden rings with birdsong. And now, beneath those high avian voices weave those of my sisters from the chapel, singing a hymn to the Virgin; a hymn of my own composition. *Ave generosa, gloriosa et intacta puella.* This is a place of peace; Our Lady walks here. I pray for a spirit free from anger, and for the ability to know with certainty which decisions are God's and which my own.

A voice within me whispers, *Did you ever know that, Hildegard? Surely you thought it unlikely that God would choose a frail woman—a sickly child, you were when it began—to be the recipient of His divine wisdom. Did you not sometimes wonder if the visions and messages and ideas sprang, not from Heaven, but purely from your own imagination?*

"Begone," I mutter aloud, driving in the spade with all the vigour I can summon. "You are the voice of the devil, and you must know by now that I am too old and stubborn to listen to you. Besides, I'm busy."

"Sister Hildegard?"

I start as one of the young novices appears on the pathway beside me. It's hard to straighten up. My body does not obey me as it once did.

"Let me help," says the girl, reaching for the spade. What is her name, Agnes? Mathilde? I cannot recall. "You should rest—you should go in and sit down—"

The voices float out from the chapel, high and true. The girl looks at me; I look back at her.

"We're missing Terce," she says.

"God will be content to hear our prayers under the trees, with earth on our hands." Ah! I've remembered her name. "Shall we kneel, Sister Barbara?"

We lift our voices in song. I can no longer reach the high register required by this hymn; I did not compose it for old women. I restrict myself to the final, providing a sort of drone. Barbara surprises me. She tackles the melismatic chant with perfect confidence, every note clear and accurate despite the wide range of the melody and the particular challenges of the third mode. The birds continue their distinctive contribution.

I had a good voice once. God has many ways of teaching us humility.

The hymn over, we rise to our feet. Our habits are muddy, our sandals clogged with earth.

"You are something of a musician," I tell my companion.

Sister Barbara blushes and holds her silence. Instructed, no doubt, to avoid prideful thinking. We have many talented women here; if our reputation for piety and scholarship does not draw them to this particular convent, our music surely does.

"Lift that voice of yours only in praise of God," I say, "and there's no more personal pride in you than there is in those birds up in the trees. Like yours, their song is a song of joy. Joy in God's creation. Joy in being alive and free."

"Sister Hildegard," says Barbara, "please let me do the digging."

I sit on the bench and watch her awhile. She understands the task. Word has got around, no doubt, of my fury at the letter from the bishops: a letter ordering me to have poor Matthias's earthly remains dug up and removed from hallowed ground. A letter stating in blunt terms that if I refuse, they will send someone to do it for me.

So we are turning a gravesite into a vegetable garden. Seedlings await their places; stakes and cord lie ready for neat bean-rows. We may even fashion a clerical scarecrow. Matthias had farms, crops, animals. He'll forgive us a cabbage or two.

I measure out my breathing. Slowly, my calm returns. I close my eyes, considering the difficult question that never quite leaves my mind: *Did you ever lie about your visions? Once they were credited by the Holy Father as true, did you ever interpret them in ways that would serve your own ends? There's no denying they were often convenient.* I let myself drift back into the past. Many, many years...almost a lifetime of years...

◊Δ◊Δ◊Δ◊Δ◊Δ◊

I was seven when they enclosed me with Jutta in her cell at Disibodenberg monastery. It was meant to be for life. I thought the anchoress looked like an angel, and on that first day I told her so. Jutta chided me, gently, for presuming to know how an angel might appear. I told her I did know; I had seen them. It was not a lie.

When I was a little older, and understood what the life of an anchoress was, I realised that my mother and father, in their decision to commit me to enclosure at such a tender age, had not been cruel and unfeeling as some might have thought. They had done me a great service. In locking me away, they granted me the lifelong gift of freedom. Freedom to learn; freedom to think; freedom to create. Freedom to love God with all I had to give.

By the time I was seventeen, there were twelve of us sharing the cell. I no longer spoke of my visions. Among my sisters, and even among the monks of that foundation, there were some who believed that what I told them was self-aggrandisement or the product of an undisciplined imagination. Others thought I suffered from a disorder of both body and mind. True, when the visions came I had a kind of fit, or so folk told me. My body went rigid or fell into trembling spasms, and although my eyes were open, I did not see what was before me in the real world. I looked into God's world; I saw what He wished me to see. I was indeed an unlikely vessel for His wisdom. But there it was. In the beginning the visions came unsought. They overtook me; they left me much weakened in body. But in spirit, much refreshed and full of wonder. Full of the need to share my new insights.

But I learned to keep silent, knowing I would be misjudged. *Hildegard is in frail health,* they said. *She has never been strong.* With the wisdom of my eighty years, I believe that they were only half right.

When I was twenty-seven, our number had grown to sixteen and the confines of the cell, even with its two chambers, became intolerable. I had by then negotiated access to the monastery garden at certain times of day, though Jutta held firm in her vow of seclusion and would not go out. A new door was made, with its bolt on the inside, and we had the freedom to come in and out at our own choosing. A privy was constructed for our exclusive use; the old system with the buckets was abandoned. The general health of the sisters improved greatly with the increased sunshine and fresh air. We grew vegetables. We kept chickens. On the subject of my visions I held my silence.

By the time I was thirty-seven, Jutta's health was uncertain; the beautiful young woman of my childhood had become worn and weary. There were five-and-twenty sisters living in the cell; I had persuaded Abbot Kuno to extend our quarters when other parts of Disibodenberg were rebuilt. But the requests kept coming, for another girl to join us, and another. They were drawn by Jutta's piety.

◊∆◊∆◊∆◊∆◊∆◊

"Sister Hildegard?"

Young Barbara's voice breaks into my thoughts. I sit up with a start, and see on her face that she thinks I have fallen asleep.

"Shall I begin putting in the seedlings?" she asks.

She has done a good job of preparing the garden; she's dug over three times the area I could manage in the same time. Who would know, now, where the repentant sinner Matthias lies? Under this fertile soil rest both nuns of our convent and local folk of noble family, buried since we made the move to Rupertsberg. A contentious move, opposed by Abbot Kuno and the brethren, since our departure from their foundation meant the loss not only of our good selves, but of the endowments we brought with us when we entered the religious life. But God had shown me what I must do. The vision was powerful. It was plain that God intended me to take my sisters over the river where we would form our own foundation in order to provide succour and ministry to the community at large. We were to leave the comforts of Disibodenberg and fend for ourselves in far poorer surroundings. And we would offer burial within our walls to worthy Christian folk of the district.

I explained this to the Abbot. I told him we would take our few possessions, the wherewithal to establish a small scriptorium, a library, an infirmary where we might treat both our own sick and those of the community. We would take what was required to maintain ourselves in simple fashion, and we would uplift ourselves to Rupertsberg in the district of Bingen.

Abbot Kuno refused outright. Having expected this, I did not engage him in a war of words. I did not accuse him of venal motives. Instead I wrote letters to folk who could help me, folk of influence. Letters had long been my strength, my way of reaching out to make change in the world from within my convent walls. Through letters, as much as through the books I have written, I have been able to pass on the wisdom God has given me, as to how a life should best be lived, how a church or a monastic foundation should best be governed, how God might wish us poor men and women to act and speak and deal with one another during our brief span on earth.

I did not speak to Abbot Kuno on the matter again, for very soon after he refused me I was overtaken by another vision, this time so strong that it lasted from one evening's Vespers until the next day's Prime. They told me, afterwards, that my body had lain rigid on my bed, and that my eyes had remained open but unseeing as first my sisters, then my dear mentor and friend Brother Volmar—oh, how I still miss him—then the monastery's Infirmarian, and lastly the Abbot himself came to my cell to witness it. That was a remarkable visitation, so powerful that I was not able to write of it with any clarity until much later. *A divine correction*, Kuno called it. He had no choice, afterwards, but to relent in the matter of our move to Rupertsberg.

We raised the funds to buy our chosen land—many of our sisters are from wealthy families—and removed ourselves as promptly as we could to Bingen, and to the then somewhat dilapidated accommodation here at Rupertsberg. Our convent grew; it is no longer the makeshift establishment of those early days. I will die within these walls. Perhaps next winter, perhaps the one after; my bones grow weary. Will my sisters plant cabbages on my grave? I believe I would prefer herbs. Rosemary, for a strong woman. Sweet alyssum, to moderate anger. Bay for healing. Chamomile to bring me peaceful sleep.

My mind has been wandering again. Sister Barbara has been joined by two others, and the cabbage seedlings are going in, row on neat row. They'll be bedded in straw to keep out both the chill and the caterpillars. God willing, I will see them grow full and healthy; I will be here to enjoy a hearty cabbage soup. We have good cooks among our lay helpers.

"Sister Hildegard?" Barbara holds my little sack of herb roots and seedlings, ready for planting. Cress, winter purslane, sorrel, parsley. In spring I will add comfrey, a herb that not only forms a fine basis for compost, but also deters insects fond of a leaf diet. Have I time to write a new book on herbs, an extension of my *Natural History*? My hands are crabbed with age; I can no longer hold a steady quill. If only Volmar had lived a little longer… I have Guibert, of course, and Guibert has his uses. But there is nobody like Volmar. If not for that kind and clever man, I would never have had the courage to speak out about my visions. Not once did he doubt me; not once did he patronise me. He guided me as no other ever did, for Jutta, well-meaning soul as she was, was limited in her scholarship. Were it not for Volmar, I would never have recorded in writing the divine secrets

God had shown me since I was a little child. I would not have reached out to the world through my books and my letters, and the world would not have come to me. Who would have believed, when Volmar first took on the duty of teaching me a scholar's Latin, that in time the Holy Father himself would hear of my writings, and would read parts of *Scivias*, and would officially declare my visions genuine?

"Sister Hildegard, would you like to plant these yourself?"

Sister Barbara brings me back to the here and now once more. This girl may be young, but her instincts are sound. She does not know me well; cannot, as her time in the convent has been short. But she sees that I am no doddery old woman, content to sit by and watch while others work. Busy hands keep the mind alert. I will not let my faculties wither and fade away. Barbara recognises that within the carapace of a wrinkled ancient, I am still the same woman I was when young. But wiser. I hope I am wise enough to deal with whatever may come from this day's work. One thing I know: the bishops will be much displeased.

The herbs go in at each corner of the new garden plot. I tuck the last seedling in place, dust off my hands then rise with some difficulty to my feet. Barbara hovers; she will not help me up unless I ask her to.

"A good job, Sister," I say. "Tell me, can you read and write?" Her voice and manner indicate she is of good family; her singing suggests a young lady's education.

"Yes, Sister Hildegard. My Latin is rather limited, but I can read it quite well, and I can read and write in German."

"Good. I'll arrange for Brother Guibert to give you some further tuition in Latin; he may grumble a little, but we need scholarly women here as well as pious ones. What about the notation of music? Have you ever learned that?"

Her cheeks have turned pink again. "I can read music, Sister Hildegard. I have not had the opportunity to write it. I would like that very much—that is, if I can help the work of the convent by learning that skill, I would be glad to do so."

I recognise a kindred spirit; she is struggling for humility as I have done on more occasions than I can count. "This must be with Sister Elisabeth's permission, of course." Elisabeth is our Mistress of Novices; she will do as I bid her.

"Of course." Barbara is trying to suppress a grin of pure delight. "Thank you, Sister Hildegard."

"The best thanks you can give me will be to work hard, learn quickly, then use your gifts in the service of God. And to be brave, Sister. Brave in the face of those who doubt you; brave in the face of those who mock you; brave in the face of those who consider you weak, unworthy or ignorant. Brave in the face of those who do not believe a woman can have her own voice."

"But you—" she starts, then holds back her words. What was she going to say? *But you surely never had to deal with that? You are so highly regarded—who would ever have doubted you?*

"Best go now and wash your hands," I say. "I will speak to Sister Elisabeth later today. No point in wasting time."

~Year of Our Lord 1179: Spring~

Three written requests over winter, each less courteous than the last. One group of clergy from Mainz, knocking on our gates. They asked to inspect our burial ground, but if they thought the placement of the vegetable garden odd, they did not say so. They confronted me in the privacy of our library. I responded that in the matter of Matthias's burial, as in all matters, I would not act against God's will. The clerics stayed for supper. We fed them cabbage soup.

And now, a letter from the church authorities. I expected castigation. I anticipated some form of punishment. But this… How can this be borne?

I break the news to my sisters at the supper table, in place of the usual reading from scripture. I can hardly bring myself to say it. With an effort I make my voice steady. "Sisters, it is an interdict. From this moment on, we are forbidden to celebrate Mass at Rupertsberg. The Divine Office may no longer be sung before a congregation. Indeed, it may not be sung at all. We must whisper or murmur, and only behind closed doors."

My sisters gasp in distress; their faces are stricken. The music is our spirit. It is the powerful voice of God, sounding from our weak human instruments. It is joy and celebration, adoration and mystery, sacred discipline and spiritual freedom. Our music is everything.

"Sisters," I tell them, "I will pray for God's guidance. You must do the same. Meanwhile, if you would not risk excommunication, you must abide by the interdict, as I will. We will not hear the music with our ears; but it will sound in our souls."

◊∆◊∆◊∆◊∆◊∆◊

I pray for a vision. I pray for some wisdom to illuminate the way forwards. The interdict is a dark cloud hanging over Rupertsberg—not only over my sisters and me, but over the good folk accustomed to making their way up the hill to hear us sing Mass, the folk whose daughters, drawn at least in part by our music, have chosen to join us and dedicate their lives to God. This has cut a jagged rent in our whole community. How can anyone believe it is God's will?

I spend long hours on my knees, so long that I become too ill to continue, and must submit to the ministrations of our Infirmarian, Sister Clothilde. She tells me I should remember my age and not expect so much of myself. My response is somewhat short.

In the past, in times of strife or crisis, I have prayed for divine guidance, and it has always come. God has sent me a vision, often hard to understand, but containing the seeds of wisdom I needed, provided I could interpret them correctly. This time there is no illumination. As I have grown older, God has chosen to visit me in this way less and less often. I am too close, perhaps, to the moment when I will see Him face to face and make my final confession. But I wish He would grant me just one more answer. If not for myself, then for my sisters, for young Barbara and the other girls whom I have set to work with Brother Guibert, to be educated as the clever young men of a monastery might be. What Guibert does not teach them—how to speak up, how to be heard—I will impart myself. But I want them to have the music, too, for the scholarship is hard work, and the music is sheer joy.

I hope I am not selfish. But I would be well pleased if, after I die, my sisters might lay me in earth to O *quam mirabilis* in my own composition. I hope I am not arrogant.

Though I have respected the church authorities all my life, as was proper, I have never lain down and let them walk over me. I will not do so now. Only, in the past, I have always had the strength of my visions, sanctioned by the Pope himself. That authority, backed up by my sound arguments, has rendered me persuasive. But this time God remains silent, and therefore so do we. Our Divine Office is a sorry thing, conducted with sombre faces and in an undertone. We move about like sad ghosts; the whispering extends itself to daily conversation, as if our natural energy has been somehow dampened. An odd phenomenon; I wonder if I have time to write about it?

As I lie sleepless on my pallet, waiting for the vision that does not come, I hear that insidious voice again. *Use your imagination, Hildegard! Create what you need. Tell the authorities God wants the interdict lifted. Invent a vision to fit; you're more than capable of that. Indeed, you're a fool not to do so. What harm will it do?*

I do not dignify this with an answer. I will die soon; if he thinks I want to die with a lie of that magnitude on my conscience, it's the devil who is a fool. But I am tempted, all the same. It would indeed be easy. And my heart aches to think that my last days will be devoid of music. Besides, I am quite certain I am right. Why would God want this interdict? God forgives sinners as long as they repent. Matthias repented; he was absolved. Therefore he should lie in hallowed ground. Why would God want our voices silenced?

To teach you humility, Hildegard. This is what I hear as I fall asleep at last, but whether the voice is God's or that of my own conscience, I cannot tell.

◊Δ◊Δ◊Δ◊Δ◊Δ◊

Days pass, and the grey silence that has fallen over Rupertsberg remains unabated. I pray each night for a vision, and nothing comes. I wish God had devised a lesson in humility that did not extend itself to our entire community.

Guibert tells me he is writing an account of my life and works. I cannot imagine what will be in it. I hope Guibert's book does not end with the convent in silence and myself dead in my cell, taken while still praying for answers. I tell my scholarly brother, as courteously as I can, that I would greatly prefer him to spend his time teaching our young women, who are soaking up their learning eagerly. I tell him I trust their education will continue once I am gone, and that I am taking steps to ensure that will happen. Guibert smiles a little strangely, and says he hopes he can find time for both. How odd to think that folk will learn of my life through that man's words. I wish Volmar had written my life instead.

I sit at my desk with quill, ink and parchment before me, knowing that any letter I write will not be in the clear hand I learned long ago, but in the uncertain script of a sick old woman. I should ask one of the others to pen it for me. But I cannot. I am on the verge of giving in to the devil's counsel and writing a lie. This has gone on too long, this silence, these whispers, the feelings of shame and unworthiness that come with the interdict, when we have done nothing but follow God's word. Is there a way to write this letter without fabricating a vision? The quill shakes in my hand; ink splashes onto the parchment, a careless waste of precious materials. I cannot do it.

Sister Clothilde makes me take a draught to ease the pain in my joints and help me sleep. At first I refuse it; if God wanted me to be without pain, he would not visit on me the maladies of old age. Clothilde reminds me that I myself set out the ingredients for this potion in my *Natural History*, making especial note of its efficacy for conditions such as the one from which I currently suffer. I swallow the draught, if only so that she will leave me in peace. I lie down on my pallet. *Dear God, let me have the blessing of music once more before I die.*

I sleep, and dream. I dream of angels, rank on rank of them, and if their faces are beautiful to behold, their voices are beyond loveliness. I see among them my beloved friend Volmar, and Sister Richardis who was so dear to me. I see my mother and father, my departed brothers. I see Jutta, a young woman as she was when first she took the child Hildegard under her wing, and I see Matthias the repentant sinner and many others, their faces familiar, their names forgotten. The singing rises and falls in patterns too complex to analyse, celestial, transformative, rich with the mystery of God; a music far beyond the human voice. When I wake before dawn, my old cheeks are bathed in tears. Dear God! You have given me a foretaste of Heaven.

I write my letter. It is to Archbishop Christian of Mainz, and it takes a very long time. But I will not entrust this to a younger, firmer hand; I must do it myself. There is no longer any need to pray for a vision. The dream has brought me the arguments I require, clear and perfect in every detail.

In the past, however hot my anger, however pressing my need to see justice done, I have kept the tone of my letters humble, courteous, self-effacing. Always, my missives have spoken of God's will, not the will of Hildegard. I have done my best to be His true servant.

This time my voice is less conciliatory. I set out, first, the doctrinal arguments in support of my decision to provide Matthias with burial in hallowed ground. I tell the Archbishop of the shadow that lies over our convent now that our music has been silenced. I speak of Adam's voice as he sang in the Garden, before the Fall—so pure and powerful that we weak mortals could not have borne to hear it. Truly the voice of an angel. I tell how God in His wisdom allows the faithful to raise their lesser voices in songs of praise, and to compose music, and to make instruments on which it may be played—weak echoes of that first voice, indeed, but nonetheless gifts of beauty and meaning. It is God's intention that we use them in His praise. I expound on that point at some length.

The devil, I write, is driven mad by such music, for in it he hears the divine beauty of that which he left behind when he quit the Heavenly realm, and it is to him a torment and punishment. So he seeks to silence it, by setting ill thoughts in the hearts of certain authorities, and leading them to acts of repression against those who would lift their voices in the adoration of God.

My quill moves more quickly now, urged forward by the argument that stirs my blood. I end my letter with the wisdom of last night's wondrous dream. Those who silence the praise of God without sound reason, I write, should beware. For when, after death, they rise to Heaven, they will find themselves unable to hear the voices of the angels. God in His eternal wisdom has shown this to His humble servant, this weak woman, I write, reverting briefly to my more usual mode of expression. There is no need to state precisely how God has done so. No need to mention that this time, it was not through a vision. My heart tells me that the dream, as clear and direct as Sister Barbara's soaring voice, was a gift straight from Heaven.

The letter is finished. I sign it: Hildegard of Bingen. In orderly fashion I sprinkle the parchment with sand to help it dry; wipe the quill; cap the inkpot. My heart is beating too fast. Angelic music rings in my mind, though the scriptorium is silent save for the voices of birds out in the garden. I sit awhile, breathing slowly, thanking God for my life, for the visions, for the music and the scholarship and the fine friends along the way. For the warmth of morning sun; for the taste of vegetables fresh from the garden; for the smiles of young women who love learning. I thank Him for the gift of a good intellect and the opportunity to use it. I thank Him for the challenges—there have been many—and the strength I have gained from them. I wonder, for a little, what course my life might have taken had I spoken out about the visions when I was younger, and not waited to share them until my life was half over. What will Guibert put in his book about those thirty years of silence? I do not suppose I will be here to read it. *Dear God,* I pray, *let this letter achieve its purpose. Allow an old woman one selfish wish. Let me hear Lauds sung at Bingen one more time.*

◊Δ◊Δ◊Δ◊Δ◊

The letter is despatched, and we wait. We study, we pray, we harvest our spring vegetables, we tend to the sick, and we whisper our way through the Office. Guibert teaches my girls and writes his book; he does not speak to me of the interdict.

The weather warms. Blossoms appear on the trees, and one of our hens settles hopefully on a clutch of eggs. I am aware, through certain messages that pass between our convent and the foundation at Disibodenberg, that witnesses have been heard in the matter of Matthias's absolution, and that certain influential clerics have argued our case, while others have continued to condemn our action.

At last an answer comes, carried to Rupertsberg by young Brother Johannes, a long-legged country boy. I read the document in the scriptorium, with Sisters Elisabeth and Clothilde hovering at the door. I must show my sisters an example. I must be strong and calm, even if this is bad news.

I break the seal; cast my eyes over the first line or two. My heart leaps. God be praised! I blink back sudden tears.

"The interdict has been lifted." My voice shakes. But I will not weep, either before my sisters or alone in my cell. "Please let our sisters know that we will sing Vespers this evening. And send someone down to the village with the news. Thank Brother Johannes and offer him food and drink before he starts his long walk home."

◊Δ◊Δ◊Δ◊Δ◊

Later, as the voices of my sisters rise in a hymn of praise, their echoes ringing back from every corner of our chapel, I ask myself whether I have won this dispute on the strength of a half-truth. A dream is not a vision. A vision is from God; a vision holds you in its grip and will not let go until a time of its own choosing. I know this. A dream might be from anywhere. Even, perhaps, from the devil himself. Yet that dream, surely, could not be the devil's work. The music in it was all divinity, all spirit, ineffable, unknowable, holy and pure. *Dear God,* I pray, *if I have sinned, forgive me as you forgave Matthias. If I have taken too much upon myself, if I have indulged in prideful action, I am sorry. Humility has always been my hardest lesson. But in the end we are all dust. I suppose, very soon, my earthly remains will be in the garden out there, providing good nourishment for a new crop of plants. And to become compost is a humble state indeed. Dear God, thank you for this music. For the voices of women and of angels. Spread your sheltering hand over my sisters. When I am gone, let them walk on with piety, courage and, above all, wisdom. Let each in her own way sing.*

Glorious
Faith Mudge

I grieve and dare not show my discontent;
I love and yet am forc'd to seem to hate;
I do, yet dare not say I ever meant;
I seem stark mute but inwardly do prate.
— Elizabeth I

Dear God, that I should be brought to this!

It is nearing a month since I was brought to Whitehall and the queen has at last decided what to do with me. She did not summon me to tell me so herself; no, Mary would rather pray for my miserable soul than see my living face. She sent Sussex and Winchester to deliver my sentence.

I am to go to the Tower. Oh God in Heaven help me, I am to go to the Tower.

I demanded to see Mary; when this was denied, I begged leave to write her a letter. Winchester would have refused even that, but Sussex overrode him. It will be of little use, I am sure—there is no woman in England more implacable than my sister—but I may win myself a respite, be it only a day, be it only an hour.

While I wait for the paper and ink to be brought, I cross to the window, staring out across the river and folding my hands tightly to hide their shaking. Bitter words burn my lips from the inside. *You prove our father wrong, Mary! He thought no woman could rule because no woman could be as ruthless as he, but he did not know you at all. Is this righteous, sister? How heavy is his crown?*

"My lady," Sussex murmurs, "pray write."

I walk slowly to the chair and seat myself, straightening my skirts meticulously before taking up the pen. I have often been complimented on my fine penmanship. In that, let this letter do me credit!

If any ever did try this old saying that a king's word was more than another man's oath, I most humbly beseech your M. to verify it in me and remember your last promise and my last demand that I be not condemned without answer and due proof, which it seems that now I am, for that without cause proved I am by your Council from you commanded to go unto the Tower, a place more wonted for a false traitor than a true subject...

Never have I written with more care and made less sense. My mind measures the minutes, for if I can only delay long enough, the changing tide will not be safe for travel. Even Queen Mary cannot command the Thames.

Their lordships grow impatient, even the courtly Sussex. When they press me to be done, my pen scurries with obedient speed, only to be recalled by a blot or mistake. I write a word—I cross it out—I sigh and bow my head, the image of contrition. I know how to don *that* guise. Were it a dress, it would be ragged with wear.

At length, my inspiration runs dry. I sign the last page and hesitate; there is nothing left to say, yet I am reluctant to leave any space for a forger's falsehoods, so I score lines across the paper, lest my plea become a confession before it reaches my sister's hands.

"God's oath!" Winchester mutters. "She writes slower than a blind brat."

"Watch your tongue, man. She is the queen's sister."

Winchester raises his voice. "Is it written, my lady?"

I incline my head. He snatches the missive with a hasty bow and goes to quit the room, but is stopped at the door by Sussex. They confer again in whispers, but the room is quiet and my ear is keen. I hear enough.

"It's too late. We have missed the tide."

"The queen has commanded she be taken today!"

"The next tide is not until midnight. If we take her by darkness, I fear an ambush. The lady Elizabeth must remain here until the morrow."

It is a small victory, but sweet. I keep my head bent and my smile hidden. Mary must not know I smiled.

◊∆◊∆◊∆◊∆◊∆◊

It was not always this way between us. Once, we understood each other. Who else can know what it is like to be a princess one day, and a royal bastard the next?

Three children by six wives is a disappointment in anyone's arithmetic. For two of the number to be daughters was an injustice of fate that preyed ever on our father's mind. When Mary's mother lost favour, he threw her aside so that mine might take her place; when the Pope refused to grant him a divorce, he threw Rome aside and married the woman he wanted regardless.

For a time it seemed there was nothing the king would not do for his beloved Anne Boleyn, but like her predecessor, she failed to give him a son. Scandal coalesced around her like smoke and she was imprisoned in the Tower of London for treason. The last gesture of her husband's love was to send for a skilled French swordsman—a quicker, cleaner end than the clumsy axe.

I was not quite three years old. No one ever told me outright what had happened. I pieced together the tale for myself from baleful sermons and incautious whispers. *Sorceress. Traitor. Harlot.* I understood that I'd had a mother, and that I had her no more.

Mary, seventeen years my elder, remembered vividly the loss of her own mother. The grievances they had endured together gave her strength, a will to rival the king's and a temperament exactly calculated to rouse his ire. It took all the privations and humiliations he could devise to make her accept her new place as the king's bastard.

I, on the other hand, was a pretty pet of a child with a Tudor's red hair to prove my birthright and a knack for making the king laugh. I saw little of my father, but heard much. When I *did* see him, it was generally within the giddy whirl of court, where he was at his most glorious. I remember the roar of his laugh, his beringed hands swinging me up high.

Then he married for the third time, and my brother was born.

I was four. The rejoicing in my own household told me that a son was a great thing, better than a daughter. If it meant that I was called by a different title—if it also meant, when summoned to court for the christening, my father had little time for me—I was expected to accept my new place without complaint.

I was not wholly forgotten. My part in the ceremony was to carry the christening robe, a garment so heavy with gems and embroidery that I was in turn carried in order to keep up with the parade. I was curious about this baby, and jealous too, though this I hid as best I could beneath high spirits. Even then, I knew better than to speak my mind.

Perhaps I was not careful enough, or perhaps she felt something of the same, because as we left the chapel in stately procession Mary came to my side and stooped to take my hand.

"Smile, Elizabeth," she said softly, her breath warm on my ear.

"Why?" I demanded, but I whispered too.

"We are being watched," Mary said, and straightened, my hand clasped firmly in hers. It was true.

We were always watched.

◊Δ◊Δ◊Δ◊Δ◊Δ◊

My letter has done me no good. Even Sussex is stern today, and all my ploys are for naught.

Winter has ended since I came to Whitehall, but there is no sign of that in the ashy clouds and steely river, or in the rain streaming ceaselessly between them. I am escorted through the gardens and down the river steps to a waiting barge with all courteous speed, as though the weather is the worst I am to face today. At least I am allowed my retinue: three of the Queen's ladies and three of my own, and two gentlemen besides. We shelter in the cabin, each landmark we pass diminishing my time left as a free woman. As we reach the water gate beneath St. Thomas's Tower, my heart squeezes so tight that I fear I will faint. This is where the traitors go.

"Let me enter by another gate," I plead. "Any gate but this."

I might as well have asked the rain to stop falling. The barge judders beneath me, echoing my protests, and for a moment I think we will run aground beneath the bridge, but no—we are through. The Tower looms above us, greyer than the clouds, greyer than iron. How many names have fed that stony maw? Katherine Howard, my fifth stepmother, young and lovely still in my mind's eye. Thomas Seymour and the brother he loathed, their hatred of each other overcome at last by the impartiality of the axe. Little Jane Grey, who held the title of queen for nine days and none of the power. Mary wept for her, but that did not stay her hand.

My mother came this way, and never came back again.

The boatmen tip their oars and begin to tie moorings. I am seized by terror; the barge has become a final refuge and I will not shift from it. My lord captors, the first to disembark, are forced to turn back for me.

"You have no choice," Winchester says baldly. He looks at me and hesitates. I do not know what he sees in my face, but the next moment he has unclasped his cloak and is holding it out. I feel scalded by his pity. Knocking aside the cloak, I hold my chin high and climb the landing steps. The yeoman warders of the Tower are lined up to receive me. These men will remember me for the rest of their lives, no matter what comes to pass.

"Here stands as true a subject as ever landed at these stairs," I say loudly, demanding I be heard. I will not disappear in silence. "Before God I speak it, having no other friend but He alone!"

"If that were so, my lady," Winchester remarks, drily, "it would be the better for you."

It is true, those who called themselves my 'friends' have brought me to this. The men who would have raised me onto the throne of England have stretched my throat beneath the axe. Their leader is in the hands of Mary's most loyal men, being compelled by any means to confession, and I would be a fool indeed if I didn't know the word they want most to drag from his lips is my name. So far, it would seem Thomas Wyatt has not obliged them, but in the eyes of a man like Winchester I am already guilty.

It is good, then, that my words are not for him.

"Oh Lord! I never thought to have come here as a prisoner," I cry aloud, clasping my hands tight before me, as if in devotion. "I pray you all bear me witness that I come in as no traitor but as true a woman to the Queen's Majesty as any now living."

A ripple of movement passes through the ranks of the yeomen. One man steps forward, then another, another. As they kneel before me, the first cries out, "God preserve your Grace!" and it is all I can do not to weep. *I will not enter the Tower.* There is a great stone by the gate, slick with the day's rain; I sink upon it, heedless of the cold and damp, and refuse to move one step further. My retinue gather in a doubtful huddle while Winchester and Sussex mutter in conference. They are loathe to compel me by force whilst loyal men watch on.

Their consultation is brought to an end when the Lieutenant of the Tower himself comes forward to stand at my side. I know Sir John Brydges to be a devout Catholic, and as such he has no reason to be kind to me, but his voice is gentle.

"You had best come in, madam. It is unwholesome here."

"Better sit here," I retort, staring fixedly at the ground, "than in a worse place, for God alone knows where you will bring me."

A sob breaks the quiet, but the tears are not mine, nor even those of my devoted ladies—it is one of my gentlemen who weeps. I surge to my feet in such a fury I almost slap him. My people are supposed to give me strength. What right has *he* to tears?

I have often been told my temper will be the death of me, and perhaps today I make it true, because it is not trust in my innocence or belief in God's will that at last pushes my foot across the threshold of the Tower. It is anger, and pride. I will not be wept over as though I am already dead!

The sky is replaced by stone.

◊Δ◊Δ◊Δ◊Δ◊Δ◊

My brother was named Edward. My stepmother died of a fever less than a week after his birth and he was sent away from the dirt and disease of

London to join Mary and I in the country, under the care of my nurse Lady Bryan. This was another change I was expected to take with good grace, but I had not the poise for that. Why could he not be given a nurse of his own? Why must he have mine?

"Because he is the king's son, Elizabeth," Mary told me patiently. "Don't cry so, there's no use in it. Come out into the gardens. Shall we see if the rose trees have budded yet?"

I did not reward my sister's kindness that day, dragging my feet through the dirt and beheading flowers with a stick. It was one thing to understand a son's importance, another to experience being put aside.

We three had our separate households, but often moved about from one royal house to another and in consequence spent a good deal of time together. Mary liked to play with Edward, though she thought him already over-indulged, and I think I made a good show of liking him too. It became easier as the months passed and my sense of grievance diminished, for he was quick to learn and could be a marvellous playmate. Lady Bryan had tended Mary before me and knew the king's changeable temper as well as anyone; she meted out her love with care, never wholly rejecting me or my sister, but cautious not to display an excess of favour. Her new charge came first in everything.

I was instead placed under the eye of a governess. Katherine Champernowe had a manner vastly different to that of Lady Bryan. Though in possession of far greater learning than any other woman I knew, she had a wicked sense of fun and unlike my other ladies, was disposed to answer my questions instead of scolding my curiosity. Best of all, she liked me, and was not afraid to show it. How could I not love her?

My father placed no obstacles in the way of my education. Kat taught me to read and write, to dance and ride and sew, among other courtly accomplishments. By the time I was five, we had begun a study of Greek and Latin. When news of the king's fourth marriage reached us a year later, I wrote a pretty letter to the woman who shared my mother's Christian name, hoping to win her approval. It was important, I had come to understand, to have a voice at court.

That voice would not come from Anne of Cleves, for the king took against her from the first. It is true that she was not lovely of face, and could have used a strong dousing in scent, but she was and remains the most even-tempered woman I have ever met. She had patience enough to manage us, fractured and fractious as we were. She mothered us all, even our father, when he would let her.

She was queen for only seven months. Her choices were to resist divorce and risk his rage, or submit with all speed and hope for beneficence. Anne chose the latter path and was well rewarded with property and an assured income, her reputation intact. She asked for only one favour: that she might have me to stay with her sometimes.

Oh, Anne. It would have been the better for us had he let you stay.

◊∆◊∆◊∆◊∆◊∆◊

I am taken to the Bell Tower and an apartment of four rooms. Chief of these is a large chamber with a good fireplace and three windows. It would be quite comfortable, were the windows not so narrow and the walls not so thick. As it is, one can sit anywhere and not forget that this is a prison.

My women are much depressed in spirits, conversing in whispers. Kat is worst of all. During the first days of our incarceration, she stuttered every time footsteps passed the door, and that set the mood for us all. I keep my patience as best I can. It is not her fault she is afraid.

I never know when my inquisitors will arrive. Sometimes they come very early and stay for hours; other days pass with no sign of them. Today they come at midday, and Stephen Gardiner is among them.

Of all the councillors, he is the one I fear most. When the door opens and I see his face, my heart drops like an anchor, but I do not permit my hands to quiver. I am not a hounded beast, whatever he might think. I am the daughter of King Henry VIII, and well may he remember it!

The questioning commences at once. "You may recall, madam, the request you made of Her Majesty to leave court and take up residence at the estate of Ashridge," Gardiner begins, walking back and forth before the windows, so that his silhouette is cast across the floor at my feet. Even if I do not look at him, I must look at his shadow. "Why, pray, did you make such a request? Was life in the presence of your good queen irksome to you?"

"Certainly not," I reply, in tones of quiet outrage. It is the hardest thing to keep my voice low when I am angry, but it serves me well, for all men like better a soft voice from a woman. "I am unused to staying such lengths of time in London, and became unwell."

"Illness has indeed plagued you of late, madam. Was it not illness that repeatedly prevented you from attending Mass at the palace?"

"Ill health is not treasonous, I believe."

"Did not similar complaints trouble my lady of Cleves?"

"Her ladyship is not young," I observe. "To be cautious of her health is only prudent."

"Prudence!" Gardiner exclaims. "Oh yes, that is truly a woman's virtue."

I do not answer him. Winchester is also in attendance today, with the Earl of Arundel, but both say little and remain seated.

"You declare, madam, that you knew nothing of Wyatt's plans," Gardiner muses aloud, resuming his pacing. "And so you expect me to believe that, wholly ignorant of Wyatt's doings, you arranged to leave your establishment at Ashridge?"

My fingers tighten in my lap of their own accord. "I do."

"Why chose you the fortress in Berkshire?"

I stare at him, my tongue frozen. I know not how to answer. *I am not a fool, sir! Anyone with ears knew trouble was abroad.* That is the truth he is so diligently digging to uncover, but it will not help my case.

"It is passing strange, would you not say, that Wyatt writes to you of forces massed at Donnington, and that is precisely where you most wish to go!"

"Donnington!" The words burst from my mouth like a flock of panicked birds. "What is Donnington to me! How should I know where it is?"

I am shaking, with rage and with fear, for Gardiner's eyes have come alight. I have thrown him a fool's lie and cannot snatch it back.

"I know not what Wyatt wrote," I tell him, my tone as cool as I can contrive, "for I never received any such letter. Why should I not go to any house of my own, have I the mind to do so?"

"Then you *do* know where Donnington is, my lady?"

"I understand it to be my estate." I take a careful breath, measuring my words. "Having never been there, that I can recollect, I have little else to say."

"You would stake your word that you had no consultation with Wyatt or his fellow traitor James Crofts? What would you say, my lady, were Crofts to stand before you himself?"

"I have nothing to say to him, nor to any other prisoner of the Tower. If they have done evil, and offended the Queen's Majesty, let them answer accordingly. I beseech you, my lords, not to join my name with these offenders."

"Your Grace speaks truly." Arundel astonishes me by dropping to one knee in formal apology. "We are sorry indeed to have so troubled you in vain."

I gather dignity about me as a cloak. Arundel has never raised his voice in my favour at court; that he chooses to show such unwarranted kindness now is a sign I do not know how to interpret. Perhaps he, like Sussex before him, recalls my birthright and is tempering his actions accordingly. If that's so, he must believe I will leave the Tower alive.

"My lords, you question me very closely," I say aloud, eyes demurely downcast, "but assured as I am that this is God's will, He will forgive you all."

When in doubt, devout modesty is a woman's armour.

Still the questioning goes on, day after day. Sometimes their inquisition follows me into my dreams, but in my mind's eye the questions come not from the lips of the councillors. A parade of the dead mount the scaffold before me, their familiar faces twisted into grief or rage. Last of all is a woman cloaked and veiled. She comes very close, and whispers softly in my ear: *daughter*.

◊Δ◊Δ◊Δ◊Δ◊Δ◊

I had not long to wait before I met the lady who had so easily supplanted Anne's place. Her name was Katherine Howard.

I was seven years of age when, in the space of two weeks, my father cast off one wife and took another. Mary, never disposed to think well of the king's excesses, was disgusted by his choice. "She has not a thought in her head!" she muttered to me, well out of *his* hearing. "The godless little whore may have charmed her way into his Majesty's approval, but I see her for what she really is. Another Boleyn—"

She fell quickly silent, with a wary glance at me. I was already aware that the young queen was my mother's cousin, but I knew little of her and was not yet sure what the connection would mean for me.

Katherine soon made her feelings known. On the day she was announced as queen, there was a grand feast at Hampton Court and she asked that I be placed opposite herself at the table. What a scene it was! The banquet hall was bright with candles, alive with the playing of the king's musicians and the chatter of the court. At the heart of the spectacle was the king's dais, and his new queen.

Where Anne had been tall and thick of figure, Katherine was little and dainty; where the former was peaceable and placid, the latter brimmed with vivacity. Though the king was swollen and gout-stricken, his age showing in unsightly blotches and creases, Katherine attended to him as if to a young lover, responding with giddy peals of laughter to everything he said. She glittered with jewels and mischief, and the king could not have his fill of looking at her.

"You'll be well-off now, my lady," Kat whispered to me that night, in the chamber we shared. "She asked after you so particularly—'for she is of my own blood and lineage', that is what she said. His Majesty cannot do enough to please her and if she likes to have you near, you will be much at court, methinks."

I had never been granted such a place of honour before. That I owed it to my Boleyn blood was a baffling contradiction in the natural order of things

Those were golden months. My new stepmother was always seeking revelry and just as Kat had predicted, invited me to join the fun. When the royal party went to Chelsea, she made sure I was among them. After a few days in the house by the river, we continued on to Essex to see my brother. There were feasts and rides, dancing and games. After so long away from court the round of gaiety was dizzying, and having Edward near was an unexpected comfort. Though very prone to pomposity for so small a boy, he was quick and full of funny thoughts.

Katherine did not understand half of what we talked of, but she liked to have us sit by her sometimes in the gardens, playing with her little pet dogs and entertaining her with our 'pretty nonsense'. That pleased our father too, for he joined us once or twice. If we were happy amusements for the young queen, she was the same in her turn for the king.

Once, when the king was busy rough and tumbling with Edward, Katherine drew me close and toyed with my curls. I did not much like that, but didn't protest. "I should like to have a daughter like you, Elizabeth," she remarked. "After I have given His Majesty a son, of course. Would you like a sister?"

I already had a sister, but I nodded obediently. That was safer.

"Such a pretty child," she sighed. "You look so much like Anne."

I did not understand at first, thinking she meant the stepmother before her, whom I resembled not a jot. The name Anne, though, had belonged to another queen. Realising what she had said, Katherine pressed a hand to her mouth.

"Oh, Elizabeth," she breathed. "Don't tell the king."

I never did. It was Katherine who didn't know how to keep her secrets.

Those were the last good times. When she returned to London, the court was thick with ugly gossip, denouncing her as a whore and a traitor. It was all familiar; this was how Anne Boleyn fell, every tongue and hand turned against her, the king's love crumbling to dust. They had been married not quite two years when Katherine was taken to the Tower, and the axe.

Love is a word I will never trust.

◊∆◊∆◊∆◊∆◊∆◊

Spring does not come to the Tower. There is, I suppose, no call for it among the condemned. From the height of the battlements I can see the scaffold, an omen of death ever on the horizon.

Thankfully, the Lieutenant of the Tower's conduct remains cordial. Sir John remembers I am sister of the queen and daughter of the late king and grants me liberties no other prisoner might enjoy. I take my meals at his table, and on days when the weather permits I walk along the battlements with as many as five of my attendants. Kat is always among the number; she is more like herself in the open air, though never the same light-hearted, wicked-tongued friend I knew as a child.

The wind is chill this morning but I will not go inside. I brace my hands against the parapet and close my eyes, light speckles of rain stinging against my cheeks.

"I wonder what it is like," I say aloud, "when the axe falls. Do you think it hurts?"

"My lady!" Kat is horrified. "What a thing to say!"

"I think it must. One hears that it is so often blunt. Perhaps I might apply to the queen, and ask that a swordsman perform the deed, as our father did for my mother. Surely she would not begrudge me a quicker end?"

"My *lady*." Kat's voice is choked. "I beg you, don't say such things."

I bow my head. "Oh Kat," I whisper, "how many have passed through that gate and come out again alive?"

She places her hand on my arm and holds tight. "Why, I myself," she says, her voice so thick the words can scarcely be discerned. "Did I not come out again?"

We both know the reassurance is hollow.

Later, as I lie awake listening to the rain, I wonder what proof of my innocence the queen will consider sufficient. She must know, if she knows me at all, that I would have no hand in this mad rebellion. Why would I ally myself with their plotting, when all I need do is quietly wait my turn? Mary is not young. Her husband has no love for her, and it grows ever more unlikely that she shall bear a child to take the crown after her death. Who should be her heir but me?

And in the dark the answer comes like the whispering of dead women at my bedside: *any other, if the Queen sends you to the block.*

◊Δ◊Δ◊Δ◊Δ◊Δ◊

The king alternately raged and mourned the loss of his 'rose without a thorn'. Mary was quietly relieved, for Katherine had never liked her; Edward echoed our father's recriminations. I suffered bad dreams for many months afterwards and Kat held me as I wept.

Study had always been a refuge to me and so it was again now. "You have a most superior mind, my lady," Kat sometimes sighed. "I wonder how I shall keep up with you."

For once she was fully in earnest. That year my education was placed in the hands of Doctor Richard Coxe, tutor to Edward, so my brother and I were often in the same household. Mary, we saw less. I have never discovered whether this was our father's choice, or her own.

There was always gossip about the king. Kat was at first convinced he meant to remarry Anne of Cleves, holding up the gifts they had exchanged at New Year to be positive proof, but all that came to nothing. Early the next year, an odd piece of news: the king had gone to see Mary, and seemed intent to stay awhile.

"A lady in her household has caught his eye, you may depend upon it," Kat told me. "There will be word of an engagement before the spring is out."

She was right. On the twelfth of July I was summoned to Hampton Court to witness my father's sixth wedding. I was nine years old.

I do not know quite how to describe Catherine Parr. Her face was pleasant, her temper calm, and though I never had reason to suppose she loved—or even liked—my father, she hid any dissatisfaction with the greatest care. Her chief gift was the art of speaking well and her chief duty was to soothe the king's increasingly capricious temper.

I was not inclined to love my new stepmother; I was, however, curious. Catherine was a well-educated woman. Observing that she preferred conversation above flattery, I did all I could to capture her attention, offering pretty speeches in French and Italian, and reciting verses from the great poets.

Though I was dismissed from court shortly after the wedding, she still took an interest in me. I was included in Edward's lessons, studying logic and theology, rhetoric and philosophy. Edward was a boy and a prince, but he could not keep up with me. My stepmother soon found me a tutor of my own so I might learn at a quicker pace.

Even when not at our books, Edward and I spent much of our time together. There was so much we could talk of between ourselves, and so many interests we had in common, that we came to know each other better than we ever had before. It was good to have a brother, even if he did parrot my father's complaints about 'women's arguments' whenever I trounced him at debate.

Though Catherine had no ill will against Mary, I still saw little of my sister. In her letters her main concern was my study of theology. She had accepted the king's changes to the Church with deep reluctance; nothing could sway her private principles, and she wanted mine to be the same. I did not know what to tell her. She could not keep me safe any more; my stepmother could.

Catherine did more than that.

For almost a year after the wedding I saw nothing more of the queen, and though Edward and Mary had both been summoned to court, I was troubled by pains in my teeth and could not go. It was an unlucky happenstance I felt most keenly and took without much grace. I was in the sullen state of lethargy that follows a grand tantrum when the letter reached me at St. James's Palace.

My father had restored Mary to the succession, and me behind her.

I was, once more, a princess of England.

◊∆◊∆◊∆◊∆◊∆◊

Pox and plague on the Popish bastard! As if I have not enough reason to be miserable, the Constable of the Tower has taken it upon himself to correct Sir John's lenience. My walks have been put to an end. If I wish to exercise I must walk in the royal lodgings, the windows all being shut first, so that I might not mistake myself as anything but a prisoner. *Damn* him. I feel as if I am being slowly nailed into a coffin.

Even in these straits, Kat hears things I do not. How she comes by her gossip I can't say, but in my present circumstances I dare not disregard any scrap of knowledge. Yesterday, she tells me, Sir John received a warrant for my execution. Bless the man a hundred times over—I shall remember him in my prayers this night—for he doubted its veracity and instead of acting upon it, made haste to the queen to confirm her intentions. Mary denied sending any such order. But does she deny it because she wishes me alive, or because she fears what will happen if my head rolls at her word? The people of England remember their late king had two daughters—there may be unrest if I am seen to suffer injustice.

I hold my hopes close.

Last night I dreamed I walked through the unlit halls of Hampton Court. I was not alone; skirts twitched out of sight at the corner ahead of me, and snatches of a woman's singing drifted in the dark, a nonsensical lullaby as one might sing to an infant. I was seized by the conviction that I *must* catch her, but when I turned the last corner and ran out into the gardens, I found myself standing upon a scaffold, and a woman's headless body gushed blood across my bare feet.

I woke choking on tears.

When I was a little girl my tutor would take me to watch cocks fight, and he taught me to handle a bow as well as any lady of the hunt. Surgeons have bled me with knives and leeches. I have witnessed more public executions than I can easily number. Blood holds no fear for me, yet in my dreams I drown in the horror of it.

They said my mother went mad in the Tower. Dear God, may that not be my fate.

◊∆◊∆◊∆◊∆◊∆◊

In the summer of 1544, the king resurrected his youthful valour to lead a military expedition into France and appointed his wife as regent in his absence. Women, I had heard a thousand times, were destined by the laws of Heaven to make poor leaders, but Catherine showed no qualm. When I was summoned to Hampton Court in July to join Mary and Edward, my stepmother was much engaged with affairs of state. It was a wondrous thing to see the great men of court defer to her, and her own calm acceptance of the role. It was, of course, all a reflection of the king's glory; still, it did not sit ill on her.

Throughout the summer she kept me with her, and my brother and sister too. She was not motherly, as Anne of Cleves had been, nor as indulgent as Katherine Howard. She was an arbiter in disputes and a voice of consistent good sense. The contrast struck me greatly when the king returned, his health and temper both noticeably worsened by the French campaign. From his wife, he wished only smiles and soothing words; he never learned to appreciate the warmth of her true approval. What reason had he to look for it? He already owned her.

Queen Catherine liked to hear me read, but rarely when Mary was present. My sister was a staunch Catholic, my stepmother a quiet advocate of the Protestant faith, and the texts one woman deemed appropriate for my mind were necessarily opposed by the other.

As to the king's convictions, they were as changeable as his tempers. He had renounced the Catholic church when the Pope refused to grant his first divorce, yet attended Mass as many as five times a day. The ceremony of English services changed with every royal decree. Catholics were hanged. Protestants burned. No one was permitted to question a passage of the Bible but the king himself.

The year I turned thirteen, a woman named Anne Askew was arrested for the disbursement of Protestant books and tortured in the Tower. Several of Catherine's ladies were suspected to have been among her readers. My stepmother was shaken by the incident, and reacted less wisely than usual; she argued with the king and left him in such a rage he ordered her arrest. I was there that day, watching as her women whispered and wept and threw papers on the fire. Any disgruntled letter, any incautiously recorded thought—the least scrap of evidence might be enough to incriminate us all.

Familiarity does not make fear any more bearable. In a matter of hours I descended to frantic doubt. Should I leave, disassociating myself from all present, or would that only make me appear as guilty at the rest? How could I best present myself as blameless before my father's eyes? Would my stepmother be granted the dignity of a divorce, or trumped up with a trial and beheaded at the Tower?

Then Catherine herself came in. "His Majesty believes it may rain," she remarked serenely, and took up a book.

It was from Kat I heard what had happened. That morning, silver-tongued Catherine had gone to the king and persuaded him her argument had been but a ploy to distract him from the pain in his leg—that indeed, she knew he had been right all along.

Less than six weeks later, the king announced his intention to abolish Mass, and set about ridding himself of all Catholics.

Five months after that, he was dead.

All my life, I had tried to understand my father, as one might watch the clouds to predict a storm. What would please him? What would gain his favour? His presence had always been so intensely vital that to contemplate his death seemed almost sacrilegious.

The news was brought to my door by Edward Seymour, uncle of my brother. He came to Hatfield, where I was then in residence, with the prince at his side. He had not told my brother the reason for the urgent journey—he considered it more appropriate to tell us together. Edward was ashen when he arrived, half sick with dread. When Seymour spoke the words aloud we clung together, my brother and I, weeping uncontrollably. I will always remember him that way, a white-faced little boy with his arms around my neck, shaking with tears for the father who had loved him above all.

My stepmother met the event with her customary composure. It was arranged that I would live with her and continue my education—which is to say, a Protestant's education. With the death of my father, the crown passed to my brother, but until he came of age the governance of England really lay in the hands of the Council of Regency. Most held strong Protestant sympathies. Catherine had no cause to hide any more.

Chief among the Council's number was Edward Seymour, newly Duke of Somerset. He had carried me at my brother's christening. I remembered him as a strict, stern-faced man—his brother Thomas, I had little memory of at all.

God knows I have had reason to wish that was still so.

◊∆◊∆◊∆◊∆◊∆◊

The Tower is crowded with the queen's enemies. I am kept most carefully from reach of their eyes or words, but the guards can be amenable to a well-worded inquiry. On the eleventh of April, Thomas Wyatt was taken to the scaffold on Tower Hill. Even at the end, his loyalty held firm—he declared my innocence to the watching crowd. I weep when Kat tells me, for such a noble fool.

My interrogators are in a predicament. Their best hope of conviction lay in Wyatt's testimony. Now, despite their cruellest efforts, I am exonerated by his word. Yet as the days drag on, my fate remains undecided.

It is not in Mary's nature to act in haste. But it would be no more like her to forget a wrong—and never did she feel more wronged than by Anne Boleyn.

◊Δ◊Δ◊Δ◊Δ◊Δ◊

Appointed Lord High Admiral of England shortly after my brother's accession, Thomas Seymour was handsome, rowdy and recklessly ambitious. He had at one time wished to marry Catherine, but withdrew when the king made his own interest plain. With my father out of the way, he lost no time in resuming his suit, and Catherine—so wise in all other matters—lost her heart to him completely. It was shocking enough that the widowed queen would marry again; Catherine chose to marry Seymour in secret only months after the king's death, and left the court dumbfounded when the truth was revealed. Mary was appalled, perhaps the more so because I was staying with my stepmother at the time and was therefore at great risk of moral decline.

The marriage did not quite take me by surprise. Living as I did in Catherine's household, the odd comings and goings, voices raised late at night, all spoke eloquently of a secret and Kat was not long in uncovering it. Having just escaped one marriage, for Catherine to shackle herself into another! I could not understand it.

When the marriage was formally announced, Edward gave his pardon, and Seymour came to live with us at Chelsea. He was tall and brawny with an uproarious laugh that made even weak jokes sound hilarious. In his presence my patient, careful stepmother bloomed with girlish excitement. *Elizabeth*, she would cry, *did you hear what Tom said?*

Though Catherine owned several properties, we were most often at Chelsea. This household was much livelier than any I had lived in before, for my stepmother was fond of music and her new husband fond of fun. As for me, I had a pretty face, a keen mind, and a sharp tongue. Away from the intrigues of court, with a steady circle around me, I flowered.

I knew little of men, though there had been one or two youths I had admired in the past. It was Tom who undertook my lessons in flirting, joking and jostling under Catherine's fond eye, laughing at my blushes. Though his ribaldry shocked me at first, I soon learned to take each jest with an easy smile and a light retort. If sometimes I noticed the swell of muscle beneath his sleeve when he took my arm, or I shook a little when he suggested I measure his shoulders with my hands—well. I was fourteen, and he was handsome.

Nor did the horseplay end in the banquet hall. Tom liked pranks; nothing pleased him more than to shock and amaze. Early one morning he came suddenly into my room, before I was dressed, to wish me a merry 'good morrow!'. I felt his eyes on my nightgown and gathered it close around myself, hot-faced with a mixture of gratification and shame. When he left, Kat burst into breathless giggles.

"Well, he makes no secret of his fancies, that's a fact," she whispered in my ear. "The Admiral planned to ask for your hand before your father died, you know, and afterwards he would have asked again if the poxy Council had not frowned so hard on the match. He settled for Lady Catherine at last…"

"Oh, stop it!" I swatted at her words, tossing my head. "He's far too old. Besides, you shouldn't say such things about my stepmother."

Kat merely shook her head with a smile of satisfaction. "As you like, Lady Elizabeth."

Tom's morning visits to my bedchamber became a regular occurrence, and the more often he came, the more outrageous his behaviour. He so liked to surprise me that sometimes he would come before I was even out of bed, and lunged as if to leap in beside me. I'd laugh and shriek, alarmed and excited in equal measure, retreating beneath the covers until he left the room. Once, kneeling over me, he bent as if for a kiss, and only Kat's startled admonition sent him away.

My stepmother knew of her husband's antics. She laughed at them, as she laughed at all his japes, but she began to accompany him in the mornings and in her presence they became funny again. I no longer wanted to be alone with Thomas Seymour.

One day the three of us were walking together in the gardens at Chelsea—or rather, Catherine and I were walking, while Tom strode some way ahead, unable to check his pace. Every so often he would turn about and come back to us with some bold remark. At length, he said, "Good Lord! What sort of pace do you call this, my ladies? It is the fault of your gowns—I have never liked the look of them. A woman need not be so heavily robed. It weighs her footsteps. It makes her looks too solemn."

"If you do not like it, my love, I will have different gowns made," Catherine promised.

Tom was not listening. He seized a handful of my skirt and I cried out in surprise, then tried to laugh, but when I stepped back he would not let go and I must stop or fall.

"As my helpmeet, Catherine, you must help me free her!" he declared. "If we do not act at once, she shall become a bloody Roman nun!" As he spoke, he drew his dagger, and cut a sliver of fabric from my skirt. Louder than my exclamations, he called to Catherine again, and she took my arms with an uncertain laugh.

"Oh, Tom! What silly play this is!"

Tom laughed, long and merry, and cut a slice between my knees. Catherine stood behind me; she did not see him lift his head, did not see his look as he met my eyes.

"God in heaven, what has happened?" Kat demanded when I burst into my bedchamber, my dress cut all to tatters, my face wet with humiliated tears. With as much dignity as I could muster, I told her the story, and for a moment was soothed by her outrage. The comfort did not last.

"Whatever can you have been thinking?" she hissed. "Your *reputation*—when people hear—you should have left at once!"

"How could I?" I shouted. "Catherine held me down!"

The tale of Thomas Seymour's rude courtship came out, of course, as dirty truths always do. By the time it did, I was far from Chelsea. Coming into my rooms one day to find her husband attempting to take me in his arms, my stepmother's credulity was strained beyond endurance. With no delay, I was sent away, the excuse being that Catherine was pregnant and needed much rest. As if I was ever the one to disturb her! I suppose it is harder to banish a husband.

A week after giving birth, Catherine died and the baby with her. Kat knew not what to do with me—one moment I was tolerably composed, the next throwing shoes at the maids and shouting. When she said I should send condolences to the grieving widower, I refused to pick up my pen. "He needs it not," I told her, bitterness barbing the words. Later, my treasurer Thomas Parry came to convey word from Seymour himself, offering me use of a house in London. Parry made the same presumption as Kat, that it was only a matter of time before Seymour proposed.

I will never marry him, I thought. *I will never marry at all.*

I was not well myself. Assailed by violent headaches, I took to bed for days at a time. One of the royal physicians was sent to examine me, but I wanted no cures, only to hide behind the bastion of sleep until I could bear the world again.

But Thomas Seymour was too bold for his own good. His ambitions for a royal wife were part of a more daring game: to topple his own brother, the Lord Protector, and seize power through my gullible young brother. As if Edward had not known such schemers all his life! Inevitably, the conspiracy was uncovered and Seymour was sent to the Tower. Parry was taken with him, and my Kat.

An interrogator was sent to ascertain my knowledge of the plot. I was in a fearful state of mind; I wonder that I managed to speak at all. Sir Tyrwhit did not want me to be guilty, that much was plain—he wanted my testimony to convict Kat and Parry, for only I could do it. I wept a good deal, and answered every question I was asked in so vague a way that Tyrwhit could do nothing with me.

Hardest of all was when he placed depositions before me, signed each by Kat and Parry, relating things said and done at Chelsea in humiliating detail. Because Tom had not been stopped, he must have been invited. Even Kat, it seemed, believed that.

She spoke in fear of her life, I know. It was betrayal just the same.

News of the scandal spread swiftly. When I learned that my illness was rumoured to be the sickness of pregnancy and Seymour the father, I wrote in wrath to the Lord Protector, charging him to disavow all slander of my name. I offered to come to court, so all might see me as I was: the virgin princess, Edward's sweet sister. Let them speak such rumours to my brother's face!

Though no confession could be wrung out of me and no wrongdoing could be proven, I was punished nonetheless. My interrogator's wife replaced Kat as my governess, planting a tattling tongue at the heart of my household. I extracted every small vengeance I dared and wrote letters until my fingers were stained with ink. Kat and Parry might never hold my trust again, but they were my people. I would not abandon them.

After pleading that made my pride ache, they were at length released. Thomas Seymour was not so fortunate. Condemned as a traitor, he was beheaded on Tower Hill.

There died a man with much wit, and very little judgement.

◊Δ◊Δ◊Δ◊Δ◊Δ◊

Oh God preserve me, God save me, they've come.

The Constable and Lieutenant of the Tower have both been put aside. In their place stands Sir Henry Bedingfield, who has come with his own men and orders to take me away. A hundred soldiers in blue livery have claimed the Tower in bloodless triumph.

My ladies cling together, crying or praying; the only word I can discern from Kat's sobbing babble is 'please'. I stand alone, facing this stolid servant of my sister, who calls me 'your Grace' with such courtesy. I would rather a villain who wore his hatred on his sleeve. *Him* I could scathe with my scorn, but Bedingfield makes me feel defenceless as a child. When I demand, as coolly as my trembling lips can manage, whether the old scaffold still stands or if there's need to erect another, he speaks gently.

"Your Grace, you have no need for fear. I come not with an order of execution. Her Majesty has placed you in my charge—I am to take you to the royal manor at Woodstock until current matters are resolved."

I look at him. What cleaner resolution than an axe? But I do not say so.

I have thought overmuch of Death in recent days. He haunts this place so faithfully. In my dreams, brave souls walk to the block and offer their necks with a look of scorn or words of valour, and sometimes I have seen myself amongst them. Now I realise my mistake. I am not ready to die, I will never be ready to die. I will go to my death as Anne Boleyn went to hers, hoping for a miracle to the bitter end.

◊Δ◊Δ◊Δ◊Δ◊Δ◊

When the disgrace of the Seymour affair finally ebbed, I paid a visit to my brother in London with as grand a retinue as I could manage. To some at court my name might always be besmirched, but I wished to appear exactly as a sister of the king ought. I discarded my more fanciful gowns, dressing with strict modesty.

I had seen very little of Edward or Mary since our father's death. My brother had grown into a cool-eyed cynic, a true man of politics at the ripe age of fourteen and a passionate Protestant besides. Despite his casual affection towards me, I was careful to observe all royal protocol.

"Court is ugly, Elizabeth," he said, watching the acrobats cavort for his entertainment. He looked too pale, his cheekbones distinct beneath the skin. "You would not thrive here. No good woman could."

I left court not long after that, and never saw my brother again.

Edward was ever surrounded by advisors. With the fall of the Seymour brothers, the loudest of the flock was now the Duke of Northumberland. A fierce Protestant, he disliked Mary on principle, a feeling that was entirely mutual. His cause against me was less clear. Perhaps he was simply frightened that when I spoke, Edward heard me.

Regardless of his reasoning, I felt the effects of Northumberland's interference soon enough. The severity of Edward's latest illness was kept from me; when I tried to visit, I was turned back. I hope he read my letters before he died, that he knew I was thinking of him.

This is what I know: striking both Mary and myself from the succession, Edward named our cousin the Lady Jane Grey as his heir, a fact only revealed after his death. Northumberland proclaimed Lady Jane as Queen of England with all haste, and Mary reacted exactly as I imagined she would: with the righteous outrage of a true heir. She gathered Catholic supporters and marched on London.

I stayed quietly at Hatfield and did nothing at all. I am no one's pawn, not even my sister's.

Mary, a true Tudor, won the day. The duke and his failed queen were sent to the Tower and I set off at once to join the new monarch. It seemed that all of London was rejoicing the pretender's defeat—as we rode through the streets, the crowds cheered and the bells rang out. What a day that was! If only King Henry could have seen his daughters, would he have believed his eyes?

It would be untrue to say I had no fears about Mary's ascension—it had been years since we had been intimate, but still I knew her. Just as she would fight for her throne, she would fight for her faith. Those who sought her favour must go to Mass, and my claims of illness could only excuse me for so long. I sought delays of a different nature, requesting books to tutor myself in the Catholic religion. Mary understood me too well to be convinced, but my pretence earned her tolerance a while longer. When at last I could dissemble no more, I commenced my attendance.

Mary arranged a Mass to be said for our brother. That, I would not attend. Edward lived and died a Protestant; not even the queen could make me pretend otherwise.

My show of submission earned its reward at Mary's coronation, at which I was the first to take the oath of allegiance and the first to follow the queen from Westminster Abbey. By the terms of succession, *I* was heir to the throne, and I had every intention of remaining there. Mary gave me pretty things, fine clothes and jewellery, much the way she had once bought me baubles as a child. And there was one other thing she wished to give me: a husband.

It was inevitable there should be talk of a marriage. My hand, once that of a traitor's bastard, was suddenly very valuable indeed, and should I be married to a foreigner there was the added advantage of my enforced absence from England. This thought pleased Mary's advisors very much. The favourite of the candidates was, however, an Englishman—Edward Courtenay, a young man long incarcerated in the Tower for the wrong political sympathies, now restored to wealth and liberty and to all appearances enjoying them very much indeed. Best of all, in Mary's eyes, he was a devout Catholic.

He was pleasant enough to dance with; inconceivable as a husband. Truthfully, I could imagine no man who would tempt me to willingly cast my freedom at his feet, though I took great care not to say so aloud. I saw a good deal of Courtenay, smiled often, and agreed to nothing. Mary soon lost interest in my nuptials in favour of her own. If her attempts to restore the Roman faith had been met with resistance from the English people, her choice of husband—a Catholic! A *Spaniard!*—appalled them, but nothing daunted her. I think she truly loved Philip. She needed to love someone.

The intrigues of court took their toll. Whether I meant ill by her or not, I was Mary's rival, and plots swirled about me wherever I went. With my red Tudor hair and black Boleyn eyes, I was the embodiment of old miseries, wearing down what real fondness she had once had.

When Mary's favour waned, I requested permission to return to the country, retreating to my house at Ashridge with Catholic priests to say my daily Mass and save my wicked Protestant soul. I was there in Hertfordshire when the long-simmering resentment against the queen boiled over. Leading the revolt was Thomas Wyatt. His plan was to depose Mary and place me upon the throne, Courtenay at my side.

I believe it's plain how Mary felt about that.

◊∆◊∆◊∆◊∆◊∆◊

What will God make of my soul? Born in the dying throes of Catholic England, raised amidst the persecution of Protestants, I have acted not from conscience but the desire to live. It must be wrong, to think so much of my own life, but who else is there to guard it?

I am not taken to the scaffold. Bedingfield brings me to a boat and we travel downriver. Cannons fire off a salute as we pass the gunners' wharf—for me? I was two months in the Tower. How much has changed?

We spend the night at Richmond, and ride on the next day for Windsor. I am in a state of the most fearsome confusion. Bedingfield is somber; I am surrounded by guards and sit upon a broken-down litter—this is not the journey of a validated princess. And yet, lining the roads are crowds who gather as close as they can, tossing flowers and sweetmeats into my litter, calling 'God Save Your Grace!' When I answer with a smile and gracious nod, hats are thrown in the air, so I wave until my arms ache. At Windsor, the schoolboys of Eton College come gravely forth to greet me. On the road the next day, so many cakes are tossed into my litter that I must ask the people to stop. Bedingfield does nothing to prevent them.

I do not feel like a woman going to her death.

Mary has not ordered my execution. She has not banished me abroad, or removed me from the succession. Truly, who is there to replace me? How many uprisings can she withstand? In all ways we might be at odds, yet there is this common ground: our mothers were wives who died. We were the daughters who lived.

I am still her heir, and all the people of England know it.

The love of a kingdom is a fairweather gift. Crowds gather this way for Mary, with cries as raucous in their affection. They gathered for Edward, and our father before him. I was there for each hour of triumph, long enough to see it pass and fade. This intoxication is not to be trusted, but how can I resist it?

Today, if only today, I truly believe that I will live.

That one day, I will be queen.

And that hour will be glorious.

Contributor Biographies

Liz Barr (@_lizbarr) is the co-editor of *Companion Piece: Women Celebrate the Humans, Aliens and Tin Dogs of Doctor Who* (Mad Norwegian Press, 2015). She blogs about politics, pop culture, media and social justice with Stephanie Lai at no-award.net, and can be relied upon to have strong feelings about historical and fictional women. She lives in Melbourne, Australia, where she works as a legal secretary and occasionally moonlights as a chew toy for a cat with an anxiety disorder.

Deborah Biancotti is the author of two short story collections, *Bad Power* and *A Book of Endings*. She is the co-author of the upcoming Zeroes series, along with Scott Westerfeld and Margo Lanagan. Deborah's work has been nominated for the Shirley Jackson Award and the William L. Crawford Award for Best First Fantasy Book, as well as the Aurealis and Ditmar Awards. Her most recent short stories appeared in *The Review of Australian Fiction* and her new novella, "Waking in Winter", will be available from PS Publishing in 2015. You can find Deborah online at deborahbiancotti.com and on Twitter @deborah_b.

Born in Singapore but a global citizen, **Joyce Chng** writes mainly science fiction (SFF) and YA fiction. She likes steampunk and tales of transformation/ transfiguration. Her fiction has appeared in *Crossed Genres, the Apex Book of World SF Vol II* and *We See A Different Frontier*. Her YA science fiction trilogy is published by a Singapore publisher, Math Paper Press. She can be found at A Wolf's Tale (http://awolfstale.wordpress.com). She tweets too: @jolantru.

Thoraiya Dyer is an award-winning Australian writer. Her short science fiction and fantasy stories have appeared in *Clarkesworld, Apex, Analog, Nature* and *Cosmos*, among others (for a full list, see www.thoraiyadyer.com). Her collection of four original stories, *Asymmetry*, available from Twelfth Planet Press, was called "unsettling, poignant, marvellous" by Nancy Kress. A lapsed veterinarian, her other interests include bushwalking, archery and travel. Find her on Twitter @ThoraiyaDyer.

Dirk Flinthart resides in Tasmania, where he raises children, teaches martial arts, writes (not enough!) and studies. He's been responsible for a range of short stories and at least one novel, and is currently in the process of creating more. You can find scattered musings from him at https://dflinthart.wordpress.com/, but the internet access in his part of Tasmania is too primitive to support Twitter...

Lisa L. Hannett has had over 55 short stories appear in venues including *Clarkesworld, Fantasy, Weird Tales, ChiZine, Year's Best Australian Fantasy and Horror (2010, 2011 & 2012),* and *Imaginarium: Best Canadian Speculative Writing* (2012 & 2013). She has won three Aurealis Awards, including Best Collection for her first book, *Bluegrass Symphony*, which was also nominated for a World Fantasy Award. Her first novel, *Lament for the Afterlife*, is being published by CZP in 2015.You can find her online at http://lisahannett.com and on Twitter @LisaLHannett.

Kathleen Jennings is an illustrator based in Brisbane, Australia. Her work has won several Ditmars and twice been shortlisted for the World Fantasy Award. She blogs at http://tanaudel.wordpress.com and frequently posts sketches at Twitter and Tumblr (@tanaudel). Her portfolio is at http://kathleenjennings.com.

Sylvia Kelso lives in North Queensland, Australia. She mostly writes fantasy and SF set in analogue or alternate Australian settings, and likes to tinker with moral swords-and-sorcery and elements of mythology. She has published eight fantasy novels, including *Amberlight* and *The Moving Water*, which were finalists for best fantasy novel in the Australian Aurealis genre fiction awards. Her short stories appear in Australia and the US, including anthologies from DAW and Twelfth Planet Press. Her novella "Spring in Geneva", a riff on *Frankenstein*, appeared in October 2013 with Aqueduct Press. www.sylviakelso.com

Stephanie Lai (@yiduiqie) is a queer Australian of Chinese descent (and a left-handed archer). She writes about identity, racism and Asian ladies, and has yelled about things in *The Lifted Brow, Peril Magazine,* and *The Toast*. She blogs about politics, pop culture, media and social justice (and drop bears) with Liz Barr at no-award.net. She likes penguins, infrastructure, and Asian steampunk, and is often paid to train people in surviving our oncoming dystopic future. Stephanie hates everything you love.

Laura Lam is an author originally from California but now based in Scotland. Her debut fantasy, *Pantomime* (2013), was a Top Ten Title for the 2014 American Library Association Rainbow List, won the Bisexual Book Award for Speculative Fiction, and was nominated for other awards. The sequel, *Shadowplay*, followed in 2014. Her next book is *False Hearts* (2016 Tor/Macmillan), a thriller featuring conjoined twins, cults, brainhacking, and the dark underbelly of near future San Francisco.

Juliet Marillier was born and brought up in Dunedin, New Zealand, and now lives in Western Australia. Her historical fantasy novels and short stories for adults and young adults have been published internationally and have won a number of awards including the Aurealis, the American Library Association's Alex Award and the Sir Julius Vogel Award. Her lifelong love of folklore, fairy tales and mythology is a major influence on her writing. Juliet is currently working on *Tower of Thorns*, second book in the Blackthorn & Grim historical fantasy/mystery series for adult readers. The first novel in the series, *Dreamer's Pool*, was published in 2014. When not busy writing, Juliet is active in the animal rescue field, and she has her own small pack of waifs and strays. Her website is at http://www.julietmarillier.com

Kirstyn McDermott has been working in the darker alleyways of speculative fiction for much of her career. Her two novels, *Madigan Mine* and *Perfections*, each won the Aurealis Award for Best Horror Novel and her most recent book is *Caution: Contains Small Parts*, a collection of short fiction published by Twelfth Planet Press. After many years based in Melbourne, Kirstyn now lives in Ballarat with her husband and fellow scribbler, Jason Nahrung, where she is currently pursuing a creative PhD at Federation University. She can be found online (usually far too often) via @fearofemeralds on Twitter or at www.kirstynmcdermott.com.

Sandra McDonald's first collection of fiction, *Diana Comet and Other Improbable Stories*, was a Booklist Editor's Choice, an American Library Association Over the Rainbow Book, and winner of a Lambda Literary Award. She writes adult and young adult books with gay, transgender and asexual characters, including the collection *Drag Queen Astronaut*, the thriller *City of Soldiers* (as Sam Burke) and the award-winning *Fisher Key Adventures* (as Sam Cameron). Her short fiction has appeared in *Asimov's Science Fiction, Fantasy & Science Fiction, Lightspeed*, and many other magazines and anthologies. Visit her at www.sandramcdonald.com and @sandramcdonald.

Foz Meadows is a bipedal mammal with delusions of immortality and fantasy writer. Her YA novels, *Solace & Grief* and *The Key to Starveldt*, are both available through Ford Street Publishing, and in 2014, she was nominated for a Hugo Award for Best Fan Writer for her blog, Shattersnipe. She can also be found on Twitter, tumblr and the Huffington Post, as well as reviewing for *Strange Horizons* and *A Dribble of Ink*. An Australian expat, Foz currently lives in Scotland with a toddler, not enough books and her very own philosopher. Surprisingly, this is a good thing.

Faith Mudge is a Queensland writer with a passion for fantasy, folk tales and mythology from all over the world—in fact, almost anything with a glimmer of the fantastical. She also spent a disproportionate amount of her childhood watching history documentaries, getting overly invested in dead monarchs. Her stories have appeared in various anthologies, the most recent of which include *Kaleidoscope, Phantazein* and *The Year's Best Australian Fantasy and Horror 2013*. She posts regular reviews and articles at beyondthedreamline.wordpress.com. Somewhere in the overcrowded menagerie of her mind, there are novels. She is even writing some of them.

Between teaching part-time and and studying Anthropology and English Literature at university full-time, **Havva Murat** still finds precious moments to devote to her true passion: writing. Nora of Kelmendi was an easy pick for Havva as all her grandparents were born in Albania and feisty Albanian women have surrounded her all her life. Being the first woman in her family to attend university and the first writer, she fully intends to model herself on the Cranky Ladies featured in this anthology, striking out on interesting paths no matter how thorny, and hopes other will be inspired to do the same.

L.M. Myles is the editor of the Hugo Award nominated *Chicks Unravel Time* with Deborah Stanish, and *Companion Piece* with Liz Barr. She's written for Doctor Who in prose and on audio, and her essays have been published in *Chicks Dig Time Lords, Outside In,* and *Chicks Dig Gaming*. She co-hosts the Hugo Award nominated Verity! podcast, where she says extraordinarily sensible things about Doctor Who. She thinks lots more people should be interested in legal history cause it's fascinating stuff. Too often she can be found procrastinating on Twitter @LMMyles.

Garth Nix was born in Melbourne, Australia. A full-time writer since 2001, he previously worked as a literary agent, marketing consultant, book editor, book publicist, book sales representative, bookseller, and as a part-time soldier in the Australian Army Reserve. Garth's books include the award-winning young adult fantasy novels *Sabriel, Lirael* and *Abhorsen*; the dystopian novel *Shade's Children*; the space opera *A Confusion of Princes*; and a Regency romance with magic, *Newt's Emerald*. His latest book, *Clariel*, is a prequel to the Old Kingdom trilogy. Garth lives in a Sydney beach suburb with his wife and two children. http://www.garthnix.com/

Amanda Pillar is an award-winning editor and author who lives in Victoria, Australia, with her husband and two cats, Saxon and Lilith. Amanda has had numerous short stories published and has co-edited the fiction anthologies *Voices* (2008), *Grants Pass* (2009), *The Phantom Queen Awakes* (2010), *Scenes from the Second Storey* (2010), *Ishtar* (2011) and *Damnation and Dames* (2012). Her first solo anthology was published by Ticonderoga Publications, titled *Bloodstones*. Amanda is currently working on the sequel, *Bloodlines*, due for publication in 2015. Amanda's first novel, *Graced*, will be published by Momentum in 2015. In her day job, she works as an archaeologist.

Tansy Rayner Roberts is the author of the Creature Court trilogy, *Love and Romanpunk, Ink Black Magic* and other works of SF and fantasy, and has edited for the Science Fiction Writers of America's *Bulletin* and AGOG! Press. She has won several Aurealis, Ditmar and WSFA awards for her work, and won the Hugo Award for Best Fan Writer in 2013. You can find Tansy on Twitter at @tansyrr, and on both the Galactic Suburbia and Verity! podcasts. She is currently writing and publishing *Musketeer Space*, a gender-swapped space opera retelling of *The Three Musketeers*, at http://tansyrr.com/tansywp/tag/musketeer-space/

Barbara Robson (@bjrobson) is a research oceanographer at CSIRO who doesn't write as often as she should. Her husband, Nathan Cassidy, suggested Theodora as a subject for a story and helped with historical fact-checking, but is still disappointed that Barbara didn't take up his first suggested subject: the wife of Socrates. Some of Barbara's other publications include "Baby Steps" in *One Small Step* (Fablecroft), "Mrs Estahazi" in *Belong* (Ticonderoga), "Lizzy Lou" in *Year's Best Fantasy 5* (Harper Voyager) and "State of the Art in Modelling of Phosphorus in Aquatic Systems" in *Environmental Modelling and Software* (Elsevier).

Nisi Shawl's story collection *Filter House* won the James Tiptree, Jr. Award. She was a Guest of Honor for WisCon 35 and SFRA 2014. Shawl coauthored *Writing the Other: A Practical Approach*; edits reviews for the literary quarterly *Cascadia Subduction Zone*; and co-edited *Strange Matings: Science Fiction, Feminism, African American Voices, and Octavia E. Butler.* Two more anthologies are forthcoming in 2015: *The Year's*

Illustrious Feminist Science Fiction and Fantasy and *Stories for Chip: A Tribute to Samuel R. Delany*. Shawl's Belgian Congo steampunk novel *Everfair* is due out from Tor this fall. She's fairly active on Twitter and Facebook, and promises to update her homepage soon.

Bram Stoker Nominee and Shirley Jackson Award winner **Kaaron Warren** has lived in Melbourne, Sydney, Canberra and Fiji. She's sold almost 200 short stories, three novels (the multi-award-winning *Slights, Walking the Tree* and *Mistification*) and four short story collections including the multi-award-winning *Through Splintered Walls*. Her latest short story collection is *The Gate Theory*. Kaaron is a Current Fellow at The Museum of Australian Democracy at Old Parliament House, where she is researching Robert Menzies, Sir William Ashton, and the Granny Killer, John Wayne Glover. The resulting crime novel should see print in 2016.You can find her at http://kaaronwarren.wordpress.com/ and she tweets @KaaronWarren.

Tehani Wessely (@editormum75) started FableCroft Publishing in 2010 and has produced more than 20 publications since then, including original and reprint anthologies, novels and one shot stories. Work published by FableCroft has been shortlisted for awards in Australia and overseas, and has won Aurealis and Ditmar awards. Tehani herself won the Best New Talent Ditmar in 2008, and for her non-fiction writing has twice won the William Atheling Jr. Award for Criticism or Review (for conversational reviews). She continues to write about Doctor Who with David McDonald and Tansy Rayner Roberts, and has an essay in the forthcoming Doctor Who collection *Companion Piece*. fablecroft.com.au

Jane Yolen, often called the Hans Christian Andersen of America, has over 350 books published. *Time Magazine*'s recent list of 100 best children's books named her *Owl Moon* #6 on the list. Her books and stories have won the Caldecott, Nebula, Golden Kite, World Fantasy Award, Mythopoeic Award, Rhysling, and had a nomination for the National Book Award, among many others. She was the first writer in Western Massachusetts to be honored by New England Public Radio's Arts & Humanities Award and the first woman to give the Andrew Lang lecture in Scotland since the speech's inception in 1929. Six colleges and universities have given her honorary doctorates. www.janeyolen.com.

Guardian
by Jo Anderton
ISBN: 978-0-9922844-4-2

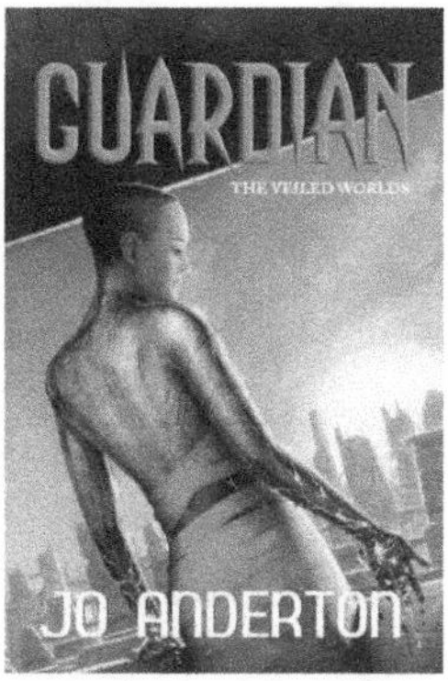

The grand city of Movoc-under-Keeper lies in ruins. The sinister puppet men have revealed their true nature, and their plan to tear down the veil between worlds. To have a chance of defeating them, Tanyana must do the impossible, and return to the world where they were created, on the other side of the veil. Her journey will force her into a terrible choice, and test just how much she is willing to sacrifice for the fate of two worlds.

"...a tremendously satisfying conclusion to an already celebrated series. ...Anderton is to be commended for her ability to create such rich and original settings." — Alex Stephenson, Aurealis #72

"Refreshingly original..." — The Guardian

"Impressively combines far-future world-building, conspiracies, and a redemption quest..." — Publishers' Weekly

"Anderton demonstrates a mastery of storytelling and world building" — Library Journal

The Bone Chime Song and Other Stories
by Joanne Anderton
ISBN: 978-0-9807770-9-3

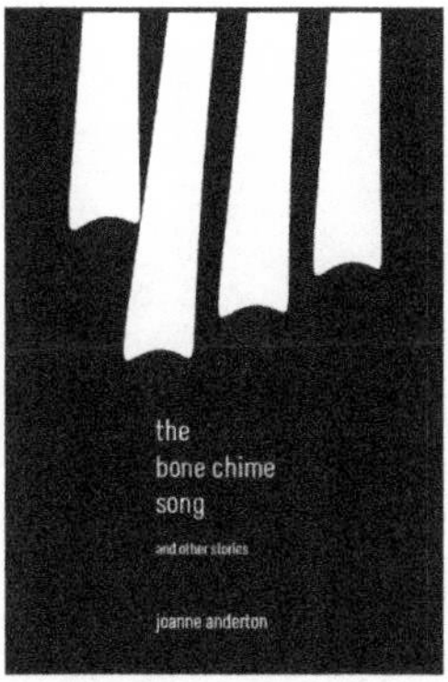

Enter a world where terrible secrets are hidden in a wind chime's song; where crippled witches build magic from scrap; and the beautiful dead dance for eternity

The Bone Chime Song and Other Stories collects the finest science fiction and horror short stories from award-winning writer Joanne Anderton. From mechanical spells scavenging a derelict starship to outback zombies and floating gardens of bone, these stories blur the lines between genres. A mix of freakish horror, dark visions of the future and the just plain weird, Anderton's tales will draw you in — but never let you get comfortable.

...follows a fine horror lineage from Shirley Jackson's The Lottery through The Wickerman... — Scary Minds

Dark, unexpected and tightly written, Anderton makes a fantasy world seem completely real, while using a premise that spirals from a shadowed and lonely place. — ASif!

...a stunning descent into dark decay and the grisly madness of eternity ... a chaotic and beautiful fairy tale with a patina of gangrene. — Specusphere

[Anderton] has a real mastery of the surreal ... and somehow manages to make the surreal seem normal ... reading this book will fill you with horror, wonder, awe, sorrow, delight, surprise and admiration." — Kaaron Warren

Winner of 2013 Aurealis Award and 2013 Australian Shadows Award for Best Collection

Phantazein
edited by Tehani Wessely
ISBN: 978-0-9922844-9-7

You think you know all the fables that have ever been told. You think you can no longer be surprised by stories. Think again. With origins in myth, fairytales, folklore and pure imagination, the stories and poems in these pages draw on history that never was and worlds that will never be to create their own unique tales and traditions…

The next generation of storytellers is here.

Faith Mudge / Twelfth
Tansy Rayner Roberts / The love letters of swans
Thoraiya Dyer / Bahamut
Rabia Gale / The village of no women
Jenny Blackford / The Lady of Wild Things
Suzanne J. Willis / Rag and bone heart
Nicole Murphy / A Cold Day
Vida Cruz / How the Jungle Got Its Spirit Guardian
S.G. Larner / Kneaded
Charlotte Nash / The Ghost of Hephaestus
Cat Sparks / The Seventh Relic
Gitte Christensen / The nameless seamstress
Foz Meadows / Scales of Time (poem) reprint
Moni / Illustrations Scales of Time
Kathleen Jennings / Cover Art

…kudos to the writers who took long raked over material in a lot of cases and breathed life and originality in to them. — Sean Wright

…there wasn't a story that disappointed… — A Fantastical Librarian

One Small Step
edited by Tehani Wessely
ISBN: 978-0-9874000-0-0

Sixteen stories of discovery from Australia's best writers. Each story in some way addresses the idea of discoveries, new beginnings, or literal or figurative "small steps", but each story takes you to places you far beyond the one small step you imagine… Journey through worlds and explore the reaches of the universe with this collection.

Marianne de Pierres / Foreword
Joanne Anderton & Rabia Gale / Sand and Seawater
Deborah Biancotti / Indigo Gold
Jodi Cleghorn / Firefly Epilogue
Rowena Cory Daniells / The Ways of the Wyrding Women
Thoraiya Dyer / The ships of Culwinna
Kate Gordon / Shadows
Lisa L. Hannett & Angela Slatter / By Blood and Incantation
Kathleen Jennings / Ella and the Flame
Penny Love / Original
Michelle Marquardt / Always Greener
DK Mok / Morning Start
Faith Mudge / Winter's Heart
Tansy Rayner Roberts / Cold White Daughter
Barbara Robson / Baby Steps
Cat Sparks / Daughters of Battendown
Suzanne J Willis / Number 73 Glad Avenue

A very strong slate of stories… — Publishers Weekly

Recommended reading for anyone interested in SFF with a feminist bent… — Foz Meadows

Smart, heartfelt and a little bit otherworldly… — Dave Versace

…very strong collection of stories showcasing the talents of eighteen very talented women. — A Fantastical Librarian

Winner of 2013 Aurealis Award for Best Anthology

Ink Black Magic
by Tansy Rayner Roberts
ISBN: 978-0-9874000-0-0

Because sometimes, it takes cleavage and big skirts to save the world from those crazy teenagers.

Kassa Daggersharp has been a pirate, a witch, a menace to public safety, a villain, a hero and a legend. These days, she lectures first year students on the dangers of magic, at the Polyhedrotechnical in Cluft.

Egg Friefriedsson is Kassa's teenage cousin, a lapsed Axgaard warrior who would rather stay in his room and draw comics all day than hang out with his friends. If only comics had been invented.

Aragon Silversword is missing, presumed dead.

All the adventures are over. It's time to get on with being a grownup. But when Egg's drawings come to life, including an evil dark city full of villains and monsters, everyone starts to lose their grip on reality. Even the flying sheep.

Kassa and Egg are not sure who are the heroes and who are the villains anymore, but someone has to step up to save Mocklore, one last time.

True love isn't all it's cracked up to be. Happy endings don't come cheap. You really can have too much black velvet.

All this and more in the third and final adventure of The Mocklore Chronicles!

...surprisingly layered...complex and ambitious... — Jim C Hines

...fun fantasy adventure...that brings to mind Terry Prachett's Discworld...
— Carolyn Cushman, Locus

Path of Night
by Dirk Flinthart
ISBN: 978-0-9807770-8-6

Michael Devlin is the first of a new breed. The way things are going, he may also be the last.

Being infected with an unknown disease is bad. Waking up on a slab in a morgue wearing nothing but a toe-tag is worse, even if it comes with a strange array of new abilities.

Medical student Michael Devlin is in trouble. With his flatmates murdered and an international cabal of legendary man-monsters on his trail, Devlin's got nowhere to hide. His only allies are a hot-tempered Sydney cop and a mysterious monster-hunter who may be setting Devlin up for the kill. If he's going to survive, Devlin will have to embrace his new powers and confront his hunters. But can he hold onto his humanity when he walks the Path of Night?

...action driven, laced with humor...I am hoping that there will be a sequel. —Roger Ross

...a darkly humorous thriller with cracking one liners and plenty of action.
—Sean Wright

... excellent and feels thoroughly authentic. —Alan Baxter

Look out for our ebook-only collection and more FableCroft books at our website:

http://fablecroft.com.au/

Havenstar by Glenda Larke
Phantazein edited by Tehani Wessely
Pratchett's Women by Tansy Rayner Roberts
50 Roman Mistresses by Tansy Rayner Roberts
The Bone Chime Song and Other Stories by Joanne Anderton
Guardian by Jo Anderton
The Mocklore Chronicles by Tansy Rayner Roberts
Splashdance Silver
Liquid Gold
Ink Black Magic
Isles of Glory trilogy by Glenda Larke
The Aware
Gilfeather
The Tainted
Worlds Next Door edited by Tehani Wessely
Australis Imaginarium edited by Tehani Wessely
After the Rain edited by Tehani Wessely
Epilogue edited by Tehani Wessely
One Small Step edited by Tehani Wessely
Focus 2012: highlights of Australian short fiction
edited by Tehani Wessely
Canterbury 2100: Pilgrimages in a New World
edited by Dirk Flinthart
Path of Night by Dirk Flinthart
"Sanction" by Dirk Flinthart
"Flower and Weed" by Margo Lanagan
To Spin a Darker Stair
by Catherynne M Valente & Faith Mudge

Coming soon…

Insert Title Here… edited by Tehani Wessely

With thanks to our Pozible supporters...

Adelia Croser
Aidan Doyle
Aimee Lindorff
Aja Romano
Alan Baxter
Alex Pierce
Alex Rankin
Ali Nolte
Alisa Krasnostein
Alison Grahame
Alison Simmonds
Amanda Dettrick
Amanda Pillar
Andrej Pavković
Andrew Finch
Andrew Finch
Andrew Macrae
Andrew Waddington
Angela Hellewell
Anita
Anne Croft
Anthea Hawdon
Avril Hannah-Jones
Barbara Robson
Beks Raymond
Benjamin McKenzie
Bethwyn Walker
Brenda Tronson
Caroline Mills
Carrie Smith
Cath Sherwin
Catherine Braiding
Catherine Green
Catherine Lundoff
Catherine Macdonald
Catherine McArdle
Cathie Tasker
Catriona Sparks
Charles Tan
Cheryl Morgan
Chris Bobridge
Chris Barnes
Chris Brandon-Jones
Chris Keogh
Claire McArthur
Clara White
Claudia Nugent
Damien Saunders
Daniel Franklin
Danielle Venning
Dave Winterbotham
Deb Stanish
Deborah Biancotti
Deidre Tronson
Donna Zillmann
Elanor Matton-Johnson
Eleanor Smith
Elissa Nguyen
Elizabeth Alpert
Elizabeth Shayne
Ellen Blackburn
Ellen Kuehnle
emilly
Emma Kate
Emma Wearmouth
Erin Brown
Fiona Beckwith
Frances Menting
Georgina Ogivlie
Glen Collins
Hana Kramer
Havva Murat
Heath Graham
Heather Garnett
Heather Smith
Heidi Stabb
Helen Merrick
Holly Brett Masone
Ian Mond
Ian Nicholls
Janika Bischof
Jason Nahrung
Jean Hollis Weber
Jeanette Gormley
Jen White
Jenni Hughes
Jess I
Jess Lethbridge
Jessica Gravitt
Joanna Kasper
Jodi Cleghorn
Johanna Mary Motteram
Johanna Qualmann
John Devenny
John Richards
Joris Meijer
Ju Transcendancing
Julia Meyer
Julian Barr
Julie Blake
Julie O'Brien
Juliet Marillier
Karen McKenna
Karin Landelius
Kate Cuthbert van der Veer
Kate Eltham
Kate Gordon
Katharine Stubbs
Katherine Ellis
Kathleen Hanrahan
Kathryn Linge

Kathy Sinclair
Katrina McDonnell
Keith Mullumby
Kelly Kleiser
Kelly Osterberg
Kendra Leigh Speedling
Keri Bas
Kerryn Hands
Kim Lowe
Kim Wilkins
Kimberly Bea
Kirsten J Bicica
Koa Webster
Kyna62
Lara Hopkins
LaShonda Hill
Lavinia Gent
Leah Mcdougall
Lee Winter
Leife Shallcross
Linda Sengsourinho
Louise Williams
Lyn Battersby
Mandy Tonks
Marcia Watson
Margaret Davis
Margaret Wieringa
Maria Gerhardt
Maria Messmer
Mark Webb
Mary Gardiner
Matthew Morrison
Matthew Sheahan
Meg Caddy
Melina Dahms
Michael F Stewart
Michelle Goldsmith
Michelle Schoemaker
Michelle Walsh
Mieneke van der Salm
Mikayla Micomonaco
Mindy Johnson
Miriam Mulcahy
Mitenae
Molly Tebo
Narrelle Harris
Natalie Bannister
Nicholas Schiller
Nicky Strickland
Nicola Foxworthy
Nicole Murphy
Nikki Clark
Omega Howell
PaperBarkTree
Patricia Scott
Poppy Carpenter
Rachel Sonntag
Rat Reardon
Rebecca Dominguez
Rebecca Dridan
Rebecca Murrie
Robyn Jelleff
Rochelle
Sarah Bassett
Sarah Brown
Sarah Liberman
Sarah Smith
Satima Flavell
Saxon Brenton
Scott Leis
Sean Wright
Shane Nixon
SirLinda Gale
Sophie Burnham
Stephanie Gunn
Steve Cameron
Stu Barrow
Stuart Reeh
Sue Ann Barber
Sue Collins
Sue McCarthy
Susan Loyal
Suyin Hor
Suzanne Willis
Tania Duffield
Tanya Bailey
Terry Frost
Thomas Bull
Thoraiya Dyer
Tiki Swain
Tori Tyrrell
Tsana Dolichva
Vanessa Ronan-Pearce
Vicki Rogers
Victoria Vyvyan
Wendy Hanna
Zoe Walton

We also thank the supporters who prefer to remain anonymous—we are very grateful!

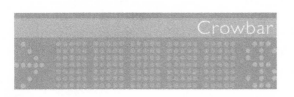

And to **Arts Tasmania** for the Crowbar Grant that has supported the production of this book.